interactive SCIENCE

Chapter Activities
and Projects

PEARSON

Boston, Massachusetts   Chandler, Arizona   Glenview, Illinois   Upper Saddle River, New Jersey

Note to Teachers

This book is designed to provide you with a way for students to investigate and apply their knowledge of the chapter concepts in the *Interactive Science* program through open-ended activities. You can use this book as a source of project-based activities for use in science fairs or class projects. Projects are typically designed to span the length of one chapter.

Extensive Teacher Support

The first two pages of each project are notes for you. These notes are designed to guide you in introducing the project and include tips about group size, deadlines, and handing out worksheets. The notes detail any advanced preparation necessary, as well as provide you with tangible checkpoints to keep students on track. Additionally, there is guidance for running final presentations and closing the project with a class discussion, as well as ideas to extend the project either as a class or for accelerated students.

Overview for Students

Each project contains two pages of overview for your students that can accompany your project assignment. These pages explain the nature of the project to students and outline the steps and guidelines they must follow. They are generally open ended, but include a list of possible materials and hints to assist students in the process. There is also a timeline specially designed for you to assign interim dates for the stages of the project. Try aligning tasks with each lesson of the chapter.

Tools for Self-Monitoring

Worksheets related to the project provide additional guidance for the student. They are not self-contained but rather typically step the student through two major parts of the activity. These worksheets encourage students to create a design, question scientific concepts, or make inferences from research and results. The last page of each project is a rubric that will help students understand the grading criteria and expectations to effectively evaluate or peer-evaluate their work.

ISBN-13: 978-0-13-369853-4

ISBN-10: 0-13-369853-X

1 2 3 4 5 6 7 8 9 10   V084   14 13 12 11 10

Contents

Contents

Science in the Community

The following steps will walk you through the Chapter Project. Use the hints and detailed directions as you guide your students through gathering information about science in their community, analyzing their data, and presenting their findings to the class.

Chapter Project Overview

To introduce this project, lead a class discussion on scientific literacy. Point out that people who have been out of school a long time may not think much about science and, as a result, may hold unscientific and fanciful notions about the natural world. Point out that some people even think the sun revolves around Earth, rather than the other way around. Ask students what scientific information they think every person should know, whether involved in science or not. Make a list on the board of student suggestions about basic scientific information. Then ask students to predict the scientific literacy of people in their community on a scale of 1 to 10 (10 being the highest) and explain their predictions. After students have expressed their opinions, explain that in this project they will have a chance to investigate that question.

Explain that they will develop a questionnaire for use in a survey of basic science literacy. They will also ask questions that check if people can tell the difference between statements of evidence and statements of opinion. Finally, they will investigate whether people use science at work or home. Explain that after conducting the survey, students will choose people to interview in-depth about science in their lives.

Have students read the Project Overview. Review the Project Rules, and hand out the Scoring Rubric, which you will use for scoring students' work. Discuss with students what will be expected of them. You may also want to set deadlines for the completion of the different stages of the project, including completion of the questionnaire, the survey, the interviews, their analysis, and completion of their report. Encourage students to record these dates on the Project Timeline.

Divide the class into groups. Tell students they will be working in groups as they develop their questionnaires, conduct the surveys, do the interviews, draw their conclusions, and write their reports.

Distribute copies of Project Worksheet 1. Explain that this worksheet should help them think about questions that will be included in their group's questionnaire. Have students individually complete this worksheet and then take their written questions when they meet with their group. Group members will decide together which questions to include in the survey. Groups will also write new questions after discussing which questions would be best for checking scientific literacy and the use of science at work or home.

After students have conducted their surveys, distribute copies of Project Worksheet 2. Make sure students understand that the questions they ask in the interviews should be formed with the idea of eliciting valuable information about where people get and evaluate scientific information and whether they use science at work or home. Explain that each student should individually complete the top of the worksheet and then share their questions with their group for consideration. Point out that the bottom of the worksheet can be used to help in analysis after the interviews have been done.

Remind students to refer to the hints in the Project Overview to help them form their questions, conduct the survey and interviews, and then analyze their results.

Materials and Preparation

Students will need access to a computer to compose and print their questionnaires. You could photocopy a neatly hand-written questionnaire as an alternative. For conducting the survey, students will need pencils for respondents to use and clipboards to hold the questionnaires.

Keep Students on Track—Tasks 1–3

Once groups have completed their questionnaires, check to see that the questions are well written and easily understood. Then talk with groups about where they could conduct a survey. You might need to get permission from the school for students to conduct this survey at a school event. Other possible places include a community center, a supermarket, or a shopping mall. Talk over students' ideas before they conduct the survey, and make sure responsible authorities are aware of students' plans before giving approval.

Keep Students on Track—Task 4

Review the questions students will use in the in-depth interviews. Make sure the questions are well-written and can be easily understood by people interviewed. Advise students that they should plan on taking notebooks with them to write down people's responses.

Keep Students on Track—Tasks 5–6

After students have completed the interviews, discuss with each group how it should prepare for writing its report. Tell students that the first step should be for each student to finish Worksheet 2. Then groups should tally the results of their surveys, make calculations, create graphs or charts, and draw conclusions from the results of the surveys and the interviews. Make sure students know that conclusions must be based on results.

Chapter Project Wrap Up

As students write their reports, discuss with each group its findings and analysis of the information the group collected. Encourage groups to draw conclusions about scientific literacy in their community, how people find science information, and whether they use science at work or home.

Provide class time for discussion after all reports are turned in. You might read aloud findings or conclusions from different reports and then ask for comments from the class. Have volunteers describe their experiences in conducting the survey and doing the interviews. Encourage students to reflect on what they found most surprising and on what they learned from carrying out the project.

Extension

Students might review the survey results and interview responses from all groups and see if they can identify similarities and differences in the results. Ask students to compare and contrast the conclusions different groups drew. Students might also put together a survey using the best questions from all groups and then conduct a survey of adults and students who attend a school function, such as a football game or a school play. Once the survey has been conducted, students can analyze the results and present their findings to the class. Students might consider submitting an article about this survey to the school newspaper.

PROJECT OVERVIEW
Science in the Community

For this project, you will investigate scientific literacy in your community. You will also investigate where people acquire their scientific information and whether people use science at work or at home. Your investigation will involve developing a survey questionnaire and conducting a survey of at least 20 people in the community. This survey questionnaire will include questions about basic science, the difference between evidence and opinion, and use of science in the workplace or at home. After you have conducted the survey, you will choose five people to interview about where they get science information and whether they use science at work or home. You will then analyze the results and write a report of what you found.

Project Rules

- Develop a survey questionnaire with 15 questions to investigate scientific literacy and science in the lives of people in your community. The questionnaire should include five basic science questions, five questions that test the difference between evidence and opinion, and five questions about careers in science or the use of science information at work or home.

- Obtain your teacher's approval of your survey questions. Discuss with your teacher where and how to conduct the survey.

- Give your survey to at least 20 people of various ages.

- Choose five people who took your survey to return to for an in-depth interview about science in their lives, including where they get science information and how they use science at work or home.

- Analyze the results of your survey. Your analysis should include such information as the number of correct responses, calculations of averages, and graphs or charts of results.

- Write a report that includes your analysis of the survey as well as any conclusions you draw from the results of your survey and interviews.

Suggested Materials

- Consider using a computer and printer to develop the questionnaire and print out copies. A copy machine could be used to make copies of a neatly hand-printed survey as an alternative.

- Pencils and a clipboard for people to take the survey.

Hints for Conducting Your Survey and Interviews

- Your survey questions should be written in a way that people can quickly and easily mark the correct answer and you can easily tally the results. For instance, you could write True/False questions in which people simply circle either *True* or *False*. For Multiple Choice questions, people could simply circle their responses.

- You need to conduct your survey someplace where there is a diversity of people—people of all ages and types. This place might be a community center, a city building, or a school event. You'll need permission from your teacher once you've decided on a place. You may need to get permission from an authority at the location as well.

- When choosing people for in-depth interviews, you should pick a variety of people, not just those who have good scientific literacy. In fact, you should choose at least one person who seems to have little understanding of science.

- Prepare at least four questions for the five in-depth interviews. These are questions that should elicit a longer, thoughtful response from a person.

- Plan for each in-depth interview to take about 10 minutes.

- After conducting the surveys and interviews, analyze your results. Your analysis should first involve tallying the responses to the survey questions. Then, you can calculate averages, such as the mean number of correct answers (the number of correct answers divided by the total number of questions) and the mode of correct answers (the number of correct answers that most often occurred). You can use your tallies and calculations to create illustrations in the form of graphs or charts that illustrate your results.

- Draw conclusions based firmly on the results of your surveys and interviews.

Project Timeline

Task	Due Date
1. Complete development of survey questionnaire	_____
2. Obtain teacher's approval of survey location	_____
3. Complete at least 20 surveys	_____
4. Complete five in-depth interviews	_____
5. Complete analysis of surveys and interviews	_____
6. Complete a written report	_____

Science, Society, and You

PROJECT WORKSHEET 1

Developing a Survey About Science

What questions would you ask to find out whether people in your community have scientific literacy? For your survey questionnaire you need to write True/False questions, Multiple Choice questions, and Evidence/Opinion questions. Answer the questions below, and then write similar questions that you could use in your group's survey on a separate sheet of paper.

Here are two examples of True/False questions. Circle the correct answer.

1. The sun revolves around Earth.   T   F
2. Spiders don't have backbones.   T   F

Write two more True/False questions.

Here are two examples of Multiple Choice questions. Circle the correct answer.

3. What is the basic unit of structure and function of a living thing called?
   a. tissue   b. cell   c. atom   d. organ
4. The amount of matter in an object is called its
   a. weight.   b. volume.   c. mass.   d. density.

Write two more Multiple Choice questions.

Here are two examples of Evidence/Opinion questions. Circle either *Evidence* or *Opinion*.

5. The scale indicates that the dog weighs 75 pounds.   Evidence   or   Opinion
6. The dog is too heavy for its breed.   Evidence   or   Opinion

Write two more Evidence/Opinion questions.

Here are two examples of True/False questions about whether people use science in their jobs or at home. Someone would respond by circling either *T* or *F*.

7. I often use science in my daily life.   T   F
8. I sometimes use my knowledge of science in a hobby.   T   F

Write two more True/False questions about using science at work or home.

PROJECT WORKSHEET 2

In-Depth Interview Questions and Analysis

In-Depth Interviews

After completing the survey, choose five of the survey responders to interview about science and society. The following are examples of questions you might use. Write your own responses to each question on a separate sheet of paper.

1. Do you think an understanding of science is important for a person to have? Why or why not?

2. When deciding about a public issue requires knowing some science, what source(s) do you use for scientific information?

3. When you hear opposing claims about an issue related to science, how do you decide which is correct?

Write two or more questions your group could use in the in-depth interviews.

Analysis of Results

Answer the following questions to help you analyze the results of your survey and interviews on a separate sheet of paper. Answering these questions will help you prepare for your presentation.

4. Which question was answered correctly by the most people? For each of these questions, make a pie or bar chart to display how many people chose each answer choice.

5. What was the average number of questions answered correctly by all taking your survey? (You can calculate the average by dividing the total number of correct answers by the total number of questions.)

6. What was the most frequent number of correct answers for the people taking your survey? (This is the mode, the number that appears most often in a list.) Make a bar graph showing the number of people who answered one question correct, two correct, and so on.

7. Based on your survey, do you think most people understand the difference between evidence and opinion? Explain your answer.

8. How many of the people you surveyed use science on a daily basis? How many claimed not to use science at all?

Name _____ Date_____ Class_____

Science in the Community

In evaluating how well you complete the Chapter Project, your teacher will judge your work in four categories. In each, a score of 4 is the best rating.

	4	3	2	1
Developing Survey and In-Depth Questions	Student contributes several good questions and takes a lead in development of the survey and in preparation for the interviews.	Student contributes some good questions and fully participates in development of the survey and in preparation for the interviews.	Student contributes at least one question and adequately participates in development of the survey and in preparation for the interviews.	Student does not contribute a question and participates only minimally in development of the survey and in preparation for the interviews.
Participating in Collection of Survey Data	Student takes a lead in organizing and carrying out collection of survey data.	Student participates fully in organizing and carrying out collection of survey data.	Student helps in some aspects of organizing and carrying out collection of survey data.	Student only minimally participates in collection of survey data.
Participating in In-Depth Interviews and Analysis of Results	Student plays a lead role in the in-depth interviews and the analysis of results.	Student participates fully in the in-depth interviews and the analysis of results.	Student participates in most aspects of the in-depth interviews and the analysis of results.	Student participates minimally in the in-depth interviews and the analysis of results.
Writing of Final Report	Report is very well written and thoroughly in describesing survey and interview results, includes several informative well-done illustrations in the form of graphs or chartsgraphs or charts, and draws conclusions well based directly on the results.	Report is fairly well written and thoroughly in describesing survey and interview results, includes somemostly good illustrations in the form ofseveral graphs or charts, and draws conclusions somewhat based on the results.	Report is adequately written and only somewhat thorough in describingdescribes survey and interview results, includes at least one good illustration in the form of a graph or chart, and draws conclusions somewhat based on the results.	Report is poorly written and/or not thorough in describing describes some survey and interview results, includes no good illustration in the form of arelevant graphs or charts, and does not drawss conclusions not not based on the results.

Science, Society, and You

Is It Really True?

The following steps will walk you through the Chapter Project. Use the hints and detailed directions as you guide your students through design, test phase, presentation, and reflection.

Chapter Project Overview

In this project, students will work individually to develop a hypothesis about a common belief, design an experiment to test that hypothesis, carry out the experiment, and create a poster as part of their conclusion. The hypothesis should be testable, and the experiment should be a controlled experiment, with a manipulated variable, a responding variable, and variables kept constant. Through this project, students will become familiar with the process of scientific inquiry.

In introducing the project, call on volunteers to describe common beliefs other than the ones listed in their text. Examples include: "it's always darkest before dawn," "the early bird gets the worm," and "walking under a ladder brings bad luck." Beforehand, you might use an Internet search engine to find common beliefs, with such search terms as *superstitions, folk wisdom,* and *rules of thumb.*

In a class discussion, focus on ways in which scientists might investigate a common belief. For example, in the case of the walking under a ladder and bad luck, a scientist might first have to write an operational definition of *bad* before any experiment can be designed.

Also discuss with students why some common beliefs may be difficult to investigate. For example, one belief is that warm water freezes faster than cold water. If this belief were investigated, students would have to record temperatures of water as it becomes ice, and the periodic opening of a freezer would probably interfere with the freezing process.

Distribute Project Overview. Review the Project Rules. You may also want to hand out the Scoring Rubric, so students will understand what is expected of them. Make sure students understand that each student will investigate a common belief and create a poster that summarizes the experiment for the class.

Set a deadline for the presentation of posters and some interim dates for the different stages of the project, and have students copy the dates in their Project Timeline.

Distribute Project Worksheet 1. After students read the worksheet, ask if they have any questions. Encourage students to talk to friends, relatives, and adults in their neighborhoods as they go about making their lists of common beliefs.

Materials and Preparation

The materials each student will need depend on the common belief investigated and the design of the experiment. For example, if the belief involves whether a slice of buttered bread always lands buttered side down, bread and butter will be needed. No special measurement tools will be needed because the quantitative observation is the number of times it falls one way or the other. In contrast, suppose a student wanted to investigate the belief that a person's height is equal to the fingertip-to-fingertip measurement of his or her extended arms. That investigation would require some type of standardized measurement tool, such as a tape measure. As students design their experiments, an important component will be to list the materials needed to carry out the experiment. You should check procedures and materials for attention to necessary safety procedures.

All students will need poster board as well as markers to complete their posters after concluding their experiments. Some students may want to use chalk, crayons, or colored markers to complete their posters.

Keep Students on Track—Tasks 1 and 2

As you review each student's common beliefs, encourage students who lack ideas to talk with their classmates, other students in the school, and people in their neighborhoods. Also, check to see that students have some idea about how they might investigate each common belief listed. Point out that a good experiment often includes the collection of quantitative observations.

Check each investigative idea for safety considerations. Caution students not to design experiments that would be too dangerous to carry out. Advise students to review the Science Safety Rules in Appendix A. Also, talk to students about the length of their proposed investigations. Explain that an investigation that would take weeks or months is impractical for this project. A good investigation might entail only an hour or two.

Distribute Project Worksheet 2. Make sure students understand that they will need to work on the worksheet as they learn more about scientific inquiry. As in Worksheet 1, students should work independently, but they might confer with classmates or consult you as they design their experiments.

Keep Students on Track—Task 3

Check to see that each student has chosen a common belief to investigate, developed a testable hypothesis, and designed a controlled experiment. Discuss with each student whether the experiment planned will result in the collection of data that will allow students to draw a conclusion about the hypothesis. Review the student's list of materials and discuss how the student can obtain whatever is needed to carry out the experiment. If the experimental design involves observing the behaviors of other students, help in organizing subjects for the experimenter. You may have to make a schedule so that students can be the observer for their own experiments and the subject of other experiments. For some experiments, you may have to find a location in the classroom or the school for students to carry out their experiments.

Keep Students on Track—Tasks 4–7

Check to see that students have carried out their experiments and collected their data. Discuss with each individual student about whether the data support the original hypothesis or not. Review students data tables, and advise students about making graphs from their data in order to reveal patterns. If necessary, review how to determine percentages and create labeled diagrams.

Make sure students have the materials to make their posters once their experiments have been carried out. Distribute poster board, markers, and other materials students might need to complete the project.

Chapter Project Wrap Up

As you review each student's poster, check to see that there is an identification of the common belief investigated, inclusion of the hypothesis tested, and a description of the controlled experiment carried out to text the hypothesis. Also, the poster should include the data collected in the form of a data table or a graph. Each student should also include a conclusion about whether the original hypothesis was supported or not.

You may want to provide class time for each student to present his or her poster to the class, or you could choose outstanding examples for class presentation. Whether or not students make presentations, find places in the classroom for students to display their posters.

After presentations have been made, discuss with students which common beliefs were supported and which were not, as well as which experiments were the best thought out in investigating a belief. Sum up by discussing with students their thoughts about the process of scientific inquiry after completing the project.

Encourage students to evaluate how well they accomplished what they set out to do, including how well the controlled experiment they designed yielded the expected data. Invite students to make suggestions about what they think would have made the project better.

Extension

After conducting the investigation, the class might want to discuss why they believe certain things. What makes information believable? Present the class with headlines from a variety of news sources, including some from reputable newspapers and others from a supermarket tabloid. Discuss how the source can influence whether a headline is believable.

PROJECT OVERVIEW

Is It Really True?

How do you use science skills in your life? In this project, you will develop a testing procedure to discover whether a common belief is true or false.

You will begin by making a list of common beliefs. List at least three different ones, and for each one briefly explain how that belief could be investigated scientifically. Then, you will choose one of these to form the basis of your project. As you learn about the process of scientific inquiry, you will apply what you learn to the investigation of the common belief you have chosen. You will develop a hypothesis, design an experiment to test that hypothesis, carry out the experiment, and draw a conclusion about your hypothesis. Before you begin the experiment, your teacher needs to approve your design. As part of your design, you will need to plan a way to collect data. Finally, you will draw a conclusion about your hypothesis and create a poster that summarizes your experiment for the class.

Project Rules

- Make a list of three common beliefs, and record them on Worksheet 1. For each common belief you list, briefly describe how you might test whether that belief is true or not.

- Choose one common belief to investigate further. Write a hypothesis related to this belief, and record your hypothesis on Worksheet 2.

- Design a controlled experiment to test your hypothesis. Record the manipulated variable, the responding variable, and variables kept constant on Worksheet 2. Write and record the procedure you will follow. Record the materials you will need to carry out the experiment. Describe what data you will collect and how you will organize your data.

- Submit your written plan to your teacher for approval.

- After receiving permission from your teacher, carry out your experiment. Collect and record data.

- Use the data you've collected to make a graph, if a graph would be appropriate.

- Draw a conclusion about whether the data support your hypothesis or not.

- Create a poster that summarizes your experiment for the class. On your poster, include the common belief you tested, the hypothesis you developed, a description of the experiment you designed, the data you collected, and the conclusion you drew.

Name _____ Date_____ Class_____

Project Hints

- As you make your list of three common beliefs, talk to classmates, friends, family, and adults in your neighborhood. Discuss with others how you could test each belief.

- Study the process of scientific inquiry. Your investigation of a common belief should be carried out in a scientific way.

- Make sure the hypothesis you develop is testable. You must be able to gather evidence that will either support or disprove your hypothesis.

- As you design your controlled experiment, consider how much time will be needed to carry it out. You want to be able to collect the data you need in a period of about 1 to 2 hours.

- Remember that in a good experiment, you will probably make quantitative observations. These observations will give you data that you can organize in a data table and then use to make a graph, if a graph is appropriate. Review the section Creating Data Tables and Graphs in the Skills Handbook of your textbook.

- Include as much information as you can on your poster. You may want to use chalk or crayons to add color to your poster.

Project Timeline

Task	Due Date
1. Compile a list of common beliefs for Worksheet 1.	_____
2. Plan an investigation of a common belief for Worksheet 2. Submit your written plan to your teacher.	_____
3. Carry out your experiment and collect the data.	_____
4. Make a data table and a graph from the data.	_____
5. Draw a conclusion about your hypothesis.	_____
6. Create a poster that summarizes your experiment.	_____
7. Present your poster to the class.	_____

Name _____ Date _____ Class _____

PROJECT WORKSHEET 1
Common Beliefs

Make a list of common beliefs that you have heard and that you think would be appropriate for an investigation.

1. Common Belief 1

_____

_____

How could this common belief be investigated?

_____

_____

_____

_____

2. Common Belief 2

_____

_____

How could this common belief be investigated?

_____

_____

_____

_____

3. Common Belief 3

_____

_____

How could this common belief be investigated?

_____

_____

_____

_____

Choose one of the common beliefs you've listed for further investigation.

PROJECT WORKSHEET 2

What Is Science?

Scientific Inquiry of a Common Belief

1. Common Belief

_____

_____

2. Hypothesis

_____

_____

Controlled Experiment to Test Hypothesis

3. Materials

_____

_____

_____

4. Manipulated Variable

_____

5. Responding Variable

_____

6. Variables Kept Constant

_____

_____

7. Procedure

_____

_____

_____

8. Method of Data Collection

_____

_____

_____

SCORING RUBRIC
Is It Really True?

In evaluating how well you complete the Chapter Project, your teacher will judge your work in four categories. In each, a score of 4 is the best rating.

	4	3	2	1
Developing a Hypothesis	Develops a hypothesis that is derived from an interesting common belief, is testable, and is well written.	Develops a hypothesis that is derived from a common belief, is testable, and is adequately written.	Develops a hypothesis that is derived from a common belief, is perhaps testable, and/or is not written well.	Develops a hypothesis that is not derived from a common belief, is not testable, and/or is poorly written.
Designing a Controlled Experiment	Experiment is imaginative and well thought out, effectively tests the hypothesis, includes a manipulated variable and a responding variable, keeps other variables constant, and has a superior plan to gather and organize data.	Experiment is adequately thought out, tests the hypothesis, includes a manipulated variable and a responding variable, keeps most other variables constant, and has a plan to gather and organize data.	Experiment is not well thought out, vaguely tests the hypothesis, includes a weak plan for variables, and has a poor plan to gather and organize data.	Experiment is poorly thought out, does not test the hypothesis, does not plan for variables, and/or has little or no plan to gather and organize data.
Gathering and Organizing Data	Gathers data from the experiment efficiently and competently, and creates a well-constructed data table from the data.	Gathers the data from the experiment adequately, and creates an adequate data table from the data.	Gathers some data from the experiment, and creates a poor data table from the data.	Gathers little data from the experiment, and creates no data table.
Creating Poster	Poster is attractive and informative, includes all the information from the experiment, includes a data table, and draws an insightful conclusion about the hypothesis.	Poster is neat and informative, includes most of the information from the experiment, includes a data table, and draws a conclusion about the hypothesis.	Poster somewhat informative, includes some of the information from the experiment, includes a data table, and draws an inaccurate or incomplete conclusion.	Poster is unorganized and not informative, includes little information from the experiment, does not include a data table, and/or draws no conclusion about the hypothesis.

Design and Build a Chair

The following steps will walk you through the Chapter Project. Use the hints and detailed directions as you guide your students through design, test phase, presentation, and reflection.

Chapter Project Overview

In this project, students will design and make a functional chair. Constructing a chair may seem like a large and daunting task for your middle school students. Yet, by following a simple process—namely the technology design process—your students will be able to successfully complete the project. Students will have to experiment with cardboard to figure out the best method of assembling the chair. Through this activity, students will be given an opportunity to experience the technology design process utilizing very inexpensive materials.

In designing and building their chairs, students will work through the stages in the technology design process:

- Identifying a need: The need is to develop a chair made entirely of cardboard.

- Researching the problem: Students will investigate what a standard chair height is, and they will conduct experiments to determine the strength of the cardboard materials.

- Designing the solution: Students will brainstorm possible designs.

- Building a prototype: Students will make a sketch of their design as a prototype. If there is time, you might encourage students to build a prototype using index cards.

- Troubleshooting and redesigning: After students receive a go-ahead from you, they will build their chairs. Once a chair has been made, students will test the chair to see if it will hold 20 kilograms of books. If not, students will troubleshoot, redesign, and build again.

- Communicating the solution: Each student or group will present the final product to the class.

This project could be carried out by individual students or by students in small groups. Working in a group may be more similar to the way that engineering teams work together in private industry. If small groups are your preference, make sure that students of differing abilities are in each group.

Distribute the Project Overview. Review the Project Rules. You may also want to hand out the Scoring Rubric, so students will understand what is expected of them.

Set a deadline for the project presentation and some interim dates for each task. Have students copy the dates in their Project Timeline.

Distribute Project Worksheets 1 and 2. After students have read the worksheets, answer any questions about the process they will use to design and build their chairs. Explain that Worksheet 2 reflects the steps in the technology design process that students will learn about as they read the chapter.

Materials and Preparation

You will want to make sure that there is enough cardboard for the students to complete the project. The chairs should be constructed of corrugated cardboard 5/32-inches thick, with an edge crush test (ECT) rating of 32 lb/in. "Standard duty," single-wall boxes are usually made from 200-pound per-square-inch (psi) burst-strength cardboard, which translates to a 32 psi ECT rating. Note that the cardboard should not span large, flat horizontal areas unsupported because it has limited strength in this capacity. Cardboard that has a crease or fold has had its strength compromised and therefore should be avoided. You might consider asking students to gather cardboard prior to beginning the project. It may be necessary to purchase some cardboard from an art supply store.

Students will also need a cutting tool such as scissors available for their use. Supervise the use of all cutting tools. An alternative strategy would be for you to cut the cardboard according to students' instructions, though this would be time consuming. It would also deny students the opportunity to make mistakes and redesign as necessary.

Students will also need metric rulers both in carrying out their research and constructing their chairs.

The rules of the project include that each chair should support 20 kilograms of books. Using a balance, work with students or groups to gather and find the mass of various books around the classroom. Then, put together a 20-kg stack of books for each group.

Keep Students on Track—Tasks 1–3

Talk to each group, and make sure they have done research about how chairs are put together and met for a brainstorming session to review each member's ideas about chair construction. It might be a good idea to talk with each group during the initial meeting. Make sure members take each other's ideas seriously. Point out that brainstorming involves putting forward the most creative ideas anyone can think of, and no idea should be dismissed out of hand.

Make sure groups are taking into consideration the constraints spelled out by the rules of the project, including that the chair should be completely made of cardboard, with no tape or staples holding it together. Discuss with each group how the members might go about designing interlocking pieces that would keep the chair together.

Encourage students to narrow their ideas to those that might have the best possibility of being functional. Make sure students are well on their way to making their prototype sketches. Emphasize that these sketches should show the dimensions of the chair in metric units.

Keep Students on Track—Tasks 4–5

Review the prototype made by each group. Check to see that the sketches are detailed with measurements of parts of the chair indicated. Point out that these sketches should show where students might cut slits in the cardboard pieces to push one piece into another.

Encourage students to begin collecting the cardboard necessary to make their chairs.

Explain that as they begin construction, they should stop anytime something doesn't seem to be working and examine their prototypes for flaws. Tell students that redesigning can take place at any point in the design process.

Keep Students on Track—Task 6

Check to see that all groups have completed the initial construction of their chairs. Have students check to make sure their chairs support 20 kilograms of books. For groups whose chair does not support this mass, provide hints about ways in which they could redesign their chairs.

Encourage groups to rethink their original designs if the chair does not work. Emphasize that troubleshooting and redesigning are an essential part of the technology design process.

Chapter Project Wrap Up

As you review each student or group's constructed chair, you may wish to have the members "talk you through" the presentation. Make suggestions for organizing the presentation into a logical report.

Provide class time for presentations. Allow each student or group to present its chair, explain how the chair was constructed, and describe the process that resulted in the design. Encourage other students to ask questions.

Encourage students to evaluate how well they accomplished what they set out to do, including how well the final product matched the prototype sketch that was used in constructing the chair. Invite students to make suggestions about what they think would have made the project better.

Extension

The design process can be used for a number of projects. For example, students might design cardboard tables or balsa-wood airplanes capable of gliding a specific distance.

PROJECT OVERVIEW

Design and Build a Chair

How can you make a chair out of cardboard that will support the weight of several textbooks? This may seem like a difficult task. But by following the technology design process, you will be able to complete the project successfully.

First you will do research on how chairs in your school and home are put together. Then you will meet with your group and brainstorm ideas about how your chair can be constructed in a way that it will support weight. You and other group members will make a sketch that will serve as a prototype, a model for your final product. Once your teacher has approved your design, you will work with your group in constructing a chair out of cardboard. After testing your chair, you will troubleshoot problems and redesign as necessary. At the end of the project, your group will present your finished chair to the class.

Project Rules

- Carry out research on how chairs are put together by examining several chairs found at home and at school. Make notes on design features you think could be used in constructing a chair for the Chapter Project.

- Meet with your group, and discuss individual members' research on chair construction. Brainstorm ideas about a chair design. Encourage one another to express any ideas that might work in the chair construction, and then through discussion narrow the ideas to ones that will likely be usable.

- Evaluate the constraints on the construction of the chair, including the rules about the materials that must be used.

- Use no more than 4 square meters of cardboard in constructing the chair.

- Construct a chair with a back and sides.

- Do not use tape or staples to hold the chair together.

- Make a detailed prototype sketch that includes all the dimensions of the chair in metric units.

- Construct a chair using your sketch as a guide. Test whether the chair will support 20 kilograms of books.

- Troubleshoot and redesign the chair as necessary.

- Prepare a presentation to the class of your constructed chair. As part of your presentation, you will explain the process you used in designing and constructing the chair. Your presentation will also include a demonstration that the chair can support at least 20 kilograms of books.

Project Hints

- In carrying out the research stage of the design process, examine as many chairs as possible to see how they are constructed. Antique, straight-back chairs often have pieces that fit together without using nails or staples. Examine how these chairs are put together.

- Make as detailed a prototype sketch as possible. Your sketch should have labels that show the measurements of all dimensions of the chair, such as the length and width of the base and the areas of the back, sides, and seat.

- Consider constructing the base of the chair with a series of interlocking cardboard pieces. Interlocking pieces can be constructed by cutting cardboard to the desired shapes and then using scissors to cut slits in each of the pieces so that one piece will slip into another.

- Make sure none of the cardboard pieces you use to construct the chair have a crease. Creased cardboard is weak and may cause your chair to fail when trying to support 20 kilograms of books.

- In constructing the chair, try to follow your sketch as closely as possible.

- When you have completed the chair, test whether it will support 20 kilograms of books. If it does not, redesign as necessary. When you redesign, try to use as many pieces of your original construction as you can.

Project Timeline

Task	Due Date
1. Complete research for Worksheet 1.	_____
2. Decide on the design of the chair.	_____
3. Complete the prototype sketch for Worksheet 1.	_____
4. Collect and test materials and designs.	_____
5. Construct a chair.	_____
6. Test, troubleshoot, and redesign.	_____
7. Prepare class presentation.	_____
8. Present the chair to the class.	_____

PROJECT WORKSHEET 1

Researching Chair Design

Researching the Problem

1. What chairs did you examine in your research?

   _____

   _____

   _____

2. Which design features of the chairs you examined could you use in the construction of your group's chair?

   _____

   _____

   _____

   _____

Designing a Solution

3. As your group brainstorms ways you might construct a chair, take notes of ideas that might be good to use in the design.

   _____

   _____

   _____

   _____

   _____

   _____

   _____

   _____

Building a Prototype

On a separate sheet of paper, make a detailed sketch of the design of your group's chair. Bring your sketch to a group meeting, and work together to make a final sketch of the group's design.

PROJECT WORKSHEET 2
Technology Design Process

For each of the stages of the technology design process in the chart below, you should record some notes about what was completed and done during the project. These notes will be useful as you prepare your final presentation. You may need additional sheets of paper to keep notes of what redesigning you or your group did for the project. The first box has been completed for you.

Stage	Notes
Identifying a Need	We need to design and build a chair out of cardboard. The chair must have a back and sides, must support 20 kilograms of books, and must not include tape or staples.
Researching the Problem	
Designing a Solution	
Building a Prototype	
Troubleshooting and Redesigning	
Communicating the Solution	

Name _____ Date_____ Class_____

Design and Build a Chair

In evaluating how well you complete the Chapter Project, your teacher will judge your work in four categories. In each, a score of 4 is the best rating.

	4	3	2	1
Creating Prototype Sketch	Makes a prototype sketch that shows originality of design and a thorough understanding of how to make a chair that will support 20 kilograms of books.	Makes a prototype sketch that shows some originality of design and an adequate understanding of how to make a chair that will support 20 kilograms of books.	Makes a prototype sketch that shows an adequate design, but an incomplete understanding of how to make a chair that will support 20 kilograms of books.	Makes a prototype sketch that is incomplete and/or shows a lack of understanding of how to make a chair that will support 20 kilograms of books.
Constructing Chair	Chair is attractive and well constructed with a seat and a back, uses neither tape nor staples, and easily supports 20 kilograms of books.	Chair is adequately constructed with a seat and a back, uses neither tape nor staples, and adequately supports 20 kilograms of books.	Chair is constructed with a seat and a back, uses some tape or staples to keep the chair together, and/or supports less than 20 kilograms of books.	Chair is poorly constructed, uses tape or staples to hold it together, and/or supports much less than 20 kilograms of books.
Presenting the Chair to the Class	Makes a thorough and interesting presentation that includes a clear, accurate description of the chair and an engaging explanation of the design process.	Makes a thorough presentation that includes an adequate description of the chair and an adequate explanation of the design process.	Makes a presentation that includes a partial description of the chair and/or a disorganized explanation of the design process.	Makes a presentation that is incomplete or includes numerous errors in the description of the chair and/or explanation of the design process.
Participating in the Group	Takes a lead in planning, constructing, and presenting the chair.	Participates in all aspects of planning, constructing, and presenting the chair.	Participates in most aspects of planning, constructing, and presenting the chair.	Plays a minor role in the planning, constructing, and presenting the chair.

Design and Build a Scale Model

The following steps will walk you through the Chapter Project. Use the hints and detailed directions as you guide your students through design, test phase, presentation, and reflection.

Chapter Project Overview

In this project, students will work individually or in small groups to design and build a three-dimensional model of a building or a room. Students will make metric measurements or find the actual dimensions of a structure and then build their models to scale.

To introduce this project, have students describe some models with which they are familiar. These might include doll houses, maps and globes, museum displays, and the anatomical models seen in doctors' offices, as well as hobby-shop models of boats, airplanes, cars, trains, and animals. Point out any models you might have in the classroom.

Discuss with students what a model is. Remind them that a model is a representation of a complex object or process. Models can be physical, mathematical, or computer-generated. Explain that in this project they will make a physical model. Then, explain that a scale model is a model in which all the parts are made or tested relative to all the other parts. Tell students that their models will be made by scaling down the actual measurements of rooms and buildings, as well as some objects in the rooms.

If students will be working in groups rather than individually, explain that each member of a group will make measurements of a structure or find the actual dimensions of a structure and convert those measurements to scale. Members will then collaborate in building the model.

Distribute Project Overview. You also may want to distribute copies of the Scoring Rubric. Review and discuss the Project Rules and the Scoring Rubric to make sure students understand what is expected of them. Encourage students to ask questions about the assignment.

Assign due dates for each task listed on the second page of the Project Overview. Use the following information to assign due dates. Students should be able to choose the room or building to be modeled, decide on a scale, and convert the actual dimensions during the first week. The second week should be spent choosing and testing materials and constructing the models. Students should spend the final day of the project preparing and practicing their presentations.

Set a deadline for the presentation of models and some interim dates for the tasks. Have students copy the dates in their Project Timeline.

Distribute the Project Worksheet 1 and Worksheet 2. After students have read the worksheets, ask if they have any questions.

Before students begin, make sure they realize that the major objective of this project is to create a scale model and not necessarily a realistic model. If students are unsure how to determine an appropriate scale, suggest they compare the actual measurements of the smallest and largest part or object to be included in the model. Also suggest that if rooms are being modeled, no more than ten objects in the room should be included in the models.

Materials and Preparation

Although individual students or groups will decide for themselves what materials to use in building their models, you might want to provide some basic materials and tools. Models of rooms and their contents as well as most buildings can be constructed from thin, flexible pieces of cardboard or construction paper, which can be glued or taped into place. Some students might also wish to use flexible wire, craft sticks, pipe cleaners, or toothpicks to make their models.

You might consider building a scale model of your classroom and some of its major components so that students can see an actual three-dimensional scale model of a room with which they are familiar.

Keep Students on Track—Tasks 1–3

Check to see that students have chosen a structure to model and have measured or found the actual dimensions of a room and its contents or a building.

At this time it is important to check the scales proposed by students for their models. Make sure each scale can be used to make the smallest part or object that will be modeled as well as the largest part or object.

Keep Students on Track—Tasks 3–4

Students should be making their conversions at this point in the project. To make the process simpler, you might suggest that students round the actual dimensions of the room to the nearest whole number of meters. For example, if a room is 5.46 m wide and 7.74 m long, students might round these dimensions to 5 m and 8 m.

Check to see that students are thinking about what kinds of materials they might use to make their models.

Keep Students on Track—Task 5

All students should have begun constructing their models at this point. Ask leading questions to determine if all students have begun this phase of the project. If you made a scale model of your classroom, use it to explain how you made one or two of the objects included in the model.

Students should also start thinking about what they will say during their presentations. Again, if you've made the scale model of your classroom, use it to provide a brief presentation similar to the presentations you expect from your students.

Keep Students on Track—Tasks 6–7

All students should now be finished with their projects and should be ready to present their models. You might want to provide a sign-up sheet for students to schedule their own presentations.

Lead a discussion that focuses on the limitations of any model. Then have students suggest some of the limitations of their models.

Chapter Project Wrap Up

Allow each student or group of students about 5 minutes to make a presentation. Encourage the rest of the class to provide constructive feedback on the models and presentations and ask a few questions of each student or group.

Extension

Have students pick one object or part of their models and suggest ways to make the object or part more realistic without sacrificing scale. For example, students might try to model the volume or mass of the object or part by using different materials to model the object or part.

PROJECT OVERVIEW

Design and Build a Scale Model

For this project, you will make a three-dimensional model either of a room or a building and some of the objects in it. To make your model, you will first measure or find out the dimensions of the structure to be modeled. You will record these values in a data table. After comparing the measurements, you will convert them to scale. This means that you will decide how much smaller to make each object in your model. After the measurements have been scaled, you will choose materials to build your model. Once your scale model is complete, you will present it to the class and briefly explain how you made it. You might also discuss any problems you had while constructing the model and how you solved these problems.

Project Rules

- Write a plan to describe how you will carry out this project. Have your plan approved by your teacher.

- If you are making a scale model of a building, do research to find out the actual dimensions of the structure.

- If you are making a model of a room and the objects in the room, use a metric ruler or meter stick to make the measurements.

- Decide on a scale for your model and the materials you will use. Review this information with your teacher before you begin making or converting any measurements.

- Work on your project each day so that you meet the project deadlines given to you by your teacher.

- Follow the safety guidelines as you construct your model.

Project Hints

- If you are making a scale model of a room, study the room to decide which objects you will include in your model. Choose no more than 10 objects to include in your model.

- Compare the largest and smallest dimensions of the parts/object(s) that will be modeled. This will help you choose a scale that neither is too large nor too small.

- Before you start constructing the model, use graph paper to make a sketch, to scale, of the parts of your model.

- The materials you use to make your model will depend on what you are modeling. Scissors, tape and glue, a metric ruler, and sheets of thin, flexible cardboard will probably be useful for most scale models. Other materials you might use include construction paper, scraps of fabric, plastic transparencies, thin, flexible wire, craft sticks, polystyrene shapes, and toothpicks.

- Put all of the pieces of your model in their correct positions on a tabletop, the floor, or a desktop before you glue or tape anything in place. This will give you an idea of what your finished product will look like. This trial run will also allow you to see if you've made any major mistakes in converting the measurements.

Project Timeline

Task	Due Date
1. Choose a room or a building to model.	_____
2. Measure and record the dimensions of everything to be modeled.	_____
3. Convert measurements to scale and record the values in the data table.	_____
4. Choose materials to make your model.	_____
5. Start constructing your scale model.	_____
6. Finish the model and start preparing your presentation.	_____
7. Present your model and explain how you constructed it.	_____

Name _____ Date_____ Class_____

PROJECT WORKSHEET 1
Planning the Model

This worksheet will help you get started making a design for your scale model of a building or a room.

1. Choose a room or building that you think might be interesting to model. Write the name and location of the room or the building, and tell why you chose that room or building.

_____

_____

_____

_____

_____

2. If you are going to make a model of a room, write the name of the room and the names of no more than 10 objects that you will include in your model in the first column of the data table on Worksheet 2. If you are modeling a building, write the name of the structure in the first column.

3. Compare the largest and smallest measurements. Use these values to decide on a scale.

   Actual unit   **Scale unit**

   _____   =   _____

4. Make a list of materials that you plan to use to make your model.

_____

_____

_____

_____

_____

Name _____ Date _____ Class _____

PROJECT WORKSHEET 2

Recording the Measurements

Use the table below to organize your data. Use another sheet of paper, if necessary.

Find out or measure the length, width, and height of each part/object that will be included in your model. Record these values in the appropriate columns of the data table.

Building/ Room and Objects	Actual Length	Scaled Length	Actual Width	Scaled Width	Actual Height	Scaled Height

SCORING RUBRIC

Design and Build a Scale Model

In evaluating how well you complete the Chapter Project, your teacher will judge your work in four categories. In each, a score of 4 is the best rating.

	4	3	2	1
Making and Converting Measurements and Doing Research	Accurately makes, records, and converts all measurements necessary for a complete scale model; does extensive research, if necessary	Accurately makes, records, and converts most of the measurements necessary for a complete scale model; does adequate research, if necessary	Accurately makes, records, and converts only half of the measurements necessary for a complete scale model; does minimal research, if necessary	Accurately makes, records, and converts very few of the measurements necessary for a complete scale model; does little or no research, even if it is necessary to do so
Collecting and Testing the Materials to Make the Scale Model	Collects and tests all materials necessary to make a complete scale model; collects alternative materials in case problems arise with chosen materials	Collects and tests most of the materials necessary to make a complete scale model; collects a few alternative materials in case problems arise with chosen materials	Collects and tests only one type of material to make a complete scale model; does not provide alternative materials in case problems arise with the chosen material	Collects but does not test any of the materials to make a complete scale model; does not provide any alternative materials should problems arise with chosen materials
Making the Scale Model	Makes an accurate sketch on graph paper and accurately constructs a complete scale model that includes the boundaries of the room or structure and all of the objects within the boundaries	Makes a fairly accurate sketch on graph paper and accurately constructs a nearly complete scale model that includes the boundaries of the room or structure and most of the objects within the boundaries	Makes a sketch on graph paper and accurately constructs some of the scale model that includes the boundaries of the room or structure and some of the objects within the boundaries	Makes an inaccurate sketch on graph paper and constructs some or all of the model, paying little or no attention to scale or accuracy; includes some of the boundaries of the room or structure and only a few of the objects within the boundaries
Presenting the Results	Makes a complete, well-organized presentation on how to make a scale model as well as discusses the	Makes an adequate presentation on how to make a scale model as well as discusses at least one of the	Makes an appropriate but disorganized presentation on how to make a scale model, but does not discuss	Makes a poor presentation that is hard to follow; does not explain how to make a scale model nor the limitations of a

Breaking It Down

The following steps will walk you through the Chapter Project. Use the hints and detailed directions as you guide your students through designing and conducting their experiments and preparing their reports.

Chapter Project Overview

When you introduce the project, ask guiding questions to determine what students already know about decomposition. Show them the compost chamber you made. (See Materials and Preparation below.) Explain that each student or group will need to make two chambers, one for the control and the other for testing one variable. Ask: What variables are involved in the experiment? (*Moisture, oxygen, temperature, and activity of soil organisms*)

Distribute the Project Overview, and let students review the Project Rules and procedures. Encourage questions and comments. Also distribute the Project Worksheet, which provides instructions for constructing the chambers and beginning the composting process. You may wish to divide the class into small groups. If so, let groups meet to begin discussing ideas for their experiments.

Remind students to think about how to set up the experiment so only one variable is different in the test chamber. Instruct students to consider the types of changes they will look for as evidence of decomposition. Some students may decide to measure the temperatures in the two chambers or the volumes of decomposing material. (A warmer temperature and a smaller volume indicate a higher rate of decomposition.) Encourage students to record observations of the color, odor, and particle size of the decomposing material. Emphasize that each student or group must submit its plan for your review and approval before beginning the experiment.

If students are working in groups, emphasize that group members may divide the project responsibilities among themselves in any way they wish so long as every group member takes part in planning the experiment,

observing changes in the chambers, analyzing results, and developing the project report. Emphasize that *every* group member also should be prepared to answer questions about the experiment.

Set a deadline for the project report and interim dates. Have students record those dates in the Project Timeline at the end of the Project Overview.

Materials and Preparation

Advance Preparation Before introducing the project, construct a compost chamber yourself as a prototype, following the instructions on the Project Worksheet. Fill the chamber with chopped leaves, but do not add water. After you show students the chamber, set it aside until the end of the project so students can compare their composted material with the original material.

Ask students to help you collect 2-liter, clear plastic soda bottles for making the chambers. Each student or group will need six bottles.

For the material to be composted, use chopped leaves, which will allow students to complete the project in a relatively short period of time with minimal mess and odor. The leaves can be chopped using a lawnmower with a catch bag. (Avoid oak leaves, which decompose slowly.)

Each group investigating the effect of soil organisms will need about 75 mL of ordinary garden soil—do not use commercial potting soil. The garden soil will introduce bacteria and other microorganisms to the test chamber. Students can also add earthworms, which will aerate the mixture and help break down the leaves. A class earthworm farm could serve as the source of these organisms.

Students investigating a variable other than temperature should keep their chambers in a location that does not get direct sunlight and is not exposed to heating or cooling sources. Students investigating the effect of temperature will need either a sunny (or lamp-warmed) location or access to a refrigerator.

Keep Students on Track—Tasks 1–2

When you review the experiment designs, check to see whether each student or group has identified all major variables—chamber contents, temperature, moisture content, amount of oxygen (stirring), and soil organisms—and will keep all variables the same in both chambers except the one being investigated with the test chamber.

Check each student's or group's planned data table to make sure it includes criteria for assessing decomposition and some way to differentiate between the two chambers.

Keep Students on Track—Task 3

Provide chopped leaves, water, soil, and earthworms. Also provide thermometers so students can measure and record the waste's starting temperature.

CAUTION: *As groups conduct their daily observations, make sure that any students who are allergic to molds do not sniff or handle the chambers' contents. Caution all students to wash their hands thoroughly after each observation.*

Consult with students regularly to determine whether they are encountering any problems and need to adjust their experiment plans.

Keep Students on Track—Task 4

Make your compost chamber available so students can compare its contents with the composted material in their own chambers.

Help students who are having trouble quantifying their data by suggesting that they measure the volume and/or temperature of the composted material.

Discuss with students how they will present their reports. You may want them to give an oral presentation to the class, prepare a poster session, or turn in a written report to you.

Chapter Project Wrap Up

If students are giving an oral presentation or a poster session, tell them how much time each student or group will be allowed. Encourage students to keep this time limit in mind as they prepare their reports.

As part of the project report, students might dump their chambers' contents in two piles on layers of newspaper. Let students examine each other's composted material.

As students present their reports, encourage other students to ask questions. Give each student or group positive feedback.

After all students have presented their reports, have students compare results in a class discussion. Elicit their ideas about the "ideal" conditions for decomposition, and have them list those conditions in their notebooks.

Extension

Suggest that groups repeat their experiments using one of the following options:

- Use grass clippings or whole leaves instead of chopped leaves.

- Use food scraps mixed with chopped leaves and soil as the material to be composted. (Use only fruit and vegetable scraps, not meat scraps, which produce foul odors during decomposition.)

- Moisten the test chamber with "acid rain" (a weak vinegar solution).

Name _____ Date _____ Class _____

Breaking It Down

What happens to a tree that falls or a raccoon that dies in the woods? In nature, dead and decaying materials are broken down by organisms called decomposers. Decomposers recycle basic nutrients in the decaying materials back into the ecosystem. In this project, you will take a close look at decomposition by setting up compost chambers.

First, you will think about the major variables that affect decomposition. Then you will plan an experiment to test one of those variables. You'll build two compost chambers: one, the control, to keep under "normal" conditions; and the other for testing the variable you have chosen. Your teacher will give you the instructions for building the chambers.

After your teacher reviews your experiment plan, you'll fill both chambers with chopped leaves. As you conduct your experiment, you'll check the two chambers every day to observe and compare what is happening to the leaves.

At the end of the experiment, you will analyze the data that you have recorded and make a conclusion about how the variable affected decomposition. Then you will report your results and conclusions.

Project Rules

- Choose one of these variables to test:
  - **Moisture:** Use more or less water in the test chamber than in the control.
  - **Oxygen:** Stir the leaves in the test chamber every day or two.
  - **Temperature:** Keep the test chamber in a warmer or cooler place than the control chamber.
  - **Activity of soil organisms:** Add soil to the test chamber. Soil contains bacteria and other organisms that decompose organic material. You can also add earthworms. Earthworms will break the leaves down into smaller pieces and mix them with the soil.
  - Develop a hypothesis about how the variable you chose will affect decomposition in the test chamber.
- Design an experiment to test the variable you chose. Remember to keep *all other* variables the same in both chambers.
- As part of your plan, decide what changes you will look for in the chambers' contents. You could observe its appearance and odor. You also could measure its temperature or its volume, or both. (A higher temperature and a smaller volume indicate more decomposition.) Design a table for recording your data.

- Carry out your experiment. Observe the chambers every day, and record your observations and measurements in your data table. **CAUTION:** *Wash your hands thoroughly after each time you handle the compost chambers. If you are allergic to molds, do not smell the decomposing material.*

- At the end of the experiment, analyze the data you collected. Review your original hypothesis. Then write a conclusion that states what your experiment showed you about how the variable affects decomposition.

- Prepare a report that describes the materials and procedures you used for the experiment and the results you observed. Your report could be a written summary, a poster, a bulletin board display, or another product.

- Present your report to the class.

Suggested Materials

- To build two compost chambers, you will need six 2-liter, clear plastic soda bottles. Make sure the bottles are thoroughly washed, rinsed, and dried.

- Your teacher will provide chopped leaves for filling the chambers. Your teacher will also provide thermometers, water, soil, earthworms, hand lenses, beakers, and any other materials you will need for the experiment.

Project Hints

- If you decide to do a written report, think about how you will present it to the class. Just reading it aloud word-for-word might be boring for your listeners. You might want to summarize each part of the report. You also could use audiovisual materials, such as an enlarged copy of your data table. Try to make your presentation interesting.

- If you decide to make a poster or other visual display, make sure it summarizes the major points about your experiment—the variable you chose, the procedure you used, your results, and your conclusion. Also make sure the poster or display can be seen easily by everyone in your class.

- Practice your presentation before you give it to the class. Make sure your presentation fits the time limit your teacher gives you.

Project Timeline

Task	Due Date
1. Design your experiment and present the plan to your teacher.	_____
2. Revise your plan, if necessary.	_____
3. Carry out your experiment.	_____
4. Prepare a report about your experiment.	_____
5. Present your report to the class.	_____

PROJECT WORKSHEET

How to Set Up Your Compost Chambers

These directions tell you how to make one compost chamber. You will need to make two chambers for your experiment.

Materials

- 3 clear plastic soda bottles, 2-liter size, one with screw-on cap
- wax pencil or marking pen
- drawing compass
- scissors
- pushpin

- duct tape
- masking tape
- chopped leaves
- tap water or pond water
- If you will test soil organisms: soil, earthworms

Making the Chambers *Review the safety guidelines in your student text.*

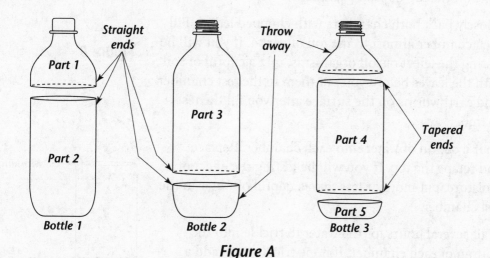

Figure A

1. With the wax pencil or marking pen, draw lines around the bottles as shown in Figure A. (*Hint:* An easy way to draw the lines is to lay the bottle down against one corner of a drawer or box, hold the pencil or pen against the bottle where you want to draw a line, and have a partner slowly turn the bottle around.)

2. With the point of the compass, poke a hole in each line you drew.

3. Push the scissors' point into one hole and cut along the line, all the way around the bottle. Cut each of the other lines the same way.

PROJECT WORKSHEET, CONTINUED

4. Throw away the screw-cap for Bottle 2 and the base and top of Bottle 3. You'll have five parts left.

5. Use the pushpin to poke small holes in parts 1, 3, 4, and 5 as shown in Figure B. Do *not* poke holes in part 2. (Part 2 will collect dripwater.)

6. Assemble the parts as shown in Figure B.

7. Tape the parts together as shown in Figure C. Use duct tape to tightly seal the joint between parts 3 and 4. Use masking tape to loosely tape the joint between parts 4 and 1 and the joint between parts 2 and 3. Masking tape will let you remove the top and the base.

8. Repeat Steps 1–7 to make a second chamber.

Starting the Composting Process

9. Take off the top of each chamber.

10. Loosely pack both chambers with chopped leaves. Fill each chamber almost to the top of part 4. If you will be testing the effect of soil organisms, mix a cupful of soil with the leaves before you put them in the test chamber. Add earthworms on the surface after you fill the test chamber.

11. Pour a cupful of water into each chamber. Replace and retape the top. If you will be testing the effect of moisture, put more or less than a cupful of water in the test chamber.

12. Wait several hours for the water to trickle into the bottom of each chamber. If none trickles out, add a little more water until about one-half cup collects in the bottom. (If you are testing the effect of moisture, more or less than one-half cup may trickle out.)

13. When you do your experiment, pour the dripwater back through each chamber every few days. To do this, unscrew the cap, remove the bottom, pour the dripwater into the chamber, quickly replace the bottom, and screw the cap on again. If you will be investigating the effect of oxygen, stir the material in the test chamber every time you pour dripwater through it.

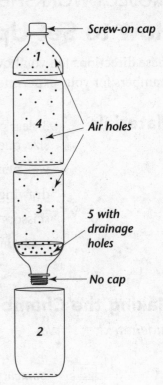

Figure B

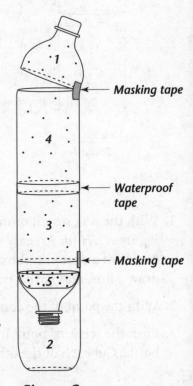

Figure C

SCORING RUBRIC

Breaking It Down

In evaluating how well you complete the Chapter Project, your teacher will judge your work in the following categories. In each, a score of 4 is the best rating.

	4	3	2	1
Designing the Experiment	Hypothesis is clear and testable. Plan involves controlling all variables except the one being tested. Data table allows daily recording of observations and two or more measurements.	Hypothesis is clear and testable. Plan involves controlling most variables except the one being tested. Data table allows daily recording of observations and at least one measurement.	Hypothesis is not clearly stated. Plan omits controlling one major variable. Data table allows daily recording of observations but no measurements.	Hypothesis is not clearly stated. Plan involves changing more than one variable or does not address controlling other variables. Data table has major flaws.
Conducting the Experiment	Closely follows original plan. Measurements and observations are precise, made daily, and recorded clearly in the data table.	Follows original plan, with minor deviations in controlling some variables. Measurements and observations are careful, made daily, and recorded clearly.	Follows original plan but does not carefully control all variables other than the one being tested. Observations are made daily but not recorded clearly.	Does not follow original plan. Observations are not made daily and not recorded clearly.
Reporting Results	Report, poster, or other product is well-organized and effectively summarizes experiment procedures and results. Class presentation is clear and interesting.	Report, poster, or other product is fairly well-organized and focuses on experiment procedures and results. Class presentation is clear.	Report, poster, or other product is disorganized and unfocused. Class presentation is clear but includes many minor points.	Report, poster, or other product is disorganized, unfocused, or incomplete. Class presentation is unclear and includes many minor points.
Working Cooperatively (optional)	Takes a lead in planning and carrying out the experiment and in preparing the report and class presentation.	Actively participates in planning and carrying out the experiment and in preparing the report and class presentation.	Participates in most aspects of planning and carrying out the experiment and in preparing the report and class presentation as directed by others.	Participates minimally in planning and carrying out the experiment and in preparing the report and class presentation.

Energy Audit

The following steps will walk you through the Chapter Project. Use the hints and detailed directions as you guide your students through their evaluation of energy uses in the school.

Chapter Project Overview

Distribute the Project Overview, and let students review the Project Rules and procedures. Answer any questions students might have. Encourage students to offer their ideas about areas they could study—their own classroom, a computer lab, the kitchen and cafeteria, the gym, the auditorium, the administration offices, school transportation, and the like. Then take the class on a tour of the school building and grounds so students can observe different energy uses. Back in the classroom, ask students to contribute to a list on the board of the different energy uses they observed.

Distribute the Project Worksheet. The first two sections of the worksheet provide instructions on how to read an electric meter and gas meter. CAUTION: *An adult must accompany students to read the school's meters and heating-fuel gauges.* The last section of the worksheet lists the different units used to measure forms of energy—kilowatt-hours (electricity), cubic feet or therms (natural gas), and gallons (heating oil and gasoline). The section also provides useful equivalents for converting the various units into one common unit, BTUs (British thermal units). Explain to students that converting different units into the same unit will make it easier for them to compare energy uses.

Divide the class into small groups, and let each group meet briefly to choose an area of the school to study. Monitor the groups' choices to avoid duplication. As an alternative, you could assign an area to each group.

Emphasize that students may divide the project responsibilities among group members in any way they wish, as long as *every* group member takes part in all aspects of the project and can answer questions about the group's work.

Materials and Preparation

Meet with your school principal—or ask the principal to visit your class—to discuss the project's requirements, particularly the need for students to visit areas that are usually off-limits to them. Work out an acceptable procedure so students can have access to these areas. For example, a custodian or teacher's aide might accompany students while they gather data.

Obtain copies of the school's utility and fuel bills. Review these bills so you can answer questions students might have.

Students will not need any special materials for the project, but they will find it helpful to use calculators.

Keep Students on Track—Task 1

Remind students to use the Project Worksheet for help in reading electric and gas meters. It might be helpful for you to take each group to the meters and gauges. Remind students that they must calculate the percentage of the various kinds of energy their study area uses.

Students may convert all fuel-specific units (gallons, kilowatt-hours, therms or cubic feet) to the common unit of BTUs. Remind them that the Project Worksheet provides the equivalents they need in order to do this. Help students work through several conversions as practice examples.

Keep Students on Track—Tasks 2–3

Check each group's data table to make sure students are collecting and recording data. Provide copies of the school's fuel and utility bills at this point. Answer any questions that students have about the bills.

Help students create a list of school personnel who are responsible for the operation of the school. Explain the project to these people before students contact them. It might be helpful for you to coordinate these contacts to limit as much as possible disruption of these people's work.

Keep Students on Track—Tasks 4–5

Encourage students to focus on major points in their reports and to look for ways to present information in visual displays. For example, students might include data tables and graphs in their reports.

If students have difficulty quantifying energy savings, suggest that they simply explain the effects of any changes they recommend. For example, if a room has drafty windows, the actual savings in energy used to heat the room is difficult to determine. Students may simply explain that by reducing the inflow of cold air from outdoors, the room will stay warm longer before the heating unit switches on.

Chapter Project Wrap Up

You may wish to coordinate the "peer review" of the reports. Groups could produce written comments on the report they review or simply discuss the report with the group that produced it. Remind students to be sensitive with their criticisms.

Discuss students' ideas about how the final proposal should be organized. You could have volunteers compile the proposal and present it to the entire class for discussion. Also discuss students' ideas about how to present the final proposal to the school principal or other official. You may want to invite the official to come to the classroom to hear students present their study results and recommendations orally. Or the class might choose to send their final written proposal to the official for his or her review. In either case, encourage the official to respond to students' ideas either in person or in writing.

Extension

Have teams survey and compare energy uses in several classrooms that are on different floors, face in different directions, or have different numbers of windows.

Let students make draft detectors to locate air leaks around windows in the classroom. Such detectors can be as simple as 15-cm strips of tissue paper taped to the sides and bottom of each window casing. Students could estimate the amount of cold or hot air leaking into the room by putting a plastic trash bag over each drafty spot and timing how long it takes for the bag to fill with air from outdoors. Based on the bag's volume and the fill time, students can calculate the volume of air coming into the room per hour.

Encourage interested students to continue their audits through the school year so they can observe how the seasons affect energy use.

Students could use the data on energy used for transportation to calculate how much fuel is needed, on average, to transport one student to and from school each day and for the year.

PROJECT OVERVIEW
Energy Audit

What types of fuel are used in your school? Electricity? Natural gas? Heating oil? How much energy is used for heating and cooling the building? How much is used for operating lights, computers, fans, and other electrical devices? How much for cooking and refrigeration in the cafeteria's kitchen? How much energy could your school save by making some changes? In this Chapter Project, you will study energy use in your school.

First, your group will choose one area of the school to study. For example, you could study your own classroom, a science lab or other special-use room, the cafeteria and kitchen, the gym, the auditorium, the school grounds, or school transportation. Your group will identify the types of energy used in that area and find out how much of each type of energy is used. As you study the area, you'll look for ways to reduce energy uses. When you finish studying the area, your group will prepare a written report of your findings and ideas for conserving energy. Then your group and another group will review each other's reports and make suggestions for improving them. The last step of the project will be to prepare a class proposal for conserving energy throughout the school.

Project Rules

- With your group, choose one area in the school to study. Survey the area to identify all the major energy uses.

- Identify the energy source for each use. Electricity, fuel oil, natural gas, and gasoline will probably be the major energy sources in your school, but you might find other sources, too.

- Determine the amount of energy used by each source.

- As you study energy uses, look for ways to reduce each use. Try to find practical ways that will not be expensive.

- Prepare a written report that describes what your group found out about energy use in the area you studied. Include your ideas for reducing energy use in the area.

- Give your report to another group so those students can give you suggestions for improving your report. Review the other group's report and give them your ideas, too.

- Revise your report based on the other group's suggestions and your own ideas. Then present your report to the class.

- Work with the rest of the class to prepare a final proposal about ways to save energy throughout the school. Your teacher may help your class present the proposal to the principal or another school official.

Project Hints

- To determine how much electricity and natural gas your school uses, you'll probably have to read some meters. The Project Worksheet explains how to read electric and gas meters. You may also need to read fuel gauges on vehicles or on a furnace. Your teacher will give you copies of the school's bills for electricity, natural gas, heating oil, and other fuels. You can use the bills to find out how much of each energy source the school used and what it cost.

- To find the energy use in some areas, you might have to ask adults who work there. If you are studying transportation, you may wish to survey students in your school. You will also need to get information from the department or company that operates the buses. Check with your teacher to find out whom to contact for information. Speak to the person beforehand to set up a convenient time for an interview. Prepare for the interview by writing out questions ahead of time.

- Observe the area you are studying at different times of the day and on different days. Patterns of energy use may vary throughout the day or from one day to another.

Project Timeline

Task	Due Date
1. Choose one area of the school to study.	_____
2. Identify the major energy uses in that area.	_____
3. Determine how much of each type of energy is used.	_____
4. Identify ways to reduce energy use in the area.	_____
5. Prepare a written report with your findings and recommendations.	_____
6. Present your report to the class.	_____

PROJECT WORKSHEET
Determining Energy Use
How to Read an Electric Meter

Electricity is measured in kilowatt-hours (kWh). Most electric meters have a row of five small, round dials, as shown below. On each dial, a needle points to a number. The first dial—the one on the far left—shows units of 10,000 kWh. The second dial shows units of 1,000 kWh. The third dial shows units of 100 kWh. The fourth dial shows units of 10 kWh. The last dial shows units of 1 kWh.

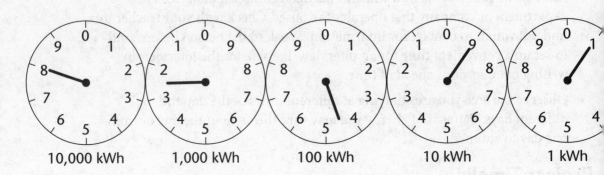

10,000 kWh	1,000 kWh	100 kWh	10 kWh	1 kWh

To take a meter reading, just write down the numbers on the dials from left to right. If the pointer is between two numbers, use the *lower* number. For the meter shown above, the reading is 82,491 kWh.

To find out how much electricity was used in a certain period, you need to read the meter at the beginning of the period and again at the end of the period, then subtract the first reading from the second reading.

1. The meter reading above was taken on February 15. The reading taken on January 15 was 81,965 kWh. How much electricity was used in the month between the two readings? _____ kWh

2. The next meter reading on March 15 was 83,023 kWh. How much electricity was used in the month between February 15 and March 15? _____ kWh

PROJECT WORKSHEET, CONTINUED

How to Read a Gas Meter

Natural gas is measured in therms or, more often, cubic feet (ft^3). Some gas meters have a row of dials like the dials on an electric meter. If the gas meter has a row of dials, you would read it just like you read an electric meter. Other gas meters have a digital display like the one shown below. With this kind of meter, you just read the number. To find out how many cubic feet of gas were used, multiply the number by 100.

3. What is the reading on this gas meter? How many cubic feet of gas were used?

_____

4. Last month's reading was 6,443. What is the difference between the two readings in cubic feet of gas?

_____

Energy Equivalents

As you saw in the above examples, different types of energy are measured in different units. How can you compare amounts of energy when the units are not the same? The answer is to convert the different units into the same unit. The common unit for measuring energy is the British thermal unit, or BTU. Use the list below to convert different energy units into BTUs.

Electricity	1 kWh = 3,413 BTUs
Natural gas	1 ft^3 = 1,000 BTUs; 1 therm = 100,000 BTUs
Gasoline	1 gallon = 125,000 BTUs
Heating Oil	1 gallon = 144,000 BTUs

5. Suppose a building used 852 kWh of electricity in one month. How many BTUs is that? _____ BTUs

6. Suppose it takes 68 gallons of gasoline to fill a school bus gas tank. How many BTUs is that? _____ BTUs

SCORING RUBRIC

Energy Audit

In evaluating how well you complete the Chapter Project, your teacher will judge your work in three categories. In each, a score of 4 is the best rating.

	4	3	2	1
Evaluating Energy Use	Correctly identifies every energy use in the area chosen for study. Collects and records data. Accurately calculates amount of each use in appropriate units and the cost. Converts all units to BTUs and calculates the area's total energy use in BTUs.	Correctly identifies all major energy uses. Collects and records data. Accurately calculates amount of each use in appropriate units. Converts units to BTUs or calculates the cost of each type of energy.	Correctly identifies all but one major energy use. Collects and records data incompletely. Calculates amount of each use in appropriate units with fair accuracy. Does not convert units to BTUs or calculate costs of energy uses.	Omits two or more major energy uses. Collects and records data only when prompted. Attempts to calculate amount of one or two uses. Does not convert units to BTUs or calculate costs of energy uses.
Preparing Written Report	Written report is well-organized and summarizes findings effectively. Recommendations for reducing energy use are practical and cost-effective. Class presentation is clear and interesting.	Written report is fairly well-organized and summarizes findings with few irrelevant details. Most recommendations for reducing energy use are practical. Class presentation is fairly clear and interesting.	Written report is somewhat disorganized and unfocused. Most recommendations for reducing energy use are practical. Class presentation is rather unclear and uninteresting.	Written report is disorganized and unfocused. Few recommendations for reducing energy use are practical. Class presentation is unclear and uninteresting.
Working Cooperatively	Takes a lead in planning and carrying out the study, preparing the group's written report and class presentation, and developing the class's final proposal.	Actively participates in planning and carrying out the study, preparing the group's written report and class presentation, and developing the class's final proposal.	Participates in most aspects of planning and carrying out the study, preparing the group's written report and class presentation, and developing the class's final proposal.	Participates marginally in planning and carrying out the study and in preparing the group's written report and class presentation. Does not participate in developing the class's final proposal.

A Precious Resource

The following steps will walk you through the Chapter Project. Use the hints and detailed instructions as you guide your students through the planning, assembly, testing, and presentation of their water treatment systems.

Chapter Project Overview

In this project, students will assemble and demonstrate a model water treatment system that consists of at least two steps.

To introduce the project, show students a container of tap water and a container of dirty water. Encourage students to brainstorm a list of ways by which the dirty water could be cleaned to look as clear as the tap water. Write the list on the chalkboard. Point out to students that in this project, they will make a model water treatment system to clean this dirty water.

Distribute the Project Overview and the Scoring Rubric. After students have read the pages, answer any questions they have and clarify what will be expected of them in this project. Set a deadline for the project presentation and some interim dates for checkpoints. Students can fill in these dates on the Project Timeline.

As students observe, create a "cleanness scale" that they can use to judge how well their model treatment systems have cleaned the dirty water.

1. Have on hand a large container of dirty water and a large container of tap water or distilled water, as well as five large graduated cylinders. Also, prepare ahead of time a container that contains a mixture of half dirty water and half clean water.

2. Place the graduated cylinders in a row on a table. Fill the first cylinder with dirty water. Fill the second cylinder three quarters full with dirty water and then fill to the top with clean water. Fill the third cylinder half full with dirty water and then fill to the top with clean water. Fill the fourth cylinder a quarter full with dirty water and fill to the top with clean water. Fill the last cylinder with clean water.

3. Have on hand a graduated cylinder that contains a half-and-half mixture of dirty water and clean water. Challenge students to compare this mixture to the mixtures in the "cleanness scale" and determine which it matches best. Point out that this will be the way in which they can determine how well they have cleaned water with their model treatment systems.

Distribute Project Worksheet 1. This activity can be done by pairs of students or in small groups.

Distribute Project Worksheet 2. This activity can be done by pairs of students or in small groups.

Materials and Preparation

You will need a supply of dirty water for both Worksheet 1 and for groups to use to test their systems. You can make dirty water by adding one teaspoon of fuller's earth per cup of tap water. (Fuller's earth is available at most hardware stores.) You can also collect a supply of dirty water from a local lake, river, or pond. Make or collect as much dirty water as you need at the beginning of the project so that the water will be consistently dirty for all groups and for every trial. Make sure that students understand that they should never taste this water, even after it is cleaned by their systems. Remind students to wash their hands with soap after they have handled the water.

For Worksheet 1, each group will need the following materials: dirty water, a 2-L clear plastic bottle with the bottom cut off, a large beaker to serve as a catch basin for filtered water, nylon fabric, a rubber band, fine sand, gravel of various sizes, activated charcoal, a coffee filter or some other kind of commercial filter, and various kinds of fabric.

Prepare the filtering apparatus for Worksheet 1 by cutting off the bottom of a 2-L clear plastic bottle, as shown in Figure 1a. Figure 1b shows how the neck of the bottle can be placed in a beaker, which will collect the filtered water.

Figure 1

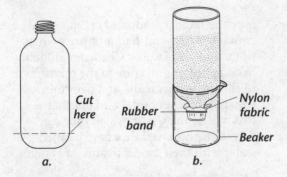

a.　　　　　　　b.

Clarify who will supply the materials needed for the model treatment systems that the students design. Materials may include those needed for coagulation, distillation, and filtration. Help students find materials that you cannot supply.

Keep Students on Track—Tasks 1–3

Review each student's design and flowchart on Worksheet 2. Help students who are having trouble designing a system of more than one step.

Keep Students on Track—Tasks 4–5

Review students' designs, making sure that each design has at least two steps. At this point, help students collect the materials they need to assemble and test their systems.

Advise students to use tap water for the first test of their treatment systems. They need to check for leaks or other problems. Encourage them to make necessary changes if leaks occur.

Keep Students on Track—Tasks 6–7

Provide each student with 1 L of dirty water to run through his or her model treatment system. Encourage students to make changes and repairs in the system in preparation for the presentation to the class. Help students troubleshoot their models.

Chapter Project Wrap Up

As you review students' model treatment systems, you may wish to have each student briefly walk you through his or her presentation to the class. Help students decide which process can be demonstrated and which process would take too long. For example, an aeration step could be presented, while a settling step would take too long.

Provide class time for presentations. Allow each student to present his or her model treatment system, demonstrate one part of the system, show the final product, and explain the processes involved in the steps of the system. Each student should indicate how much of the 1 L of dirty water the treatment system recovered and refer to the "cleanness scale" to show how well the system worked.

After all of the presentations have been made, discuss with students what conclusions they can draw from their work. Have them compare systems for similarities and differences as well as for how well each worked.

Encourage students to evaluate in their journals how well they accomplished what they set out to do and to make whatever suggestions they think could have made the project better.

Extension

Challenge students to design a water treatment system by using the best ideas from the projects presented. Encourage a few students to build and test such a system and report their findings to the class.

PROJECT OVERVIEW

A Precious Resource

Think of the water that you drink every day from a faucet at home or a drinking fountain at school. Compare that water to the water in a local river or lake. There's an obvious difference between the two, isn't there? You probably drink water from home or from a drinking fountain without thinking about it. But you might not even bathe or shower in water taken directly from a river or lake, much less drink it. Yet the water in the river or lake might just be the source of your drinking water. In this Chapter Project, you will get some idea of how dirty water is made safe to drink.

First, you will explore the filtration of water through various materials. As you will see, filtration is one way to clean water. Second, you will design a two-step model water treatment system that cleans dirty water. Third, you will assemble and test the treatment system you've designed. Finally, you will present your water treatment system to the class.

Project Rules

- Explore the filtration of water by completing Project Worksheet 1. After you have observed filtration, you may want to include this process as one of your steps. However, including filtration in your model treatment system is not required.

- Complete Project Worksheet 1. Use this worksheet to make your own design of a model water treatment system. This design must include at least two steps. That is, it should have more than one process to clean dirty water. To complete the worksheet, describe the steps, make a flowchart that represents the system, and make a sketch of the system. This design should include two steps for cleaning dirty water.

- Assemble and test the model treatment system. Gather the materials you need to assemble the system. Your teacher can provide some materials, but you may want to bring some items from home. When the system is complete, test it with tap water for leaks and other problems.

- Use your system to clean 1 L of dirty water. Find out how well your system works. Your treatment system will be evaluated according to how well it cleans water and how much water it recovers. The goal is to recover as much of the original 1 L of water as possible.

- Make your presentation to the class. In making this presentation, you and your group should describe the steps of the system, demonstrate at least one of the steps, and explain the processes involved. Also report your results.

Project Hints

- Study the figure in this chapter that shows drinking-water treatment. The processes used by a drinking-water treatment plant are those you and your group will want to consider using in your model treatment system.

- Make a list of all the ways that substances in water can be removed. Then think of simple ways such processes could be done in a model.

- Don't limit yourself to the processes described in your text. Be open to new ideas.

- Make sure the system you assemble is watertight. You want to recover as much clean water as possible. Leaks are your enemy!

Project Timeline

Task	Due Date
1. Complete Project Worksheet 1	_____
2. Complete Project Worksheet 2	_____
3. Complete design	_____
4. Assemble model treatment system	_____
5. Test system for leaks	_____
6. Test system with dirty water	_____
7. Revise design as necessary	_____
8. Make presentation to class	_____

Name _____ Date_____ Class_____

What Materials Filter Water Best?

Problem

What combination of materials filter dirty water best?

Materials

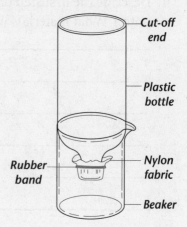

- dirty water
- 2-L clear plastic bottle with the bottom cut off
- large beaker
- nylon fabric
- rubber band
- fine sand
- gravel of various sizes
- charcoal
- coffee filter
- fabric pieces

Devise a Plan *Review the safety guidelines in your textbook.*

1. Place the piece of nylon fabric over the narrow opening of the plastic bottle, and secure it with a rubber band. Then place the plastic bottle in the beaker, as shown in the figure.

2. Study the materials provided, and think of a way that they could be used to filter dirty water. You can have as many layers as you want and use them in the order you think will work best. You can use other materials you provide yourself.

3. Pour dirty water through your filter, and observe the results.

Analyze and Conclude

Answer the following items on a separate sheet of paper.

1. Make a sketch that shows the setup and the layers of materials you used.

2. Write a description of the dirty water before you filtered it through any materials.

3. Describe the difference in the water before and after filtration. Which mixture of the "cleanness scale" does the filtered water most resemble?

PROJECT WORKSHEET 2
A Two-Step Design

What processes do you want to include in your model water treatment system?
This worksheet will help you design your system.

1. Describe the first step of the treatment system. What will this step remove from the
   water? What materials will you need for this step?

   _____

   _____

   _____

   _____

   _____

   _____

   _____

2. Describe the second step of the treatment system. What will this step remove from
   the water? What materials will you need for this step?

   _____

   _____

   _____

   _____

   _____

   _____

   _____

3. Make a flowchart that explains the steps of your model system.

4. On a separate sheet of paper, make a sketch of your design, showing the two steps
   you have described.

SCORING RUBRIC

A Precious Resource

In evaluating how well you complete the Chapter Project, your teacher will judge your work in three categories. In each category, a score of 4 is the best rating.

	4	3	2	1
Creating Design and Flowchart	Clearly describes and accurately sketches a treatment system with two excellent steps and makes a flowchart that explains how each step cleans water.	Describes and sketches a treatment system with two good steps and makes a flowchart that suggests how each step cleans water.	Describes and sketches a treatment system with at least one good step and makes a flowchart that vaguely suggests how the system cleans water.	Describes and sketches a treatment system that could not clean water and makes no flowchart or an incomplete one.
Making Model Treatment System	Model includes two distinct steps and thoroughly cleans and recovers close to 1 L of water.	Model includes two distinct steps and adequately cleans and recovers 3/4 L of water.	Model includes one good step and partially cleans and recovers 1/2 L of water.	Model includes one good step and minimally cleans and recovers less than 1/2 L of water.
Presenting the Model	Makes a thorough and interesting presentation of the system that includes a clear explanation of how each step cleans water.	Makes a thorough presentation of the system that includes an adequate explanation of how each step cleans water.	Makes a presentation of the system that includes a partial explanation of how the system cleans water.	Makes a presentation of the system that includes a weak or confused explanation of how the system could clean water.

What's a Crowd?

The following steps will walk you through the Chapter Project. Use the hints and detailed directions as you guide your students through designing and conducting their experiments and preparing their reports.

Chapter Project Overview

When you introduce the project, determine whether students have had prior experience designing and carrying out experiments. If their experience is limited, use the Skills Handbook in the student text to support development of the skills involved. In addition, Project Worksheet 1 will help students focus on the steps involved in developing a testable hypothesis, designing and conducting an experiment, analyzing data, and reaching a conclusion based on experiment results.

Distribute the Project Overview, which presents the Project Rules and hints for spacing the seeds. Ask students if they have any questions about the project. You could also distribute the Scoring Rubric, so students know what will be expected of them.

Divide the class into groups of two to four students each, and give each student a copy of the Project Worksheet 1. Advise students to use the worksheet to take notes as they brainstorm ideas for the experiment. Explain that each group's written plan should be based on the steps outlined in the worksheet. Make sure students understand that they are to submit their experiment plans to you before they plant the seeds.

Tell students that each group can divide the project responsibilities in any way they wish so long as every group member takes part in planning the experiment, measuring plant growth, analyzing results, and developing the class presentation. Emphasize that each group member should also be able to answer questions about the experiment.

Set a deadline for the project presentation and interim dates. Have students record those dates in the Project Timeline section at the end of the Project Overview.

Materials and Preparation

The preferred plants for the experiments are Wisconsin Fast Plants™ (*Brassica rapa*), a strain of radishlike plants specifically developed for their short life cycle—only about two weeks from planting of seeds to the flowering of the mature plants. Fast Plant seeds are available from biological supply houses. As an alternative, students could use radish seeds.

Provide (or have students bring in) appropriate planting containers. Each group should use identical containers for all their setups, although different groups may use different containers. The number of containers each group needs will depend on the group's experiment design. For the results of crowding to be clearly observable, each group should plant at least three containers, with one—the control—representing uncrowded conditions.

Students will also need potting soil, trowels or large spoons for filling the containers with soil, small watering cans or spray bottles for watering the plants, and metric rulers for measuring plant growth.

Set aside a location in the classroom where the plant containers will receive direct sunlight or strong indirect light for several hours each day. If sunlight is limited, set up lamps on tables.

When groups are ready to prepare their class presentations, provide materials for making posters, bulletin board displays, overhead transparencies, and other aids.

Keep Students on Track—Tasks 1–3

Review each group's plan to make sure students have accounted for and will control all the major variables that will affect plant growth. If a group has neglected to control an important variable—the amount of water, for example—ask prompting questions to help students recognize the variable and provide for it in their plan.

Allow variety in the groups' experiment designs. For example, students may decide to measure only the tallest plants in each container or to measure several plants of different heights and then calculate the average height for each container. Students could also count the number of seeds that germinated in each container and the number of mature plants at the end of the experiment and then calculate the percentage of sprouting plants that survived and grew to maturity.

Check each group's planned data table to make sure it includes all essential data, including some type of coding to differentiate among the planting containers.

Encourage the groups to post their plans near their containers so they can remember how they decided to control variables in caring for the plants.

As groups conduct their experiments, consult with them regularly to determine whether they are encountering any problems and whether any adjustments are needed in their procedures. For example, if the containers are not turned every couple of days, the plants will develop a curved shape as they grow toward the light source, making it difficult for students to measure plant height. If the containers are over- or underwatered, the plants will not grow well or may die regardless of their spacing.

Keep Students on Track—Task 4

To help students prepare their written reports and graphs, distribute Project Worksheet 2. Allow variety in the types of graphs the groups prepare. For example, students with limited graphing skills could create a simple bar graph with the vertical axis labeled *Plant Height*, the horizontal axis labeled *Container 1, Container 2,* and so forth, and the bars showing only the final height of the tallest plant in each container. More skillful students could create a line graph with the vertical axis labeled *Plant Height*, the horizontal axis labeled *Day 1, Day 2,* and so forth, and a different color line for each container showing plant heights throughout the entire experiment.

Chapter Project Wrap Up

Tell the class how much time each group will be allowed for its presentation. Encourage groups to keep this time limit in mind as they practice their presentations. As an alternative, each group could prepare a "poster session" report, where group members display their experimental procedure and results and are available to answer questions.

When each group presents its report to the rest of the class, encourage the other students to ask questions. Give each group positive feedback on its experiment and presentation.

After all groups have presented their reports, let students compare their results and discuss the factors that may have caused differences in their results and conclusions. Allow time for students to record their ideas for improving the experiment in their project notebooks.

Extension

Let students meet in their groups again to discuss members' ideas for improving the group's experiment. Encourage each group to choose the most interesting or important idea and devise a new plan that incorporates that idea. If time allows, let the groups carry out their new experiments.

PROJECT OVERVIEW
What's a Crowd?

How crowded can plants be before their spacing affects how they will grow? In this project, you will answer this question by designing and carrying out an experiment with your group.

First, you and the other members of your group will develop a hypothesis about how crowding affects plant growth. Then you will work together to plan an experiment to test your hypothesis. After your teacher reviews your plan, plant the seeds and start observing the containers. When the plants sprout, measure and record their height every day. You can record other observations, too, such as the number of leaves and buds on the plants and the color of the leaves. Continue making measurements and observations until the plants are full-grown. Then you and your group will write a report about your experiment, with a graph showing the plants' growth. At the end of the chapter, your group will present its report to the class.

Project Rules

- Develop a hypothesis about crowding and plant growth. Make sure the hypothesis is in the form of a statement that can be tested.

- Design an experiment to test your hypothesis. Any condition that can be changed in an experiment is called a **variable.** The only variable you should change in your experiment is how close together the seeds are planted in each container. Try to think of all the other variables that could affect how well your plants grow. Keep those variables the same in all your containers.

- As part of your experiment design, create a data table for recording the plants' heights and any other observations you make.

- Carry out your experiment. Take measurements and make observations every day, and record your data in the table.

- At the end of the experiment, analyze the data you collected. Review your original hypothesis. Then write a conclusion that states what the experiment showed you about crowding and plant growth.

- Write a report telling what materials and procedures you used for the experiment and the results you observed. Include a graph that shows the growth of the plants in each container.

- Submit the written report to your teacher.

- With the rest of your group, present your report to the class.

Suggested Materials

- Your group's experiment should involve planting different numbers of seeds in identical containers. You could use margarine tubs, plastic storage boxes, film containers, milk cartons with one large side cut out, or other containers.

- Your teacher will provide the seeds, potting soil, and other things your group will need. The kind of seeds you will use are ones that sprout and grow very quickly.

Project Hints

- Plan how close together you will plant the seeds in each container. One container should have plants that are not crowded—perhaps two to four centimeters apart. This container, called the "control," will show you how the plants grow when they have plenty of space.

- Decide how you will space the seeds in the other containers. You could use graph paper to make a scale drawing of each container showing how far apart the seeds will be planted. Make the spacing different in each container.

Project Timeline

Task	Due Date
1. Develop a hypothesis to test.	_____
2. Submit experiment design to teacher for approval.	_____
3. Set up containers and plant seeds (finish when the plants are full-grown).	_____
4. Complete written report and graph.	_____
5. Present report to the class.	_____

PROJECT WORKSHEET 1
Designing Your Experiment
Develop a Hypothesis

A hypothesis states what you think might happen in an experiment. For example, if you wanted to investigate how fertilizer affects plant growth, your hypothesis might be, "Plants that receive more fertilizer grow taller and bushier than plants that receive less fertilizer or no fertilizer."

1. In the space below, write a hypothesis about how crowding affects plant growth.

_____

_____

_____

Design the Experiment

An experiment tests a hypothesis. Your group's experiment design should include the following parts.

Materials

• List all the materials needed for the experiment.

Procedure

Write step-by-step directions for carrying out the experiment. Describe how one variable will be changed in the experiment and how the other variables will be kept the same. For an experiment on plant fertilizer, for example, the variable that would be changed is the amount of fertilizer the plants will receive. The variables that should be kept the same include the type of plants used and the amount of water and light the plants receive.

2. In the space below, list all the variables in an experiment that test the effects of crowding on plant growth. Mark a star next to the one variable that should be changed.

_____

_____

_____

Data Table

Create a table for recording all the measurements and observations made during the experiment.

3. On a separate sheet of paper, design a data table that you could use for your experiment.

PROJECT WORKSHEET 2

Reporting Your Results

Writing the Report

The written report that your group prepares for your teacher should include the following parts. Each part should begin on a new page.

Title Page

Give your report a simple title, such as "Our Plant Experiment" or "How Crowding Affects Plant Growth." List the names of your group's members.

Experiment Design

This part of the report should include the **Hypothesis,** the list of **Materials,** and the step-by-step **Procedure** you followed. Use the original plan you submitted to your teacher to write this part. Just make sure you revise the original plan so that this part tells what your group actually did, not what you planned to do but might have changed.

Data Table

Include a neat copy of your filled-in data table showing the measurements you recorded during the experiment. You can also include notes about other observations you made or sketches of the plants in each container.

Graph of Plant Growth

Decide how you will show the plants' growth on a graph. Do a rough sketch of your graph on a sheet of graph paper. When you are satisfied with the graph, make a neat copy on another sheet of graph paper.

Analysis and Conclusion

First, write a **Summary of Results** that explains what happened by the end of your experiment. For example, which containers had the tallest plants? Which plants had the most leaves? Which had the most flowers? In which containers did all the seeds that sprouted grow into mature plants? Next, write a **Conclusion**—one or two sentences that tell what your experiment showed you about how crowding affects plant growth.

Presenting Results to the Class

When your group has finished the written report, plan how to present your results to the rest of the class. Rather than just reading your report aloud, consider other ways to present your findings. You could use a poster, a bulletin board display, or an oral report that includes only the most important information about your experiment.

SCORING RUBRIC
What's a Crowd?

In evaluating how well you complete the Chapter Project, your teacher will judge your work in four categories. In each, a score of 4 is the best rating.

	4	3	2	1
Designing the Experiment	Hypothesis is clearly stated, testable, and quantifiable. Plan involves varying only seed spacing and controlling all other variables. Data table allows daily recording of plant heights and other quantitative data.	Hypothesis is clearly stated and testable. Plan involves varying seed spacing and controlling all other important variables. Data table allows daily recording of plant heights.	Hypothesis is not clearly stated. Plan involves varying seed spacing but does not address controlling every important variable. Data table is poorly organized.	Hypothesis is not stated so as to be testable. Plan does not include an "uncrowded" control container and does not address controlling other variables. Data table is mostly incomplete.
Conducting the Experiment	Closely follows original plan. Measurements are precise, made daily, and recorded in the data table.	Generally follows original plan, with minor deviations. Measurements are mostly precise, made daily, and recorded in the data table.	Follows original plan but does not carefully control all variables other than seed spacing. Measurements are rough, not made daily, and/or incompletely recorded.	Generally follows original plan, but measurements are not accurate, are not made consistently, or are not recorded in a data table.
Reporting Results	Written report is detailed, well-organized, and includes all essential elements. Class presentation is clear, interesting, and focuses on major points.	Written report includes all essential elements but lacks detail. Class presentation is clear but includes minor as well as major points.	Written report omits one or more essential elements. Class presentation is not focused or well-organized.	Written report includes few essential elements. Class presentation is unfocused and disorganized.
Working Cooperatively	Takes a lead in planning and carrying out the experiment and in preparing the written report and class presentation.	Actively participates in planning and carrying out the experiment and in preparing the	Participates in most aspects of planning and carrying out the experiment and in preparing the	Participates minimally in planning and carrying out the experiment and in preparing the written report and class

Variety Show

The following steps will walk you through the Chapter Project. Use the hints and detailed directions as you guide your students through the study of their plots and the development of their presentations.

Chapter Project Overview

When you introduce the Chapter Project, encourage students to offer their own ideas about nearby areas that might be good locations for the study plots. Also tell students about areas you have identified. (See Advance Preparation.) Clarify whether students can set up their plots independently or all plots will be set up in the same general area.

Distribute the Project Overview, and have students review the Project Rules and procedures. Encourage students' questions and comments. Explain whether students will have class time for their plot observations or whether they will make their observations on their own time.

Divide the class into groups of four to six students each. Pair students who have difficulty seeing and whose movements are limited with students who do not have these disabilities. (If space near the school is limited, you may also wish to give students the option of working alone on plots near their homes.)

Make sure each student or group has a project notebook for recording observations and data. Review the information to be recorded: air temperature, weather conditions, names (or drawings and descriptions) of organisms and their locations in the plot, and any changes that have occurred since the previous observation.

Distribute Project Worksheet 1, which provides instructions and a grid for making a scale drawing of the study plot. If necessary, review the procedure for making scale drawings.

Schedule the day for staking out the plots so students can plan ahead and wear suitable clothing. Also set a deadline for the project presentation and interim dates for the benchmarks identified in the Project Timeline section at the end of the Project Overview. Make sure students record all dates.

Materials and Preparation

Advance Preparation Before introducing the project, survey the grounds around the school so you can guide students to areas where they are likely to find a good variety of organisms. If the school grounds are not appropriate, locate a nearby park, field, vacant lot, or other natural area. Locate an area that is easily accessed for students whose movements are limited. Be sure the areas are free of poison ivy and broken glass or other hazards. If necessary, obtain permission to use the land.

To mark the plot, each group will need a meter stick or metric tape measure, four small stakes, a hammer, surveyor's tape or sturdy string, and a directional compass.

When students observe their plots, each group will need a thermometer, hand lenses, rulers, and trowels. Provide a variety of field guides so students can research the names and classification of any unfamiliar organisms they observe. A field guide to animal tracks will also be helpful for students who find trace evidence of organisms that have visited the plot.

When students are ready to prepare their class presentations, provide art supplies and audiovisual equipment such as cameras and videocassette recorders.

Keep Students on Track—Tasks 1–2

Ask students to disturb the land and organisms in their plots as little as possible. Their goal is to observe the organisms and abiotic factors without affecting them.

When each group has staked its plot, tell students to determine its directional orientation with a compass and mark the directions on the plot map. This will ensure that the map is oriented correctly during each observation. If necessary, show students how to use the compass to determine the plot's orientation: Hold the compass next to the plot, and when the needle stops moving, turn the compass so the marked end of the needle aligns with north, then note the direction of each side of the plot.

If students use string to mark the plot's perimeter, have them tie strips of brightly colored fabric to it at intervals so other people will notice the string and not trip over it.

Tell students that when they first stake out the plot, they can make one "base" map that includes the plants (which obviously will not move between one observation and the next), then photocopy the map so they can add animals as they observe the plot in subsequent sessions. Another way to note animals' locations each day is to mark them on tracing paper overlaid on the plot map.

Distribute Project Worksheet 2, which provides a format for recording information about organisms. Make sure students understand that they are to record information in their project notebooks, not on the worksheet itself.

In this and subsequent observation sessions, encourage students to note any animal behaviors they see, such as feeding, fighting, or cooperating in some way—for example, ants collecting food.

Keep Students on Track—Tasks 3–4

As students observe their plots, do not identify any unfamiliar organisms for them, but encourage them to draw the organisms in detail so they can identify them later using the field guides you have provided. Remind students to note abiotic factors, too.

Check each group's notebook occasionally to make sure students are making observations and recording data regularly.

Chapter Project Wrap Up

Give students a time limit for their class presentations. Emphasize that the presentations should focus on the biodiversity in their plots. Encourage students to practice their presentations beforehand, using any audiovisual aids they have prepared, to make sure the presentation fits within the time limit and also to identify any improvements that need to be made.

Before groups give their presentations to the class, meet with each group briefly to review students' plans. Suggest any questions other students might ask that may not have occurred to them.

As each group gives its presentation, encourage the other students to ask questions. Be sure to give each group positive feedback.

After all groups have given their presentations, let students compare their study results, particularly the number of different species living in or visiting each plot. You may want to make a class list of all the different organisms observed.

After students have recorded their reflections about the project in their journals, encourage them to share their reflections in a class discussion.

Extension

Students could request permission to create a bulletin board display somewhere in the school on "Schoolyard Biodiversity." They can display their artwork or photographs of organisms, plot maps, and descriptions of interactions they observed.

Let the class or selected groups present the project to a school or community nature club. Students could show their plot maps, identify and describe the organisms they observed, and summarize their findings about the diversity of species in the plots.

PROJECT OVERVIEW

Variety Show

How many different species are there in the entire world? In your state? In your own neighborhood? In this project, you will find out how many species are found in just a small plot of land. The results may surprise you!

First, you will stake out a small plot of land to observe. You will prepare a project notebook for recording your observations. You can use field guides to identify any organisms that are unfamiliar to you. At the end of the observation period, you will prepare a class presentation about your plot study.

Project Rules

- If you are working in a group, share decisions and responsibilities with group members.

- Plan your project notebook. The notebook should include the following information:

  - a map of your study plot that includes abiotic factors;

  - the date, time, air temperature, and weather conditions during each observation;

  - the names of the organisms you observe or descriptions and drawings if you don't know their names.

- Begin your study by staking out a square plot that is 1.5 meters on each side. Use Project Worksheet 1 to make a scale drawing of your plot. Label the drawing to show the compass directions.

- Make your first observation of the plot. In your notebook, record the plants, animals, and other organisms you see, as well as the abiotic factors you observe. Mark the organisms' locations on your plot map. Describe the behavior of any animals you see. If you see organisms that are unfamiliar to you, use field guides to identify them. Project Worksheet 2 will help you collect information about each organism.

- Disturb the land and organisms in your plot as little as possible. Your goal is to observe the organisms and abiotic factors without affecting them.

- Observe your plot every day for the entire study period. Record your observations and data in your notebook.

- At the end of the observation period, prepare a class presentation about your study. Your presentation should describe the variety of species you observed in the plot. Use audiovisual aids to make your presentation interesting and clear.

- Present your findings to the class.

Suggested Materials

- When you mark your plot, you will need a meter stick or metric tape measure, four small stakes, a hammer, surveyor's tape or heavy string, and a directional compass.

- Each time you observe your plot, you will need these materials:

  - a thermometer for measuring the air temperature (**CAUTION:** *Handle the thermometer carefully. If the glass tube breaks, tell your teacher immediately.*);

  - hand lens for observing organisms closely;

  - ruler for measuring organisms and their exact locations in the plot.

- Your teacher will provide field guides for identifying any organisms that are unfamiliar to you.

- For your presentation, you can create a poster or flip chart, a computer display, a video of your plot, or other audiovisual aids. Talk to your teacher about the materials you will need for making these aids.

Project Hints

- When you first draw your plot map, mark the locations of all the plants and abiotic factors such as rocks. They won't change from one observation to the next.

- If possible, make one photocopy of the map for each day you will observe the plot. During each observation, mark the locations of animals and any new, sprouting plants on a copy of the map. Remember to label that copy with the date of the observation. Another way to note animals and new plants in your plot each day is to draw them on a sheet of tracing paper laid over your first plot map.

Project Timeline

Task	Due Date
1. Plan your project notebook.	_____
2. Mark your plot and make your first observations.	_____
3. Complete the observations of your plot.	_____
4. Complete the preparation of your presentation.	_____
5. Present your findings to the class.	_____

Name _____ Date _____ Class _____

PROJECT WORKSHEET 1
Drawing Your Plot to Scale

Follow these steps to make a scale drawing of your plot.

1. Your plot is 1.5 meters on each side. You will draw it on the grid below. What would be a good length for each side on your drawing? _____ cm

2. With sides that length, what will be the scale of the drawing? Record the scale below.

3. Draw your plot to scale on the grid. Label north, south, east, and west.

4. Locate all the plants and abiotic factors such as rocks. Mark their locations on your drawing.

Scale: 1 cm represents _____ cm

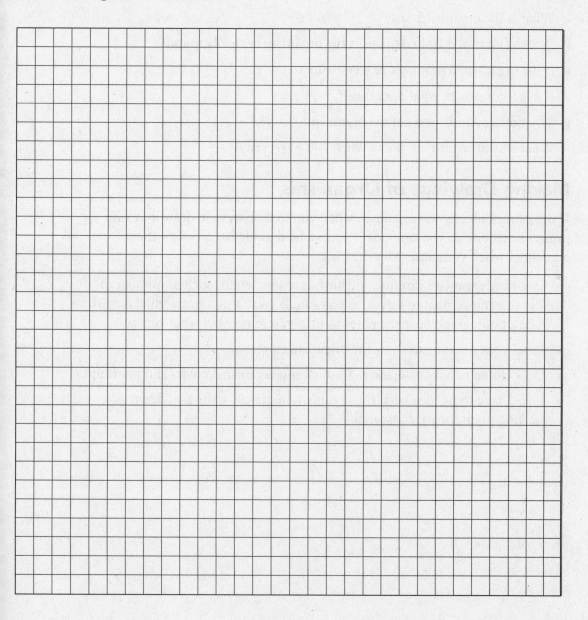

PROJECT WORKSHEET 2

Identifying and Describing Organisms

For each organism you observe, record its name and other information in your project notebook. Use the following checklist as a guide. You will need to use field guides to research some information.

Organism Checklist

✓ What is the organism's common name?

✓ What is its scientific name?

✓ What type of organism is it—alga, fungus, plant, or animal? If the organism is an animal, is it a worm, insect, amphibian, reptile, bird, mammal, or other kind of animal?

✓ What is the organism's size?

✓ Where else in the United States is the organism typically found?

✓ Is the organism a producer or a consumer?

✓ If it is a consumer, what does it eat?

✓ What other consumers eat the organism?

✓ What was the organism doing when you observed it?

Making Drawings of Organisms

If you cannot identify an organism when you first observe it, draw it in your project notebook so you can look it up in a field guide later. Follow these guidelines when you make your drawing.

- Draw the organism carefully. Include as many details, such as number of legs or arrangement of leaves, as you can. If you cannot draw small details, take a photograph or make notes to help you remember what you saw.

- Label your drawing to show the organism's size.

- Use colored pencils or markers to show the organism's colors and markings.

- If you have some idea what the organism might be, write that down as a starting point for your research.

SCORING RUBRIC

Variety Show

In evaluating how well you complete the Chapter Project, your teacher will judge your work in four categories. In each, a score of 4 is the best rating.

	4	3	2	1
Making Observations and Recording Data	Observations and measurements are precise, thorough, and carefully recorded in the project notebook.	Observations and measurements are careful and recorded in the project notebook.	Observations omit some minor details; some measurements are missing; recording is done regularly but not in a well-organized manner.	Observations and measurements are sporadic, not carefully made, and not recorded regularly and clearly.
Identifying and Classifying Organisms	All organisms are identified and classified correctly. Drawings and descriptions of unfamiliar organisms are precise and detailed. Research is thorough.	Almost all organisms are identified and classified correctly. Drawings and descriptions of unfamiliar organisms are sufficiently detailed for research purposes. Research is fairly thorough.	Most organisms are identified and classified correctly. Not all drawings and descriptions of unfamiliar organisms are sufficiently detailed for research purposes; research is superficial.	Few organisms are identified and classified correctly. Drawings and descriptions of unfamiliar organisms are missing or carelessly done; little research done.
Communicating Results	Class presentation is well organized, clear, and interesting; effectively summarizes procedures and findings; makes creative use of audiovisual aids.	Class presentation is fairly well organized, clear, and interesting; summarizes procedures and findings well; makes good use of audiovisual aids.	Class presentation is somewhat disorganized and unfocused; does not clearly summarize procedures and findings; makes little use of audiovisual aids.	Class presentation is disorganized and unclear; does not summarize procedures and findings; does not use audiovisual aids.
Working Cooperatively	Takes a lead in planning and carrying out the field study and in preparing the class presentation.	Actively participates in planning and carrying out the field study and in preparing the class presentation.	Participates in planning and carrying out the field study and in preparing the class presentation as directed by other group members.	Participates marginally in the field study and in preparing the presentation. Does not carry out all responsibilities and tasks.

Shine On!

The following steps will walk you through the Chapter Project. Use the hints and detailed directions as you guide your students through the investigation, gathering of data, presentation, and reflection.

Chapter Project Overview

As you launch the project, emphasize the importance of controlling variables for meaningful project results. Remind students that while they vary the lighting conditions of their plants, they must control other variables, such as amount of water or type of soil.

Students can vary lighting conditions in a number of different ways. If they choose to vary the amount of light, the use of plant growth lights on timers is a good choice. In this way, students can deliver controlled amounts of light to plants regardless of the amount of sunlight that is available. Students can vary the color of light that plants receive by making tents to cover the plants, using different colors of cellophane. Some students may wish to investigate differences between direct sunlight outdoors and sunlight through window glass. Encourage students to use their imaginations when deciding how to vary lighting conditions for their plants. Monitor students' choices so that a wide variety of lighting conditions is tested.

Advise students that they should keep the soil their plants are growing in moist, but not soggy. To help students keep their plants well watered, you may want to provide inexpensive soil probes to monitor soil water. These are available from garden centers and plant shops. Remind students they must control how much water the plants receive.

Have students think of other variables that might differ in different lighting conditions. *(One variable is temperature, which is likely to be higher in a brightly-lit location such as a sunny windowsill.)* Challenge students to brainstorm ways of controlling these other variables. *(For example, to control temperature differences, students might open the window to let in cool air at the brightly-lit location.)*

Students are likely to predict that plants in bright light will grow more quickly than plants in dim light, but they are unlikely, at least at the start of the chapter, to know why. Have students complete Project Worksheet 2 so they will understand why plants need light to grow. This knowledge will also help students explain their results at the end of the project.

Keep Students on Track—Task 1

Before students set up their experiment, make sure they have developed a reasonable and appropriate experimental design. For their design, they should state what type of plants they will grow, how many plants they will grow, how different lighting conditions will be achieved, how they will control other variables, and how plant growth will be measured. Urge students to measure plant growth in more than one way. Students also should have a schedule for regularly checking their plants for water and measuring them.

Keep Students on Track—Task 2

Check to see that students have set up their experiments and started to record data. By now, students should have recorded at least baseline data on their plants. Review students' data tables and point out any omissions or errors. Students may use the data table in Worksheet 1 or a table like it.

Make sure that low-light plants will not be getting too little light to survive. Students should be aware that their plants require some light just to stay alive.

Keep Students on Track—Task 3

Have students review their data tables and consider whether one way of measuring plant growth reveals changes in size better than others. If one way is better, students may wish to continue using it and discontinue using the others.

Encourage students to take photographs or draw sketches showing how their plants appear and to make notes in their data table regarding any differences they observe in their plants, such as differences in leaf color or leaf texture.

Keep Students on Track—Task 4

As students prepare to graph their data, remind them to use the graph in Worksheet 1.

In preparing their presentations, students should try to answer two questions: Under which lighting condition did the plants grow more? Why did different lighting conditions result in different growth rates?

Chapter Project Wrap Up

Students can write a report on their project, make an oral presentation to the class, or do both. In their report or presentation, students should include the graph of their data on light and growth. They also should explain why light affects growth in this way. *(Plants receiving more light undergo more photosynthesis, produce more food, and therefore grow more.)*

If students prepare written reports, you may want to bind their reports together in a booklet, illustrated by photographs or drawings of some of the plants, so students can read about the results of their classmates' projects. If students give oral presentations, try to provide extra support and encouragement to students who are nervous about speaking in front of the class.

Encourage students to evaluate how well they accomplished what they set out to accomplish. Students should consider how well they controlled the variables in their experiments and make suggestions for improving that part of the project.

Extension

Students can investigate other factors affecting plant growth, such as the amount of water or minerals that plants receive. Water, like light, is needed for photosynthesis, and minerals are needed for plants to make proteins and nucleic acids. Students also can continue the experiment with lighting conditions for longer than two weeks. In addition, they can monitor plant growth under three different lighting conditions, instead of just two.

Name _____ Date _____ Class _____

PROJECT OVERVIEW

Shine On!

You know that plants need light to grow. How much, do you think, does the amount or type of light plants receive affect how well they grow? In this Chapter Project, you will design and carry out an experiment to determine the effect of light on plant growth. The project rules outline the major steps you must take to complete the project. The project hints will give you useful tips to help ensure project success.

Project Rules

- Decide what type of plants you will use in your experiment.
- Decide how many plants you will grow.
- Decide how you will vary the lighting conditions.
- Decide how you will control the other variables.
- Decide how you will measure plant growth.
- Write a plan for your experiment and give the plan to your teacher. Obtain your teacher's approval before you begin your experiment.
- Set up a data table for recording your data.
- At the end of the experiment, graph the data in your table and analyze your results.
- Display your graph and explain your results in an oral or written report.

Project Hints

- If your teacher does not suggest a type of plant to use, choose a plant that will grow quickly. Generally, leafy houseplants such as coleus or geranium grow quickly under bright light. Bean plants will also work well for this investigation. Avoid choosing cactus plants or succulent plants, because most are slow-growing.
- Give each plant an identifying number or letter. Use a permanent marker to write the numbers or letters on the plant pots.
- Try to vary the two lighting conditions as much as possible. For example, place bright-light plants in the brightest light available—under plant growth lights, in a greenhouse, or on a sunny windowsill. Place low-light plants in very dim light, such as on a shelf in an unlighted room away from windows. Alternatively, you can keep low-light plants in a dark cupboard or closet most of the time, and place them in bright light for just an hour or two each day.
- The best way to control the variable water is to keep the soil slightly moist in each pot at all times. However, all plants should receive the same amount of water.

- You may choose to use one, some, or all of the following measures of plant growth: plant height, plant diameter, number of leaves, and average size of leaves. If plants are in bloom during the project, you may wish to add number or size of flowers as a measure of plant growth. Use more than one measure, at least at the beginning of the project. As the project continues, you may find that one measure provides better information than others and decide to rely on it alone.

- Unless plant growth is very rapid, you may need to measure plant growth only every two or three days. However, be sure to keep checking your plants' soil for water every day.

- Record your data on growth for each plant as soon as you measure it. Record the data in the table in Worksheet 1 or in a table like it. The table must be filled in for each plant each time you measure it, so be sure to leave room in the table for enough rows (number of plants × number of times measured = number of rows needed).

- At the end of two weeks, graph your data using a graph similar to the one in Worksheet 1. Plot data for the plants' grown in both lighting conditions on the same graph to make comparisons of their growth easier. Indicate on the *x*-axis how plant growth was measured (for example, by height in millimeters or by number of leaves). If you grow more than one plant under each lighting condition, you can plot the average values for all the plants grown under that condition. If you keep records on more than one useful measure of plant growth, create a separate graph for each measure.

- Completing Worksheet 2 will help you understand the results of the Chapter Project. It also may help you explain the results in your oral or written report.

Project Timeline

Task	Date Due
1. Create experimental design.	_____
2. Set up and begin experiment.	_____
3. Complete collecting and recording data.	_____
4. Graph data and analyze results.	_____
5. Present results to the class.	_____

PROJECT WORKSHEET 1
Recording and Graphing the Data

You can use this table or one like it to record your data during the Chapter Project. You should record data every day during the investigation.

Date and Time	Plant ID Number/Letter	Lighting Condition	Measures of Plant Growth			Comments
			Plant Height (mm)	Plant Diameter (mm)	Number of Leaves	

Set up a graph like the one below to plot the data in your completed table.

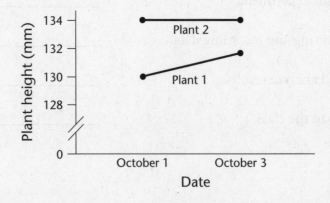

Name _____ Date _____ Class _____

Understanding Photosynthesis

Why do plants need light to grow? Plants need light for photosynthesis. As you will see, photosynthesis consists of a series of chemical reactions. However, the role photosynthesis plays in plant growth—and in the outcome of the Chapter Project—is easy to understand from the flowchart below.

Photosynthesis

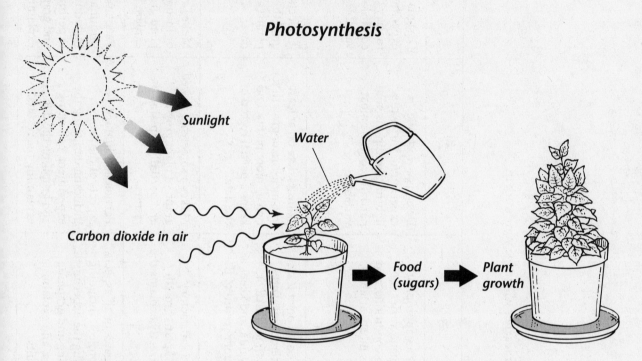

Sunlight

Water

Carbon dioxide in air

Food (sugars) ➡ **Plant growth**

Use the flowchart to answer the following questions.

1. What three things are required for photosynthesis to occur?

_____

2. What does photosynthesis produce?

_____

3. How does food affect plant size?

_____

4. Without sunlight, photosynthesis cannot occur. How would a lack of sunlight affect plant size?

_____

5. Predict how photosynthesis will affect the outcome of your experiment.

_____
_____

SCORING RUBRIC

Shine On!

In evaluating how well you complete the Chapter Project, your teacher will judge your work in the following categories. In each, a score of 4 is the best rating.

	4	3	2	1
Designing Experiment and Controlling Variables	Designs a highly appropriate experiment, successfully varies the lighting conditions, and controls all other variables, such as amounts of water.	Designs an appropriate experiment, varies the lighting conditions, and controls most variables.	Designs a workable experiment, varies the lighting conditions, and partially controls most variables.	Designs a flawed experiment and fails to vary the lighting conditions or control most variables.
Collecting and Recording Data	Collects data on at least three different measures of growth for four or more plants, and keeps a complete and detailed record of the data.	Collects data on at least two different measures of growth for three or more plants, and keeps a satisfactory record of the data.	Collects data on at least one measure of growth for two or more plants, and keeps a partial record of the data.	Collects data on plant growth for at most two plants, and records little data.
Graphing Data and Explaining Results	Makes a well-constructed graph of plant growth, and thoroughly and accurately explains the results.	Makes a satisfactory graph of plant growth and correctly explains the results.	Makes a somewhat flawed graph of plant growth and partially explains the results.	Makes a seriously flawed or incomplete graph of plant growth and fails to explain the results.
Working Cooperatively (optional)	Takes a lead in all aspects of the project, including designing the experiment, collecting and graphing the data, and explaining the results.	Participates in all aspects of the project, including designing the experiment, collecting and graphing the data, and explaining the results.	Participates in most aspects of the project, including designing the experiment, collecting and graphing the data, or explaining the results.	Participates only minimally in the project, including designing the experiment, collecting and graphing the data, or explaining the results.

Egg-speriment with a Cell

The following steps will walk you through the Chapter Project. Use the hints and detailed directions as you guide your students through the gathering of information, presentation, and reflection.

Chapter Project Overview

When you introduce the project, you may want to do the following demonstration so students can see the cell membrane they will be studying as they carry out the project. Gently crack open a chicken egg, and carefully pour the contents into a dish. Show the class the membrane that remains attached to the inside of the shell.

Be aware that students may not understand the changes they observe in their egg. Therefore, you may want to provide the class with some background information at the start of the project. First tell the class that the chalky shell of the egg, which surrounds the membrane, is made up mostly of the mineral calcium carbonate. Explain that calcium carbonate dissolves in acids such as vinegar, which is why they will first soak their egg in vinegar for two days. After the shell has dissolved, only the membrane will remain around the egg. Then introduce students to the idea of the cell membrane as selectively permeable, although you do not need to use that term at this point. Tell students that water, oxygen, and some other substances can pass easily through the membrane, while many other substances, such as salt, cannot. Ask: What do you think would happen to the egg if water passed into the egg through the membrane? (*The egg would get bigger.*) What do you think would happen to the egg if water passed out of the egg through the membrane? (*The egg would get smaller.*)

Hand out the Project Overview. Review the Project Rules with the class, and give students time to read the Project Hints.

Stress the importance of starting to soak their eggs in vinegar as soon as possible in order to dissolve the shells. Suggest appropriate containers for students to use, and advise them to find a place to put their eggs where they will not be disturbed. Also remind students to measure the circumferences of

their eggs before they start to soak them. Remind students to carefully wash their hands after handling raw eggs because the eggs may contain harmful bacteria. Advise students to clean up any broken eggs with soap and hot water.

Set dates for the various project tasks and a deadline for the project presentation. Distribute the Scoring Rubric, which you will use for assessing students' work. Also distribute Project Worksheet 1 and urge students to use it to record and graph the data they collect during the project.

Keep Students on Track—Task 1

Check that students have started to soak their eggs in vinegar. Students should not remove their eggs from the vinegar until the shells have completely dissolved.

Allow time for students to observe and measure their eggs each day. Make sure students understand how to measure their eggs and that they measure the eggs the same way each time. Students should record their data on Worksheet 1.

Students should handle the eggs carefully and work slowly to avoid breaking the eggs. Remind students to wash their hands after handling the eggs.

Keep Students on Track—Tasks 2–5

Call on volunteers to share their observations to date. Most students will have noticed an increase in the size of their eggs and a change in the eggs' appearance and texture. Students also may have noticed bubbles in the vinegar and pieces of shell floating on its surface. Explain that the bubbles are carbon dioxide, which is released when the shell dissolves in vinegar.

Remind students to start soaking their eggs in different liquids after soaking them in vinegar for two days. After using the vinegar, students should soak their eggs first in plain water for two days and then in water with food coloring, salty water, and other liquids they choose for one day each. Challenge students to predict how their eggs will change as they soak in each liquid.

Keep Students on Track—Task 6

Have students use the graph on Worksheet 1 to make bar graphs of the daily measurements of their eggs' circumferences. Remind students to indicate on their graphs in what liquids the eggs soaked each day. Suggest that they use either labels or symbols with a key to show this information.

Information presented in Project Worksheet 2 will help students understand the process of osmosis so they can interpret the results of the project. Hand out the worksheets at this point, and instruct students to complete them before they give their presentations.

Chapter Project Wrap Up

As students give their presentations, urge them to compare their results with the results obtained by their classmates.

After all the students have given their presentations, make two lists on the board: (a) liquids that students found increased the size of the eggs; (b) liquids that students found decreased the size of the eggs. The first list should include vinegar and plain water. The second list should include salt water and thick liquids such as syrup.

Challenge students to explain why some liquids caused the eggs to increase in size, whereas others caused the eggs to decrease in size. (*Liquids causing the eggs to increase in size have a higher concentration of water than the eggs, resulting in water passing into the eggs by osmosis. Liquids causing the eggs to decrease in size have a lower concentration of water than the eggs, resulting in water passing out of the eggs by osmosis.*)

Extension

Give students a chance to apply what they learned in the Chapter Project by having them explain why the body is harmed when a person drinks salt water. (*The person's body cells would lose water through osmosis.*)

PROJECT OVERVIEW

Egg-speriment with a Cell

One of the cell structures you will be learning about is the cell membrane. In the Chapter Project, you will model how a cell membrane works to let water enter and leave the cell. You will use a chicken egg as a model of a cell. After dissolving the shell in vinegar to expose the membrane, you will soak the egg in various liquids and observe how the size of the egg changes as it takes on or loses water through the membrane. You also will keep a daily record of observations and measurements of the egg.

Project Rules

- As soon as you get your egg, observe its features and measure its circumference. Record your observations and measurements.

- Soak the egg in vinegar for at least two days. Then observe and record how the egg has changed, including any changes in appearance or texture. Also measure the circumference of the egg, using the procedure described on the next page. Record your observations and measurements.

- Soak the egg in plain water for one or two days. Each day, observe and record how the egg has changed, and measure and record its circumference.

- Soak the egg in water with food coloring, salt water, and another liquid of your choice for at least one day each. Continue to keep a daily record of observations and measurements of the egg's circumference.

- Graph the data you have collected and prepare a report of your results. Be prepared to explain your results and show your egg to the class.

Project Hints

- For best results in this project, it is important to measure your egg carefully each day. This is because changes in the circumference of the egg may be slight, and measurements that are not precise may mask changes that have occurred.

- The drawing shows how to measure your egg's circumference.

- Follow these steps when measuring the egg each day:

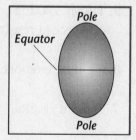

1. Carefully take the egg out of the liquid and pour the liquid down the drain.

2. Rinse off the egg in cold water over the sink and blot it dry with a paper towel.

3. Using a flexible tape measure or piece of string, measure the circumference of the egg. If you are measuring your egg with a piece of string, follow these steps:

   a. Wrap the string snugly around the egg at the equator (but be careful not to cut into the egg's membrane with the string).

   b. Grasp the string between your thumb and finger exactly at the point where the end of the string meets the rest of the string after circling the egg.

   c. Keeping your thumb and finger in place, lay the string straight on a flat surface.

   d. Use a metric ruler to measure the distance from the end of the string to the point at which you are holding it.

4. Record your measurements and any other observations about the egg in the data table on Worksheet 1.

5. Return your egg to the container and cover it with the same or another liquid, according to the project rules above.

Project Timeline

Task	Due Date
1. Finish soaking egg in vinegar and record results.	_____
2. Finish soaking egg in plain water and record results.	_____
3. Finish soaking egg in water with food coloring and record results.	_____
4. Finish soaking egg in salt water and record results.	_____
5. Finish soaking egg in a liquid of your choice and record results.	_____
6. Complete report and graph.	_____
7. Present results.	_____

Name _____ Date_____ Class_____

PROJECT WORKSHEET 1
Managing the Data

In this Chapter Project, you will collect two types of data: data on the circumference of the egg and data on changes you observe in the egg, such as changes in the egg's appearance and texture. Both types of data should be collected and recorded each day throughout the project. Use the table below, or one like it, to record your data.

Date	Liquid	Circumference (in millimeters)	Other Observations

After you have collected the data and completed the table, use the data to create a bar graph showing changes in the circumference of the egg. Label the horizontal axis of your graph "Date" and the vertical axis "Circumference (mm)." Also indicate on the graph what liquid the egg was soaking in each day.

PROJECT WORKSHEET 2

Understanding Osmosis

You learned that water can pass through a cell membrane by a process called osmosis. Osmosis occurs when water moves from an area where it is more concentrated to an area where it is less concentrated. For example, if a cell is placed in plain water, there will be a higher concentration of water outside the cell than inside the cell, because the inside of the cell contains other materials in addition to water. As a result, water will pass through the cell membrane into the cell by osmosis.

The concentration of water in a substance is the proportion of that substance that is made up of water. For example, if 10 milliliters of salt water contain 9 milliliters of water, the concentration of water in the liquid is 9 milliliters ÷ 10 milliliters, or 9/10, which is 90 percent.

Calculate the percentage of water in each of the liquids in the table, and write your answers in column 4.

Calculating Concentration

Liquid	Total Amount of Liquid (milliliters)	Amount of Water (milliliters)	Concentration of Water in Liquid (percent)
A	10	7	
B	100	92	
C	15	13	
D	28	22	

Answer the following questions in the spaces provided.

1. Many cells contain about 80 percent water. If you place them in a liquid that contains less than 80 percent water, they will lose water through the cell membrane by osmosis. If you place them in a liquid that contains more than 80 percent water, they will gain water through the cell membrane by osmosis. Which of the liquids in the table would cause many cells to gain water? To lose water?

   _____

   _____

2. Name some specific liquids that you think might contain less than 80 percent water.

   _____

   _____

SCORING RUBRIC

Egg-speriment With a Cell

In evaluating how well you complete the Chapter Project, your teacher will judge your work in four categories. In each, a score of 4 is the best rating.

	4	3	2	1
Collecting and Recording the Data	Collects and keeps an accurate and complete record of observations and measurements each day for at least five different liquids.	Collects and keeps a satisfactory record of observations and measurements each day for at least four different liquids.	Collects and keeps a partial record of observations and measurements for at least three different liquids.	Collects but fails to record, or keeps an inadequate record of, observations and measurements for no more than two different liquids.
Graphing the Data	Constructs a high-quality graph of the measurements that includes a clear representation of the liquids used each day.	Constructs a satisfactory graph of the measurements that shows the liquids used each day.	Constructs a graph of the measurements that has errors or fails to show the liquids used each day.	Graph is unclear, incomplete, or constructed incorrectly.
Reporting the Results	Prepares an informative, well-organized report with diagrams and gives a thorough and accurate explanation of the results of the project.	Prepares a satisfactory report and gives an adequate explanation of the results of the project.	Report is not well organized and gives an explanation of the results of the project that contains some errors.	Report is incomplete and/or the explanation of the results of the project are incorrect.
Working Cooperatively (optional)	Takes a lead in all aspects of the project, including planning, collecting the data, and presenting the results.	Actively participates in all aspects of the project, including planning, collecting the data, and presenting the results.	Participates in most aspects of the project, including planning, collecting the data, or presenting the results.	Participates minimally in the project, including planning, collecting the data, and presenting the results.

Life's Long Calendar

The following steps will walk you through the Chapter Project. Use the hints and detailed directions as you guide your students through the research and construction of their timelines.

Chapter Project Overview

After students have read the Chapter Project description, on the Project Overview, have them review the Project Rules and procedures, and encourage their questions and comments.

Next, divide the class into small groups, and let the groups meet to discuss the kinds of timelines they could make and the units they could use to represent millions of years. Follow up with a class discussion in which the groups share their ideas. List the possibilities on the board in two separate columns, one for models that use units of length to represent millions of years (for example, meters marked on the floor of the gym or on a wall of the classroom or a long hallway) and the second column for models that use units of time (days or months in a year, days in a month, hours in a day, minutes in an hour). Listening to other groups' ideas will be particularly helpful to students who are having difficulty thinking of possibilities.

Explain to students that each pair of timelines should include as many of the major evolutionary events as possible. Explain that you will give them a list of important events (Worksheet 2). If you want students to research more events, explain this requirement as well.

Emphasize that each group may divide the project responsibilities among themselves in any way they wish so long as *every* group member takes part in designing both timelines, helps make at least one line, and is prepared to explain how both timelines were made and answer questions about them.

Establish a date for presenting the timelines and interim dates for the benchmarks identified in the Project Timeline section at the end of the Project Overview. Make sure students record all dates.

Materials and Preparation

Students could use calculators to determine the scale of each timeline and the placements of events on them. Students will need colored marking pens for labeling the timelines and drawing organisms.

Models based on length: Provide meter sticks, metric tape measures, and a variety of materials for constructing the timelines—rolls of white shelf paper, adding machine tape, continuous-feed printer paper, wide ribbon, yarn, and the like. Students could use craft sticks to mark outdoor timelines.

Models based on time: Groups that plan to model Earth's history with a 24-hour or 60-minute clock dial will need a large sheet of posterboard or cardboard and a large drawing compass (or a length of string). Groups that plan to model days in a year or other "linear" time could use the materials suggested above for models based on length.

Keep Students on Track—Task 1

Advise students not to start making the first timeline until you have reviewed and approved their plans. If any groups have planned unwieldy timelines, meet with them individually to provide assistance.

Distribute Worksheet 1 and have each student make a scale model of his or her own life history as practice for the project. Discuss major life events that could be included on the personal timeline—taking first steps, saying a first word, starting school, memorable family celebrations or vacations, and the like. If necessary, help students calculate their timelines' scales and position the events.

Assess each student's skill in making a personal timeline. Make sure each project group includes at least one student who was successful with this practice activity.

Keep Students on Track—Tasks 2–4

Evaluate and, if necessary, correct each group's work on the first timeline before students begin the second timeline.

Distribute Worksheet 2, which lists evolutionary events in addition to those shown in the textbook. Remind students they should include at least three of those additional events on their timeline, but may include more if they wish. However, caution students not to include so many events that the timelines are difficult to read. If you want students to research other evolutionary events, provide source materials at this point.

Chapter Project Wrap Up

When students examine their own and other groups' 5-billion-year timelines, they may conclude that not very much seemed to happen for billions of years. Emphasize that during this ancient period, microorganisms evolved all the major biological processes found on Earth today—photosynthesis, cellular respiration, DNA replication, formation of organelles, and sexual reproduction.

You may want to group the presentations based on the models' locations, with in-the-classroom models, school-wide models, and outdoor models presented on different days.

Extension

Let students research the continents' locations at different times in Earth's history and add maps they have sketched themselves or photocopied from books to their timelines.

Students could make another magnified timeline that focuses on geological changes.

PROJECT OVERVIEW

Life's Long Calendar

This chapter deals with changes in living things that have occurred during Earth's history. These changes occurred over hundreds of thousands, millions, and even billions of years. Such huge time spans are difficult to imagine. The Chapter Project will help you understand these time spans by converting millions and billions of years to smaller, more familiar units.

Your group will construct two models of Earth's history—two timelines drawn to scale. One timeline will show the history of life from 5 billion years ago to the present. The other timeline will show 600 million years ago to the present. The second timeline is a magnified view of a small section of the first timeline. First, your group will decide what kind of timelines to make. Next, you will calculate the scale for each model and use these scales to construct the two timelines. Then you will mark each line to show important events in the evolution of life on Earth. At the end of the chapter, your group will present and explain your timelines to the class.

Project Rules

- With your group, decide what kind of scale models to make. You could represent billions and millions of years with units of length, such as meters, or units of time, such as months in a year. List the events you plan to include on the timelines. Include as many events in Earth's history as possible. Submit your plans and list to your teacher for approval.

- Make both lines the same size. Calculate the scale for each timeline. Because the second timeline is a magnified part of the first timeline, the two timelines' scales will be different. The Hints section of this Overview will help you calculate the scales. Also, Project Worksheet 1 will let you practice this step by making a timeline for your own life history.

- Construct the first timeline to scale. Mark it at equal intervals to show billions of years. Show this timeline to your teacher, and then make any necessary corrections.

- Construct the second timeline. Mark it to show millions of years.

- Add events to the timelines. Events that happened more than 600 million years ago should go on the first timeline. Events that happened during the past 600 million years should go on the second timeline. Use each timeline's scale to determine where to mark the events. Identify each event with a written label. You may also add drawings you have made of organisms.

- Present your timelines to the class. Explain why you chose the kind of model and the scales you used. Be prepared to answer questions about your timelines.

Suggested Materials

- Your group may want to use calculators to determine the scales of your models and where to place each event on the timelines.
- **Models that use units of length:** You will need a meter stick and a metric tape measure. To make the timelines, you can use a long strip of adding machine tape, shelf paper, wide ribbon, or other material. If your group is making outdoor timelines, you can use craft sticks or index cards to mark events on the lines.
- **Models that use units of time:** If you plan to use hours in a day or minutes in an hour to represent billions and millions of years, you'll need to make a clock dial from posterboard or cardboard. If you plan to use months in a year or some other unit of time that can be shown in a long line, you can use the same materials as models that use units of length.

Hints for Calculating the Models' Scales

- **Models that use units of length:** Suppose both timelines will be 10 meters long.

  First timeline: 5 billion years = 10 meters
  Divide 5,000,000,000 years by 10 meters. The result is 0.5 billion years for each meter.
  Scale: 1 meter = 0.5 billion years, or 500 million years

  Second timeline: 600 million years = 10 meters
  Divide 600,000,000 years by 10 meters. The result is 60 million years for each meter.
  Scale: 1 meter = 60 million years

- **Models that use units of time:** Suppose both timelines will show a 12-month year.

  First timeline: 5 billion years = 12 months
  Divide 5,000,000,000 years by 12 months. The result is 417 million years for each month.
  Scale: 1 month = 417 million years

  Second timeline: 600 million years = 12 months
  Divide 600,000,000 years by 12 months. The result is 50 million years for each month.
  Scale: 1 month = 50 million years

Project Timeline

Task	Due Date
1. Submit your plans and event list to your teacher.	_____
2. Finish constructing the first timeline.	_____
3. Finish constructing the second timeline.	_____
4. Finish marking events on both timelines.	_____
5. Present your models to the class.	_____

PROJECT WORKSHEET 1
Modeling Your Life History

This activity will give you practice in making a timeline to scale. Here, you will model your own life history.

Materials

- paper strip about 110 cm long
- meter stick or metric tape measure
- calculator

Procedure

1. On the paper strip, draw a line 100 centimeters long. Label the left end of the line *Birth*. Label the right end *Today*.

2. How old are you? (To make your calculations easier, round off your age to the nearest half year.) _____ years

3. Calculate how many centimeters on the model will equal 1 year of your life. Fill in the spaces below.
   100 cm = _____ years (your answer in Step 2)
   Divide 100 cm by the number of years. Round off your answer to the nearest whole centimeter.
   Scale:_____ cm = 1 year
   Example: 100 cm = 14 years
   100 cm ÷ 14 years = 7.14 cm/yr, or 7 cm for each year
   Scale: 7 cm = 1 year

4. Starting at the *Birth* end of the line, measure the number of centimeters to represent 1 year. Mark that place on the line and label it *Year 1*.

5. Measure, mark, and label the rest of the years in your age. Your last mark should be very close to the *Today* end of the line.

6. Now mark and label the line to show important events in your life. Use the model's scale to position each event correctly. For example, if you walked on your own for the first time when you were about 1 1/2 years old, multiply 1.5 by the number of centimeters that represent 1 year. Measure that distance from the *Birth* end of the line, and mark that event.

Name _____ Date _____ Class _____

PROJECT WORKSHEET 2

The History of Life on Earth

Your group's timelines should include as many major events in Earth's history as possible. Here are some important events in Earth's history. You may also research other events to add to your timelines. (1,000 million = 1 billion.)

Date (millions of years ago)	Event
3,800	First cells
3,000	DNA replication
3,000	First release of oxygen
2,000	Oxygen abundant in the atmosphere
1,400	First eukaryotic cells (cells with a nucleus)
1,000	First sexual reproduction
540	First organisms with shells
505	Trilobites common
500–425	First crustaceans
425–410	First wingless insects and millipedes
410–350	Ancient sharks abundant
245	Trilobites become extinct.
240	First egg-laying mammals
140	First marsupials
135	Toothed birds become extinct.
35	First monkey-like primates
22	First true monkeys and apes
6	Development of grasslands; grazing animals and large carnivores abundant
1.9	Ice ages cause extinction of many plants and large animals.

SCORING RUBRIC

Life's Long Calendar

In evaluating how well you complete the Chapter Project, your teacher will judge your work in three categories. In each, a score of 4 is the best rating.

	4	3	2	1
Constructing the Timelines	Demonstrates creativity in choosing a workable format for the timelines. Correctly calculates the scale of each model, and constructs two timelines to different scales. Precisely marks and labels many events on the timelines.	Chooses a workable format for the timelines. Constructs two timelines to different scales, but the scale for one or both models has a few minor errors. Marks many events on the timelines with fair accuracy.	Chooses a workable format for the timelines, and constructs two timelines to different scales. Incorrectly calculates the scale of one model. Marks an adequate number of events on the timelines; some events are not accurately marked.	Chooses an unwieldy format for the timelines. Incorrectly calculates the scales of both models and/or does not construct each timeline to scale. Includes only a few events on the timelines and/or most events are not accurately marked.
Presenting the Timelines	Presentation is well-organized, is complete, and demonstrates in-depth understanding of the procedures involved in constructing timelines to scale and of the relationship between the two models.	Presentation is fairly well-organized and demonstrates good understanding of the procedures involved in constructing timelines to scale and of the relationship between the two models.	Presentation is somewhat disorganized and demonstrates only a partial understanding of the procedures involved in constructing timelines to scale and of the relationship between the two models.	Presentation is disorganized and demonstrates little understanding of the procedures involved in constructing timelines to scale and of the relationship between the two models.
Working Cooperatively	Takes a lead in planning, constructing, and presenting both models.	Actively participates in planning and presenting both models and in constructing one or both models.	Participates at others' direction in most aspects of planning and presenting both models and in constructing one model.	Participates minimally in planning, constructing, and presenting the models.

Proteins From a Double Helix

The following steps will walk you through the Chapter Project. Use the hints and detailed directions as you guide your students through the construction of a model of a DNA molecule as well as the development of a presentation on the process of protein synthesis.

Chapter Project Overview

To introduce the project, show students a large, colorful image of a DNA molecule, either from the Internet or an upper-level biology text. As students examine the model, point out that an understanding of the structure of DNA and its function in cells is essential to understanding modern biology. Explain that DNA's primary purpose in cells is to store information about the production of large molecules called proteins. That function, though sounds simple but is at the heart of the growth, development, and evolution of all living things.

Hand out copies of the Project Overview. Review the Project Rules, and ask students if they have any questions. Also pass out the Scoring Rubric, which you will use for scoring students' work. Discuss with students what will be expected of them.

Set a deadline for the presentation of the model and the explanation of protein synthesis. Set interim dates for the completion of Project Worksheet 1, the DNA model, Project Worksheet 2, planning for the presentation, and the final presentation to the class. Encourage students to record these dates on the Project Timeline.

Divide students into small groups. You may want groups to begin discussing what they will do for this Chapter Project. Tell students that though they will be working together in creating a model and developing a presentation, they should individually complete both Worksheet 1 and Worksheet 2.

Distribute copies of Project Worksheet 1. To complete this worksheet, students will need to have learned about the structure of DNA. Instruct them to complete the worksheet before they meet with their groups to plan the construction of a DNA model. Each group should first decide what materials to use to make their DNA model. Materials can include anything in the classroom or materials brought from home. You can display illustrations of a DNA molecule in addition to the one in their text. Remind students to refer to the hints in the Project Overview to help them build.

After groups have completed their models, pass out copies of Project Worksheet 2, and remind students that they should complete this individually. Students need to have read about the production of proteins to be able to respond to the questions. This worksheet is designed to help students organize their thoughts about protein synthesis before they begin to develop their presentation.

After students have completed Worksheet 2, have groups develop their presentation on protein synthesis. Again, allow each group to decide how to make its presentation. Tell students they can make a poster, create a video, use a computer presentation program, prepare an illustrated report, or anything you approve that will effectively demonstrate protein systhesis. Encourage each group to use a unique method of presentation. Remind students to refer to the hints in the Project Overview to help them in developing their presentations.

Materials and Preparation

Each group will decide what materials they will use to make the DNA model. For example, they could use paper, cutting out shapes and coloring different parts with colored pencils or markers. Talk with each group about what materials are readily available at school, and point out that they can bring materials from home.

Materials needed for the presentation of protein synthesis will vary. A group that makes a poster will need poster board, markers, and colored pencils. If a group feels confident about making a computer presentation of the process, provide access to a computer loaded with a presentation program. Also, allow students to use materials of their own, such as a video camera for a video presentation. Talk with each group to help them clarify what they need.

Keep Students on Track—Task 1

Review student responses after they have completed Worksheet 1. Their answers should show who has a firm understanding of the structure of DNA and who does not. You might suggest some students review the material in the text. Tell students that group members should agree on the materials they need to construct their DNA model.

Keep Students on Track—Task 2

Answer any questions students have while they are building their models. After the models are completed, examine each group's model and suggest changes if there are obvious errors in understanding of DNA structure. If a group is off track, you might suggest that students carefully compare their model with the illustration of DNA structure in the text.

Keep Students on Track—Tasks 3–4

Have students complete Worksheet 2 and then meet with their groups to develop their presentation. As students work, be prepared to answer questions about both protein synthesis and the chosen method of presentation. Emphasize to students that a thorough outline at the beginning will result in a more complete presentation.

Chapter Project Wrap Up

As students prepare for presentations, talk with each group to determine whether students have a well-organized presentation of protein synthesis. Make suggestions if a group seems unsure about how to proceed. Emphasize that all group members should take part in the presentation.

Provide class time for group presentations. Allow each group to make its presentation of protein synthesis. Encourage other students to ask challenging questions after each group has finished. After all presentations have been made, discuss which presentation methods and/or materials worked best and why. You may also have students display their DNA models in the classroom.

Extension

Students could use a computer presentation program to show how mutations occur in chromosomes and how some mutations result in cancer. This extension would put to use students' knowledge of both the structure of DNA and DNA replication. Their presentation would need to explain how DNA replicates, how mutations can occur in the process, and how mutations can result in cells that function abnormally. An alternative would be developing the same material on a large poster that could be displayed in the classroom.

PROJECT OVERVIEW
Proteins From a Double Helix

In this Chapter Project, you will explore the structure of DNA and develop a presentation about how DNA is involved in the production of proteins. The discovery of the structure of DNA was one of the great advancements in biology during the twentieth century. In this project, you'll gain insight into why that discovery was so important.

First, you will work with a group to plan and build a model of a DNA molecule. Then, your group will develop a presentation that explains how DNA molecules are involved in protein synthesis within cells. Finally, your group will show the model and make the presentation of protein synthesis to the class.

Project Rules

- Complete Project Worksheet 1 on your own, and then share it with your group as you plan the model of a DNA molecule.

- Plan and build a model of a DNA molecule with your group using materials of your choice. Your model should be accurate in its representation of a DNA molecule, and it should have at least ten rungs on its ladder.

- Complete Project Worksheet 2 on your own, and then share it with your group as you plan a presentation about the process of protein synthesis.

- Develop a presentation showing the steps of protein synthesis. Your presentation should be clear, logical, and complete. The method of presentation is up to you and your group. For example, you can make a poster, film a video, use a computer presentation program, write an illustrated report, or another method of your choice. Get your teacher's approval of the method you choose before proceeding.

- You will make a presentation to the class in which you will show your explanation of the process of protein synthesis.

Suggested Materials

- Poster board, markers, colored pencils
- Paper for model building
- Objects found in the classroom or brought from home

Project Hints for Building a Model of DNA

- As you plan to build a model of DNA, you may want to make a detailed and labeled sketch of the molecule. Write out the sequence of bases you'll use on each side of the molecule.

- Begin thinking about your model by drawing the basic shapes you'll need: a deoxyribose molecule, a phosphate molecule, and a nitrogen base. Use the illustrations in your text or provided by your teacher as references for making these shapes.

- Make sure you use a different color for each part of a DNA molecule.

- You may want to use a marker to label each part of your DNA molecule.

- Keep in mind that a DNA molecule is in the shape of a double helix—like a twisted ladder. Your model should have that shape.

Project Hints for Presenting Protein Synthesis

- Your first task in developing a presentation of protein synthesis is to decide as a group how you will present the information. Discuss what information needs to be presented as well as the various methods each of you has used before. Consider several methods before finally deciding on the method you will use. Ask your teacher for advice if necessary.

- Write an outline of all the information you want in your presentation. Work with your group and make sure the outline includes every step of protein synthesis. Your outline will serve as the basis of your oral presentation.

- The success of your presentation may partly depend on what illustrations you include. They should clearly illustrate the steps in the process, and they should be labeled to help the viewers understand each step.

Project Timeline

Task	Due Date
1. Complete Project Worksheet 1	_____
2. Complete DNA model	_____
3. Complete Project Worksheet 2	_____
4. Finish work on the presentation	_____
5. Make presentation to the class	_____

PROJECT WORKSHEET 1

Building a Model of DNA

As you think about building your model, you need to understand what DNA is and the structure of DNA. Answer the following questions to help you understand the structure of the DNA molecule.

1. What is the relationship among chromosomes, DNA, and genes?

_____

_____

2. Describe the shape of a DNA molecule.

_____

3. Why is the order of nitrogen bases along a gene important?

_____

_____

4. How do the nitrogen bases in DNA always pair up?

_____

Your model can be made from various materials, but it should have different colors representing different parts of DNA. Before building your model, complete the table below.

Basic Part of DNA	Description	Color in Model
Deoxyribose	**5.**	
6.	A molecule that alternates with deoxyribose molecules along the sides of a DNA double helix	
Adenine	**7.**	
8.	One of the nitrogen bases that make up the rungs of DNA; represented by the capital letter *T*	
Guanine	**9.**	
10.	One of the nitrogen bases that make up the rungs of DNA; represented by the capital letter *C*	

89
DNA

PROJECT WORKSHEET 2

Understanding Protein Synthesis

In this Chapter Project, you will work with your group to develop a presentation on protein synthesis. Your presentation should be clear, logical, and complete so that everyone watching will understand. This worksheet will help you plan your presentation.

1. Describe the structure of a protein molecule.

   _____

2. What is protein synthesis?

   _____

   _____

3. What is RNA, and what is its role in protein synthesis?

   _____

   _____

4. What are the two types of RNA, and what are their functions in protein synthesis?

   _____

   _____

For each of the following sentences, fill in the blank with the correct term.

5. Protein synthesis begins in the cell's _____, where the chromosomes are found.

6. After DNA unzips between its base pairs, one of the strands of DNA directs the production of a strand of _____.

7. In the production of a strand of mRNA, adenine pairs with _____, not thymine.

8. After a strand of mRNA is produced, the mRNA leaves the nucleus and enters the _____.

9. The mRNA in the cytoplasm attaches to a cell organelle called a(n) _____.

10. Molecules of _____ and their amino acids attach to the mRNA.

11. The _____ of tRNA pair with bases of mRNA.

12. On the ribosome, _____ _____ are linked together and form a growing chain.

13. The order of the amino acids on the ribosome is determined by the order of the three-base codes on the _____.

14. Once an amino acid is added to the chain, the _____ is released and picks up another amino acid of the same kind.

Name _____ Date _____ Class _____

SCORING RUBRIC

Proteins From a Double Helix

In evaluating how well you complete the Chapter Project, your teacher will judge your work in four categories. In each, a score of 4 is the best rating.

	4	3	2	1
Understanding of DNA Structure and Protein Synthesis	Student demonstrates a mastery of DNA structure and protein synthesis.	Student demonstrates a good understanding of DNA structure and protein synthesis.	Student demonstrates an understanding of most concepts of DNA structure and protein synthesis.	Student demonstrates little understanding of DNA structure and protein synthesis.
Planning and Building a DNA Model	Student takes a lead in planning and building an excellent model of a DNA molecule.	Student participates fully in planning and building an excellent model of a DNA molecule.	Student participates in most aspects of planning and building a model of a DNA molecule.	Student minimally participates in planning and building a model of a DNA molecule.
Developing a Presentation	Student develops a presentation of protein synthesis that is clear, logical, and complete.	Student develops a presentation of protein synthesis that is reasonably clear and complete.	Student develops a presentation of protein synthesis that is fairly clear and mostly complete.	Student develops a presentation of protein synthesis that is unclear and/or incomplete.
Making the Presentation	Student makes a thorough and well-organized presentation of protein synthesis.	Student makes an organized presentation of protein synthesis.	Student makes an adequate but not well-organized presentation of protein synthesis.	Student gives an incomplete and/or disorganized presentation of protein synthesis.

Teach Others About a Trait

The following steps will walk you through the Chapter Project. Use the hints and detailed directions as you guide your students through design, construction, presentation, and reflection.

Chapter Project Overview

In this project, students will work in groups to design an interactive display board that can be used as an educational tool to teach younger students about inherited traits. In introducing the project, you may choose to follow some or all of the suggestions below.

1. Summarize the goals of the project and features of the display board:

   - choose a trait and illustrate how it is inherited

   - explain if the trait is governed by dominant, recessive, or codominant alleles

   - make a display board that has an interactive Question and Answer section including at least one probability problem

   - The display board should stand by itself and be easy to set up.

2. Present the vocabulary terms and concepts students will be working with and their definitions: alleles, dominant, recessive, codominance, probability, Punnett square, phenotype, genotype, homozygous, heterozygous. Students don't have to present all these terms to younger students, but they will need a working understanding of the terms to prepare their lessons.

3. Have students perform their own probability tests using the coin toss, calculating percentages, and working a Punnett square. Have them create several sample problems to be sure they grasp the concept.

4. Give students a list of inherited alleles that also tells which are dominant and recessive.

5. Explain, by using examples, what is meant by "interactive" display board.

   - learners should be physically involved: they can move, attach, or remove pieces working with materials such as felt or magnets.

   - instructor and learners can be involved; instructor asks a question and uses a sound effect (music, buzzer, gong, bell) or visual effect (pop-ups, puppets) to signal a correct or incorrect response given by the learner.

   - the display board might serve more than one purpose—e.g., a display on one side and a game board on its reverse side.

6. If time is a factor, you may choose to have the class work together to create a single interactive display board. Groups could be assigned tasks of the board to complete.

7. You may choose to eliminate entirely the research portion of the project by giving students a set of facts regarding traits that need to be incorporated into the board.

Distribute the Project Overview and review the Project Rules. You may also want to hand out the Scoring Rubric so students will understand what is expected of them. Set a project deadline and some interim dates for checking students' progress. Have students copy the dates on their Project Timeline.

After you discuss the timeline, organize the class into small groups. Next, lead a general discussion about interactive displays, giving a definition (activity shared by people) as well as examples. Encourage students to think about what sort of interactive components would make their display boards interesting.

Student groups will begin by researching information about a specific inherited trait. Then, they will select the key concepts they want to present in their lesson to younger students—Grade 4 or 5. Once key concepts have been chosen, students will turn their attention to the design and function of the display board.

Materials and Preparation

The display board can be made out of various materials, such as foam core or cardboard. Have rulers, tape, construction paper, paste, glue, markers, crayons, and other supplies on hand, also. Students can bring other materials from home.

Keep Students on Track—Tasks 1–2

Talk with each group during its initial meeting. At this point, students should think about the materials they could use for their displays. Encourage creative thinkers to be imaginative in developing their interactive displays.

Distribute Project Worksheet 1. Make sure students understand they will want to use this worksheet as they learn more about inherited traits and plan their lesson and display board.

Keep Students on Track—Tasks 3–5

Check to see that student groups have completed their research on inherited traits and have a rough lesson plan and sketches for their display board. They should also have a preliminary materials list ready. Check individual designs. You may also want to score individual designs as well as the collaborative design.

Students should begin building the display boards. Distribute Project Worksheet 2.

Keep Students on Track—Tasks 6–7

Review the display board built by each group. Test the interactive feature(s). If further work is required, have students work on solutions to be approved before the display board is finished.

Chapter Project Wrap Up

Provide class time for group presentations. Allow each group to present its lesson and display board. Encourage other students to make comments and suggestions about the lesson and display board.

After presentations have been made in class, groups should take turns visiting classes of younger students and teaching their lesson on inherited traits. Evaluate the presentations and younger students' responses to the interactive display.

Encourage students to evaluate how well they accomplished the assignment. Invite students to make suggestions about what they think would have made the project better.

Extension

Have students do a *Who is the child's mother?* activity. Create a fictitious child and give the child a set of traits. Give the father's traits and these traits for Mother #1 and Mother #2. Have students determine which Mother, #1 or #2, is the girl's mother. An example is given. (The correct answer is Mother #1.)

Child

Widow's peak: *WW* or *Ww*

Curly hair: *CC* or *Cc*

Free earlobes: *LL* or *Ll*

Can curl tongue: *TT* or *Tt*

Father

Widow's peak: *WW* or *Ww*

Curly hair: *CC* or *Cc*

Attached earlobes: *ll*

Can curl his tongue: *TT* or *Tt*

Mother #1

No widow's peak: *ww*

Straight hair: *cc*

Free earlobes: *LL* or *Ll*

Can't curl tongue: *tt*

Mother #2

Widow's peak: *WW* or *Ww*

Curly hair: *CC* or *Cc*

Attached earlobes: *ll*

Can curl tongue: *TT* or *Tt*

PROJECT OVERVIEW

Teach Others About a Trait

Characteristics and traits that you possess have been inherited from your parents. Some traits that people inherit, such as perfect eyesight, are beneficial while other inherited traits, such as night blindness, can present obstacles to be overcome. In this project, you will plan a lesson and design a display board that can be used to help instruct younger children about inherited traits. The table shows some examples of inherited traits and whether their alleles are dominant or recessive.

	Dominant Allele	Recessive Allele
Hair	• curly hair • widow's peak	• straight • straight hairline
Facial features	• dimples • unattached earlobes • long eyelashes	• no dimples • attached earlobes • short eyelashes
Muscle control	• able to roll tongue	• unable to roll tongue
Inherited diseases	• both parents must carry an allele for each disease listed	• Tay Sachs • cystic fibrosis • sickle cell anemia • hemophilia A

Project Rules

- Devise a plan for gathering research materials about the inherited trait your group is studying.

- Assign group members to work on different tasks: research, lesson planning, display board design, and materials collection.

- With your group, review the research and decide what concepts will be taught in your plan.

- Brainstorm ways to make the display board interactive, or involving and engaging younger students. Sketch your group's plan for the display board. Show the plan and a materials list to your teacher.

- Prepare the plan and discuss it with your teacher. Revise the plan as needed.

- Present your final plan and display board to the whole class. Make final changes if needed, and then present your lesson and display board to younger students.

Project Hints

- Begin by collecting research material about the trait that your group selected or that was assigned by your teacher. Decide if you will examine one trait or teach students about the differences between dominant and recessive alleles in general. Include a method for predicting probability and at least one probability problem for students to solve.

- Test ways to predict the probability a trait will be inherited. Use the coin toss/percentage method and Punnett square.

- Decide what worksheets you need for the students you will teach.

- Think about how the display board will be used to help present the key points of your lesson and how younger students will interact with the display.

- You need to plan how the younger students will use the interactive features and what the users will learn in the process.

- Use the outline on Worksheet 2 as a guide for planning your lesson.

Project Timeline

Task	Due Date
1. Select a trait to research.	_____
2. Gather research materials.	_____
3. Decide what information will be presented to younger students.	_____
4. Create a probability problem for younger students to solve.	_____
5. Sketch a design for your display board.	_____
6. Collect materials and build your display board.	_____
7. Refine your design as needed.	_____
8. Prepare a practice presentation for your class.	_____
9. Present your lesson to younger students.	_____

PROJECT WORKSHEET 1

Teach Others About a Trait

This worksheet will help you get started making your interactive display board about inherited traits.

Research

1. What genetic trait will you research?

   _____

   _____

2. What information will your research include?

   _____

   _____

   _____

   _____

3. What information will you include in your lesson for younger students?

   _____

   _____

   _____

   _____

Planning the Display Board

4. What interactive components would enhance your display board?

   _____

   _____

   _____

5. What materials do you need to build your display board?

   _____

   _____

   _____

6. On a separate sheet of paper, sketch a display board your group could build. Take this worksheet and sketch to your group meeting. Talk over your ideas with group members.

Name _____ Date_____ Class_____

PROJECT WORKSHEET 2
Teach Others About a Trait
Completing the Display Board and Lesson Prep

Now that you are building a final display board with interactive pieces, you may want to finalize the lesson content you will share with younger students. Use the outline below to organize your plan.

Topic _____
_____

Goal What knowledge should younger students be able to demonstrate at the end of the lesson?
_____
_____

Purpose Why should students learn about this topic? _____
_____
_____

Materials What do you need to teach the lesson? _____
_____
_____

Lesson Content What information and/or skills are going to be taught?_____
_____
_____
_____

Teaching Steps

Answer the following questions on a separate sheet of paper.

a. How will you get the younger students' attention?

b. How will you help students understand what traits are, how traits are inherited, the difference(s) between dominant and recessive alleles, and how to solve a probability problem?

c. How will you check students' understanding of the lesson?

d. How will you get the students to join in and pay attention?

e. How you will end the lesson?

SCORING RUBRIC

Teach Others About a Trait

In evaluating how well you complete the Chapter Project, your teacher will judge your work in four categories. In each, a score of 4 is the best rating.

	4	3	2	1
Developing Suggestions and Designs	Student contributes ideas that show originality of design and a thorough understanding of the purpose of the display board and the concepts to be taught, including how traits are passed from parents to offspring, the difference between dominant and recessive alleles, a method for predicting probability, and a sample probability problem.	Student contributes ideas that show some originality of design and a good understanding of the purpose of the display board and the lesson concepts, including how traits are passed from parents to offspring, the difference between dominant and recessive alleles, a method for predicting probability, and a sample probability problem.	Student contributes ideas that show an adequate understanding of the purpose of the display board and lesson concepts, including how traits are passed from parents to offspring, the difference between dominant and recessive alleles, a method for predicting probability, and a sample probability problem.	Student contributes ideas that show an incomplete understanding of the purpose of the display board and the concepts to be taught, including how traits are passed from parents to offspring, the difference between dominant and recessive alleles, a method for predicting probability, and a sample probability problem.
Constructing Display Board	Display board is well constructed and includes interactive features. The lesson presentation is thorough and well planned.	Display board is well constructed and includes interactive features. The lesson presentation is well planned.	Display board construction is a little sloppy but does include interactive features. The lesson presentation shows an effort at planning.	Display board is poorly constructed and is missing the required interactive features. The lesson presentation shows mediocre effort at planning.
Presenting the Board and Lesson Concepts	Student makes an organized and interesting presentation.	Student makes a good presentation of the display and lesson concepts.	Student makes a presentation that includes a partial explanation of the display board and lesson concepts.	Student makes a presentation that includes an incomplete and/or inaccurate explanation of lesson content and use of the display board.
Participating in the Group	Student takes a lead in planning, constructing, and presenting the display and	Student participates in all aspects of planning, constructing, and presenting	Student participates in most aspects of planning, constructing, and presenting	Student plays a minor role in planning, constructing, and presenting the display board

All in the Family

The following steps will help you execute the Chapter Project. Use the hints and detailed instructions as you guide your students through the creating, predicting, and communicating of the inheritance of traits in their paper pets.

Chapter Project Overview

In the Chapter Project, students will create a paper pet, cross it with a classmate's pet, and determine the offspring's traits. To introduce the project, discuss how puppies in the same litter look similar to each other and to their mother, as well as how they look different. Challenge students to explain how the puppies and their mother can look both similar and different.

Have students read the description of the project in the Project Overview. Then distribute the Scoring Rubric. After students have read these pages, answer their questions about the project and clarify what is expected of them. Note that students should choose their pet's traits without considering which alleles are dominant or recessive.

Set a deadline for the project presentation and some interim dates for the project tasks. Students can fill in these dates on the Project Timeline in the Project Overview.

Distribute Project Worksheet 1. This worksheet provides instructions for how to create a paper pet. While students work on their pets, make sure that the distribution of male and female pets is about equal.

Materials and Preparation

You will need blue and yellow construction paper for students to cut out their paper pets. Provide various materials for students to decorate their pets, such as markers, glitter, yarn, ribbon, sequins, feathers, buttons, and beads. If you cannot provide these materials, suggest that students take their pets home and decorate them with materials available there. Students will also need scissors and glue.

For Project Worksheet 2, student pairs will need a coin to help them assign genotypes to their pets' offspring. For their presentation, students will need poster board or other large paper on which to mount their pet families.

Keep Students on Track—Tasks 1–2

Check students' pets to make sure they have correctly assigned pairs of alleles based on the traits of the pets. Explain that XX and XY are the symbols used in genetics to represent females and males, respectively. Monitor the number of male and female pets so there is an equal number of each in the class. Make an extra pet if your class has an odd number of students.

Keep Students on Track—Task 3

Encourage students to use the terms *genotype* and *phenotype* as they carry out their crosses. Devise a method for students to find mates for their pets. You could have students choose the mates for their pets based on the phenotypes of their classmates' pets. Or you might draw names to set up the crosses randomly.

Distribute Project Worksheet 2. Using this worksheet as a guide, student pairs can create the offspring from the cross between their pets. Students should determine the genotypes of the offspring by tossing a coin.

You might suggest to students that they determine the color of the offspring first and cut the pets out of colored paper. Then students can determine the genotypes of the other traits and write them directly on the back of the offspring.

Keep Students on Track—Tasks 4–5

Give students poster board or other large paper on which they can display their pet families. Make sure students correctly label the pet parents as the P generation and the offspring as the F_1 generation.

Students should have one Punnett square for each of the five traits that correctly shows all of the possible genotypes of the offspring based on the genotypes of the parents.

If students are unsure of how to mount their pets on the poster board, show them how to make a tape hinge on the left side of the pet so that the pet can be easily turned over and read like a page in a book.

Chapter Project Wrap Up

Allow class time for students to review all the pet families in the class. You could either set up the pet family posters around the room for students to look at, or you could have each pair of students present their pet family to the class.

Encourage students to identify offspring that look identical to one or both parents or to other offspring. Also have students look for offspring that look like neither parent. Have students discuss these similarities and differences in the context of the results of the Punnett squares.

Finally, ask students to evaluate in their journals how their pet models helped them learn and understand specific concepts in genetics. Encourage students to make suggestions about how their paper pets might help them understand other topics in genetics.

Extension

Have students create an F_2 generation in their pet families by choosing two of the F_1 offspring as parents. Students should determine the genotypes and phenotypes of the F_2 offspring in the same manner as they did for the F_1 offspring.

Challenge students to set up a breeding program in which they select paper pets that have one particular trait that is especially desirable in paper pets. Students can set up crosses that will produce offspring with the desirable trait. You could have students actually construct the paper pets as they did for this project, or simply have them construct the Punnett squares for the crosses.

PROJECT OVERVIEW

All in the Family

Have you ever been surprised to see two people who looked alike but were not related? On the other hand, you're probably surprised when family members do not share the same physical characteristics. You may have wondered what causes people to look the way they do, or why offspring commonly look like their parents. These are questions that geneticists are trying to answer as they study the inheritance of traits.

In this Chapter Project, you will explore how traits are passed from parent to offspring by creating a family of "paper pets." First, you will create your own "paper pet" by choosing its characteristics. Then you will find a mate for your pet and determine the characteristics of six offspring. Finally, you will present your pet family to the class.

Project Rules

- Use Project Worksheet 1 to help you create your paper pet. Cut out your pet from either blue or yellow construction paper. Then choose the other traits for your pet: gender, eye shape, nose shape, and teeth shape. Use any materials you wish to decorate your pet.

- On the back of your pet, write the alleles it has for each trait. Use XX for females and XY for males. For the other traits, the dominant alleles are for blue body color, round eyes, triangular nose, and pointed teeth. The recessive alleles are those for yellow body color, square eyes, oval nose, and square teeth.

- Find a mate for your pet and determine the alleles that each of six offspring will inherit from each parent by tossing a coin. Construct a paper pet for each of the offspring, showing their phenotypes. Write the genotypes on the back of each offspring.

- Make a display of your pet family in which you label the P generation and the F_1 generation. Construct a Punnett square for each trait to show all the possible allele combinations in your pet family.

- Present your pet family to the class. Explain why some offspring look like one or both of the parents and why some offspring do not.

Project Hints

- Remember, if your original pet has a trait controlled by a dominant allele, you can choose whether your pet is homozygous or heterozygous for the trait.

- Construct each of six offspring. Remember that each offspring must inherit its traits from the parents according to the laws of genetics. You will toss a coin to determine which allele each offspring inherits.

- Set up your display so that it is easy to turn over the pets and read their genotypes.

Project Timeline

Task	Due Date
1. Complete Project Worksheet 1.	_____
2. Identify your pet's genotype.	_____
3. Complete Project Worksheet 2.	_____
4. Construct Punnett squares for each trait.	_____
5. Make a display of your pet family.	_____
6. Present your display to the class.	_____

PROJECT WORKSHEET 1
Making a Paper Pet

Follow the instructions to create your own paper pet with five different traits.

Materials

- blue or yellow construction paper
- scissors
- glue
- markers
- materials to decorate your pet, such as glitter, sequins, buttons, yarn, and beads

Procedure

1. Cut out the outline of the paper pet below. Trace the paper pet design onto either blue or yellow construction paper and cut it out.

2. On the front of your paper pet, draw the other four traits you have chosen for it. The table above lists the possible choices and shows how they should be drawn.

3. On the back of your paper pet, copy the chart shown on the right. Then write your pet's traits in the phenotype column. Give your pet a name, and write the name at the top of the chart.

4. Fill in your pet's genotypes. Use XX for a female and XY for a male. The dominant alleles for the other four traits are: *B* (blue skin), *R* (round eyes), *T* (triangular nose), and *P* (pointed teeth).

5. Decorate your paper pet with materials of your choice.

Possible Traits		
Color	blue	yellow
Gender	female (curl)	male (no curl)
Eyes	square	round
Nose	triangular	oval
Teeth	square	pointed

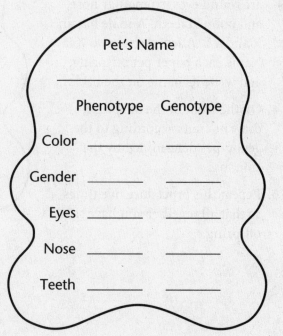

Pet's Name

_____

           Phenotype   Genotype

Color _____ _____

Gender _____ _____

Eyes _____ _____

Nose _____ _____

Teeth _____ _____

PROJECT WORKSHEET 2

Making Paper Pet Offspring

Follow the instructions to make the offspring of your paper pet.

Materials
- scissors
- blue and yellow construction paper
- glue
- markers
- coin

Procedure

1. Cut out the outline below of the paper pet offspring. Toss the coin to determine which alleles the first offspring will inherit for color from each parent. For example, "heads" could represent *B*, the allele for blue skin, and "tails" could represent *b*, the allele for yellow skin. Remember, blue is controlled by a dominant allele. Trace the outline of the offspring onto the appropriate color construction paper and cut it out.

2. On the back of the offspring, copy the chart for the phenotype and genotype of each trait. Write in the genotype and phenotype for color.

3. Toss the coin and record the results to determine the genotypes for the other four traits. Record the genotypes and phenotypes in the appropriate column. Remember, the traits controlled by dominant alleles are round eyes, triangular nose, and pointed teeth. A male has an X and a Y. A female has two Xs. Name each paper pet offspring, and write its name on the back.

4. On the front of the offspring, draw its traits according to the genotypes determined by the coin toss.

5. Repeat this procedure five times so that all together you have six offspring.

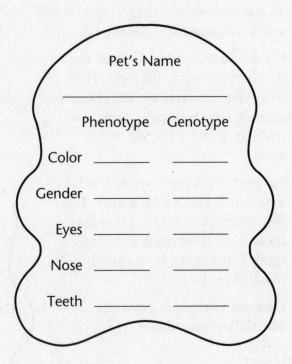

Pet's Name

_____

	Phenotype	Genotype
Color	_____	_____
Gender	_____	_____
Eyes	_____	_____
Nose	_____	_____
Teeth	_____	_____

SCORING RUBRIC

All in the Family

In evaluating how well you complete the Chapter Project, your teacher will judge your work in three categories. In each, a score of 4 is the best rating.

	4	3	2	1
Creating the Parent Paper Pet	The phenotypes and genotypes of all five traits are identified and drawn neatly and correctly on the parent paper pet.	All but one of the phenotypes and genotypes are identified and drawn neatly and correctly on the parent paper pet.	Some phenotypes and genotypes are correct, but two or more are identified and drawn incorrectly on the parent paper pet.	The phenotypes and genotypes are not completed, and/or few or none are correctly identified and drawn on the parent paper pet.
Determining the Traits of the Offspring	The phenotypes for all five traits are correctly identified for all six offspring based on the results of the coin tosses to determine genotype.	Most phenotypes are correctly identified for the offspring based on the results of the coin tosses to determine genotype.	Several phenotypes are incorrectly identified for the offspring based on the results of the coin tosses to determine genotype.	Phenotypes are incomplete, or few or none are correctly identified.
Presenting the Pet Family	Student makes a thorough, interesting presentation that shows a complete understanding of the patterns of inheritance for each trait in the pet family.	Student makes a thorough presentation that shows an adequate understanding of the patterns of inheritance for each trait in the pet family.	Student makes a presentation that shows an incomplete understanding of inheritance patterns in the pet family.	Student makes a presentation that shows a lack of understanding of inheritance patterns in the pet family.

Bird Watch

The following steps will walk you through the Chapter Project. Use the hints as you guide your students through planning, observing, recording data, and making presentations.

Chapter Project Overview

Before introducing the project, bring a bird identification guidebook to class and show the students how to use the book to identify birds. Show students how to use the range maps or a checklist of local birds to see if a bird is actually found in your area. Group students. Have them use field guides and checklists to make a list of birds commonly found in your area. Review different types of bird feeders and foods that birds eat.

Have students read the project description in the Project Overview. Review and discuss the Project Rules to make sure students understand what is expected of them. Encourage students to ask questions. At this time, you may want to hand out the Scoring Rubric that you will use in evaluating students' work. Discuss the purpose of the project and your expectations of what the final product should include.

Discuss methods for identifying and observing birds. Using binoculars may help students observe birds in detail, especially at the beginning of the project, but they are not necessary.

Materials and Preparation

Students can watch a feeder that is already in place. If they decide to install a bird feeder, they can use a ready-made one or build their own. Libraries and the Internet are good sources for suggestions on building bird feeders from inexpensive materials.

The Cornell Lab of Ornithology is an excellent resource for teachers. Their projects include Great Backyard Bird Count, Birdhouse Network, Pigeon Watch, and Project Feeder Watch. Get more information on these and other programs by mail from Cornell Laboratory of Ornithology, 159 Sapsucker Woods Road, Ithaca, NY 14850-1999, or on the World Wide Web at www.birds.cornell.edu.

One widely available bird identification guide is *Field Guide to the Birds of North America,* published by the National Geographic Society. In many cities, checklists of local birds are available from the chapters of the National Audubon Society. Donald and Lillian Stokes are authors of useful books on bird behavior: *A Guide to Bird Behavior, Volumes I, II, and III.*

Bird seed can be purchased in bulk to save money. Note that birds can choke on peanut butter unless it is mixed with corn meal, grain, or sand.

Establish a date for the final project presentation and interim dates for project tasks. Have students record these dates on the Timeline on the Project Overview. Hand out Project Worksheet 1, which helps students plan their bird feeder and its proper placement.

Also hand out Project Worksheet 2, which provides a sample data table each student should copy into a project notebook. Worksheet 2 also describes some specific behaviors. At the completion of the observation phase of this project, students should use the questions on Worksheet 2 to help in analyzing their data.

Keep Students on Track—Tasks 1–4

Check that an adequate number of birds are coming to students' feeders. If there are problems, review that the placement and food are suitable and that the feeders are being observed at different times of the day.

Encourage students to record what they actually observe at their feeders rather than ascribing human feelings or motivation to what they see. Check students' data sheets for correct bird identifications or adequate descriptions of the birds. Correct their misidentifications and review how to use field guides, checklists, and range maps.

Remind students that their observation time should be long enough to note the interactions among the different species of birds and mammals. Students may observe that some species are usually dominant.

Keep Students on Track—Task 5

Check students' observation records on a regular basis. Be sure students include details about the feeding habits of different species of birds.

Encourage students to draw the different beak shapes of birds that visit the feeder. Invite students to identify which type of food each bird species prefers to eat. Students can test this idea by separating different types of food and observing which food each type of bird eats.

Keep Students on Track—Tasks 6–7

Explain to students that analyzing their data means examining their records, summarizing their observations, finding patterns, and deciding what these patterns imply about the birds visiting their feeder.

Remind students they will be presenting their findings to the class. Tell students that their presentations can be supported with drawings, graphs, details of bird behaviors, and any other interesting observations. Encourage students to be creative, as well as accurate.

Chapter Project Wrap Up

After students give their presentations, group students and have them compare observations in order to identify similarities and differences in behaviors observed. Have students turn in any written work you require.

Extension

- Interested students may want to set up specialized feeders to attract specific birds. Examples are hummingbird feeders, suet feeders, and thistle feeders. Birds are also attracted by birdbaths and dripping water.

- Interested students may want to set up birdhouses. Encourage students to research the requirements for different types of birds. Students can build birdhouses out of simple materials.

- Make a bar graph using data on bird numbers from the whole class to estimate which kinds of birds are most common in your area.

- Suggest that interested students continue their observations through the school year.

- Invite a member of the local chapter of the National Audubon Society to make a presentation on common and not-so-common birds or other topic to the class.

- If space and time are limited, you may want to keep a bird feeder at school and allow time during class for students to regularly observe the feeder.

- Rain will ruin birdseed. Suggest that students install a cover over their feeders if necessary.

- Some students may not have a practical place to put a bird feeder near where they live. Suggest that these students use the house of a relative or neighbor. If they do this, make sure they get permission before setting up the feeder.

- Allow students to work in pairs to observe the same feeder.

PROJECT OVERVIEW

Bird Watch

For this project, you will choose an existing bird feeder or install your own to attract birds. You will then identify and make a list of the different birds that come to your feeder. You will also observe interactions between birds and also between birds and any mammals at the feeder. Different kinds of birds may have different feeding behaviors and food preferences. Your observations will be recorded on data sheets. Later, you will analyze your observations, summarize what you have learned about the birds at your feeder. Finally, you report your findings to the class in a brief presentation.

Project Rules

- Have your teacher approve your choice of bird feeder, whether it is an already established feeder or one you will put up yourself.

- Check the bird feeder daily and keep it clean and filled with birdseed.

- Make regular observations and take notes on what you observe.

Suggested Materials

- If you are going to observe a feeder you put out yourself, you will need materials to construct the bird feeder, or you can buy or borrow a feeder already made.

- Bird feeders can be constructed from milk cartons, milk jugs, plastic bottles, or wood. Cut the carton or bottle in half to make a tray. Use string or a coat hanger to hang the feeder.

- In rainy areas, it may be helpful to make a cover to keep rain out of the seed tray. Punching small holes in the bottom of the feeder will also help drain any water that gets in the tray.

- Binoculars may be useful in making observations.

- You will need data tables in a notebook to record your observations.

Project Hints

- Libraries and local birding clubs are good places to find information about birds in your area.

- If you install your own feeder, install it as soon as possible so birds can learn where it is.

- If you decide to build your feeder, you can choose from various materials and designs. The feeder does not need to be elaborate or expensive. The library is a good source for feeder designs.

- The feeder should be located so that you can easily observe it and keep it filled with food. You'll probably have more birds coming to your feeder if you put it near a tree or bushes for shelter. Have your teacher approve your feeder placement. Try to design and locate the feeder so squirrels cannot get to the food easily.

- Make your observations at various times of the day. You may find that some birds are more active at particular times.

- Your observations will include the date and time of observation and the kind of bird observed. If you don't know what kind of bird is at your feeder, write a description of the bird so you can identify it later. You will record whatever happens at your feeder: what food the birds eat, what happens when other birds are nearby, and whether the birds eat in groups or only individually. Also, list things that you think might affect a bird's behavior, such as the temperature and the weather.

- When trying to see which birds prefer which type of food, it may be helpful to add partitions to your feeder to separate the different kinds of food. By keeping track of which partitions are emptied first, you can infer which type of food is most popular. Suggestions for different foods are birdseed, sunflower seeds, breakfast cereal, and grains.

- There are many ways to present what you have learned. You might write a report, give an oral presentation, make labeled drawings on a poster, or record a summary on videotape.

Project Timeline

Task	Due Date
1. Bird feeder chosen, acquired, or constructed	_____
2. Bird feeder location approved by teacher	_____
3. Research of common area birds completed	_____
4. Observation of birds feeding and interacting among themselves and with animals	_____
5. Bird and feeding observations completed	_____
6. Analysis of observations completed	_____
7. Presentation of observations	_____

PROJECT WORKSHEET 1

Planning for Your Bird Feeder Observations

Use this worksheet to help you prepare for your bird feeder observations.

1. Research the birds of your area using field guides, the library, an encyclopedia, or the Internet. Make a list of common birds in your area.

   _____

   _____

   _____

2. Write down what books or other references you will use to identify the birds.

   _____

   _____

   _____

3. If you plan to make your own feeder, decide on a design. Make a list of materials needed.

   _____

   _____

   _____

4. If you will be installing your own bird feeder, make a sketch of the feeder you will use. Indicate on the sketch the kind of bird food, where the food goes, and any other important features of the feeder.

5. Research what is needed for a good location to hang your feeder. Whether you will be observing an existing feeder or putting up a new one, write a description of the location and whether it is safe for birds, easy to observe, easy to keep filled with birdseed, and difficult for other animals to get to.

   _____

   _____

   _____

Name _____ Date_____ Class_____

PROJECT WORKSHEET 2
Recording Bird Feeder Observations

First, in your notebook, write a brief description of the bird feeder and its surroundings, such as height from the ground, distance from buildings, observer's distance, and so on. A sketch would be helpful.

Record your observations in a data table organized like the one below. If you are unsure what kinds of birds you are watching, write down a description. Your observations should include what a bird does by itself, such as eating or grooming, and also behaviors that the bird does only when near other birds.

As your observations continue, you may notice that certain behaviors are repeated. After first describing the repeated behavior in your data table, you can give it a name to make note-taking easier. For example, many birds make a display called "head-forward," in which one bird gets ready to peck another bird, but the birds don't actually make contact. Other behaviors between birds include "crest-raise" and "wing-droop." Make up your own names for different behaviors you see.

Observer _____   Location _____

Date	Time	Bird(s)	Observations

Analyzing and Presenting

Complete the following tasks using a separate sheet of paper. When they have been completed, you are ready to start planning your presentation.

1. Write a few sentences which summarize your research methods. Describe the location and surroundings of the study site. Include the approximate distance between you and the feeder.

2. Write a paragraph or two, summarizing your observations from the data chart.

3. Decide how you want to communicate what you have learned to your classmates.

SCORING RUBRIC
Bird Watch

In evaluating how well you complete the Chapter Project, your teacher will judge your work in three categories. In each, a score of 4 is the best rating.

	4	3	2	1
Planning for Observations	Thoroughly researches local birds. Chooses an appropriate established bird feeder or chooses appropriate design and location for new feeder.	Adequately researches local birds. Chooses an appropriate established bird feeder or chooses an adequate design and location for new feeder.	Minimally researches local birds. Chooses an adequate established bird feeder or builds an adequate bird feeder and places it in a reasonable location.	Does little or no research about local birds. Bird feeder is inadequate or placement is poor.
Making Bird Observations	Makes more than 10 complete observation entries. Each entry includes what birds appeared, interactions, and foods eaten if appropriate. Applies chapter concepts to the observations.	Makes at least 7 complete observation entries. Each entry includes what birds appeared at the feeder, interactions, and foods eaten if appropriate.	Makes at least 3 observation entries. Data may be unorganized or incomplete.	Makes less than 3 observation entries. Entries may be unorganized or incomplete.
Presenting the Results	Makes a thorough, well-organized presentation. Written analysis of birds' behavior is thoughtful, well organized, and follows directly from the observation entries.	Presentation is adequate. Written analysis of birds' behavior is mostly complete, and follows directly from the observation entries.	Presentation is appropriate, but disorganized or hard to follow. Analysis of birds' behavior is incomplete.	Presentation is inappropriate and hard to follow. Written analysis is missing or unsupported by the bird observation data.

Animal Adaptations

The following steps will walk you through the Chapter Project. Use the hints as you guide your students through: planning; choosing an adaptation, a fish, an amphibian, and a reptile; constructing models; making a poster; and giving a presentation.

Chapter Project Overview

Before you introduce the project, allow students to pair off and search through the text for characteristics of fishes, amphibians, and reptiles. When they have finished brainstorming, ask each pair to report back to the class. Compile a list of characteristics on the board. Tell students they will be constructing models of fish, amphibians, and reptiles to show how they are adapted to live in their environments.

Have students read the project description in the Project Overview. Review and discuss the Project Rules to make sure students understand what is expected of them. Encourage students to ask questions. You may want to hand out at this time the Scoring Rubric, that you will use in evaluating student's work. Discuss the purpose of the project and your expectations of what the final product should include.

Materials and Preparation

Encyclopedias, books, the Internet, and magazines are useful for choosing animals and researching adaptations. Materials and tools for constructing models might include: toothpicks, pipe cleaners, polystyrene foam, cardboard, construction paper, chicken wire, balsa wood, balloons, modeling clay, papier mâché, glue, tape, scissors, paints, markers, and other decorating materials.

Establish a date for the final project presentation and interim dates for project tasks. Students' adaptations should be selected for Task 1. Each student's fish, amphibian, and reptile should be chosen before they begin making their models. Give students a week to complete each model. Have students record these dates on the Timeline on the Project Overview.

Distribute Chapter Worksheet 1. Students should be able to complete the chart based on the list that was compiled following the brainstorming activity.

Distribute Chapter Worksheet 2, which helps students plan their models. Each section of this worksheet should be completed prior to the construction of the related model. Students might need help thinking about how to construct their model. Also, having students start their model building in class might be helpful.

If time or building materials are limited, students could model only the part of the animal which shows the chosen adaptation. On their posters, students would illustrate the entire organism and show how the feature fits into the whole animal.

Another option is to have students work in groups. If done in groups of three, each student in a group could do one of the three models. Students would work together to create a poster showing how their models demonstrate the adaptation.

Keep Students on Track—Tasks 1 and 3

Explain to students that the adaptation they choose must be similar in each of the three animals, but might be different in specifics. For example, an adaptation for catching prey might be the many sharp teeth of a barracuda, the long sticky tongue of a bullfrog, and the teeth of a boa constrictor.

Direct students to choose a specific kind of fish to model. Remind students that each of the three main groups of fish has a different set of adaptations. Assist students in planning how to build their model fish given the materials available.

Keep Students on Track—Task 4–6

Make sure that students have finished their fish model. Check students' sketches of their model plans for building an amphibian. Each amphibian model must exhibit the same type of adaptation as shown in the fish model. The sketches should also include the specific kind of amphibian chosen.

Check students' lists of materials that they plan on using to build their amphibian to make sure these materials are available to the student.

Keep Students on Track—Task 7–11

Ensure that students have completed their fish and amphibian models. Check students' sketches of their model plans for building a reptile. Each reptile model must exhibit the same type of adaptation as shown in the fish and amphibian models. The sketches should also explain which specific reptile was chosen.

Encourage students to begin working on their posters. They may need help thinking about what kinds of diagrams will be necessary to illustrate their adaptations. Remind students to label the diagrams.

Chapter Project Wrap Up

As students make their presentations, ask their classmates to take notes to add to their list of animal adaptations in Worksheet 1. Have students turn in all project products.

An additional discussion of adaptations within each group of organisms—fishes, amphibians, and reptiles—might help students to use the compare and contrast skills they developed over the course of the project to review the chapter.

Extension

- Allow students to model adaptations found within the same group of organisms. For example, a student could choose to model a jawless fish, cartilaginous fish, and a bony fish.

- Incorporate mathematical skills into this project. Require students to determine the size of their model in relation to the actual organism, e.g. 1/2 size, 1/10 size. Students should include the scale in their presentations.

- Suggest that students turn their poster and models into a display, and present them at a school or local science fair.

- Invite students to research how computer models of the human body are leading to advances in sports medicine.

- Encourage students to choose animals that live in the same habitat and have them construct a realistic diorama featuring their chosen animals, similar to what they might find in a natural history museum.

PROJECT OVERVIEW
Animal Adaptations

For this project you will study how different organisms are adapted to their own environments. You will choose one kind of adaptation and use models to demonstrate how it differs in a fish, an amphibian, and a reptile. The adaptation that you choose must be different in at least two of the three animals that you model. As an example, you might choose three organisms to show how they are adapted for moving. Or you could pick three organisms that have different adaptations for eating, or for surviving in a hot climate.

Your teacher will review your choice of adaptation and your choice of animals to model. You will design your models and decide what materials to use to build them.

Project Rules

- You must model the same type of adaptation in all three of your models.

- Your models must include one fish, one amphibian, and one reptile. Since there are many variations within each of these groups, your models should be of a specific kind of organism. For example, your fish might be a lamprey, great white shark, or catfish.

- Make a sketch of each of your models and have your teacher approve it before you begin construction.

- Follow the safety guidelines for handling sharp tools in your textbook.

Suggested Materials

- Materials and tools you might use to make your models include: toothpicks, pipe cleaners, polystyrene foam, cardboard, construction paper, chicken wire, balsa wood, balloons, modeling clay, papier mâché, glue, tape, scissors, paints, markers, and other decorating materials.

Project Hints

- Encyclopedias, books, magazines, the Internet, pet stores, and zoos are all good places to look when trying to think about different adaptations and specific animals to model. They can also help you to think about how the adaptation that you choose makes your animal suited to its environment.

- Use a shoe box or other storage container to help you protect your models.

- Consider making a small model. Large models might take too long to complete, and you would need to use a large amount of materials. If your model is not life size, you should include information about the actual size of the organism in your poster and in your presentation.

Project Timeline

Task	Due Date
1. Select adaptation and get teacher approval.	_____
2. Select fish to model and get approval.	_____
3. Sketch fish design.	_____
4. Complete fish model.	_____
5. Select amphibian to model and get approval.	_____
6. Sketch amphibian design.	_____
7. Complete amphibian model.	_____
8. Select reptile to model and get approval.	_____
9. Sketch reptile design.	_____
10. Complete reptile model.	_____
11. Make poster.	_____
12. Do project presentation.	_____

PROJECT WORKSHEET 1

Animal Adaptations

All animals have adaptations that enable them to live in their own habitat and carry out necessary functions (such as eating). This chapter examines three different types of organisms: fishes, amphibians, and reptiles. Completing the following chart is a good exercise for thinking about the different ways in which animals are adapted to live in their habitats. As you fill it out, think about adaptations you might pick for your three models. And remember, you don't have to pick an adaptation or animal from the book.

Two rows of this chart have been done for you. Complete the rest. Skim through the chapter for help. At the end of the project you will use the blank rows at the bottom of the chart to record information about other students' choices of adaptations.

Organism	Adaptation	Function
angelfish	fins	move in water
catfish	whiskers	
lamprey	sharp teeth and suction-cup mouth	
balloon fish	spines	protect against predators
spring peeper (frog)		attract a mate
adult salamander	lungs	
king cobra		keep eggs safe
Jackson's chameleon	sharp claws	

PROJECT WORKSHEET 2
Animal Adaptations
Planning

Complete the following tasks using a separate sheet of paper. You should do each part after you have covered the corresponding section in the chapter.

Part I: Choosing Your Adaptation

1. Describe the adaptation that you have chosen to study.

Part II: Fishes

2. What fish have you chosen to model?

3. Make a sketch of your model fish. The sketch should be detailed enough to serve as the plan design for your model. You may need to do more than one sketch to show different views of your model. The sketches should include measurements of the height, width, and length of your model. Include a scale, if the sketch is not the actual size of the fish. Be sure that your sketches show the adaptation that you described in Part I.

4. What materials do you plan to use to build your model fish?

Part III: Amphibians

5. What amphibian have you chosen to model?

6. Repeat step 3 for the amphibian you've chosen.

7. What materials do you plan to use to build your model amphibian?

Part IV: Reptiles

8. What reptile have you chosen to model?

9. Repeat step 3 for the reptile you've chosen.

10. What materials do you plan to use to build your model reptile?

SCORING RUBRIC

Animal Adaptations

In evaluating how well you complete the Chapter Project, your teacher will judge your work in four categories. In each, a score of 4 is the best rating.

	4	3	2	1
Planning	Thoroughly researches the adaptation and how it differs in the three animals. Makes useful sketches with appropriate measurements before attempting construction.	Adequately researches the adaptation and how it differs in the three animals. Makes sketches of the organisms before attempting construction.	Minimally researches the adaptation and how it differs in the three animals. Makes sketches of one or two organisms.	Does little or no research about the adaptation. Fails to make sketches before building model.
Model Building	All models are well designed and to scale. The chosen adaptations are apparent.	Most models well designed and to scale. The chosen adaptations are fairly easy to discern.	Models are moderately well designed, but are not to scale. The chosen adaptations are fairly easy to discern.	Models are poorly designed and not to scale, and adaptations are difficult to discern.
Creating Poster	Written explanations accurately describe the adaptation. Labeled diagrams are included.	Written explanations accurately describe the adaptation. Partially labeled diagrams are included.	Written explanations partially describe the adaptation, but diagrams are unlabeled.	Written explanations fail to describe the adaptation and diagrams are missing.
Presenting the Project	Presentation is thorough and well organized. Student demonstrates the adaptation using all three models.	Presentation is adequate. Student demonstrates the adaptation using two models.	Presentation is incomplete and disorganized. Student demonstrates the adaptation using a model.	The presentation is inappropriate and hard to follow. The student is unable to clearly demonstrate the adaptation.

Animals in the Neighborhood

The following steps will walk you through the Chapter Project. Use the hints and detailed directions as you guide your students through a survey of animals, research of animal adaptations and body systems, and creation of a poster about animal body systems.

Chapter Project Overview

Introduce this project by asking students about the different animals they've seen around their own neighborhood. Students might mention seeing squirrels, various birds, and perhaps a snake or lizard. Ask if they've ever seen nocturnal animals, such as skunks or raccoons. If students don't mention insects, spiders, or snails, remind them of the many different kinds of animals classified in the Animal Kingdom. Then, turn the discussion to what each of the animals students have mentioned might eat. Students should already have learned about herbivores, carnivores, and omnivores. Ask students to classify animals according to what they eat. Explain that in this Chapter Project, they will be investigating the eating habits of various animals as well as the body systems that allow these animals to carry out daily activities.

Have students read the Project Overview, and have students review the Project Rules. Also, hand out the Scoring Rubric that you will use to score students' work. Discuss with students what will be expected of them. You may also want to set deadlines for the completion of the different stages of the project, including the animal surveys, the table in Project Worksheet 1, the research on animal systems, and presentation of their posters. Encourage students to record these dates on their Project Timelines.

For this project, divide the class into pairs or small groups. Tell students they will be working with a partner or group members as they conduct the animal survey, do the research, and make their poster.

Distribute copies of Project Worksheet 1. Talk with students about how to conduct this survey. Emphasize that students should

not to go into woods or along unfamiliar neighborhood streets alone. They should always make observations with another student or adult. You may want to have all students finish by the next day or give them several days to make their observations. Students will need time after the survey is completed for research to finish the table on Worksheet 1. If time is an issue, you could end this Chapter Project at the end of this phase. You could have pairs or small groups make a poster showing what they observed during their survey. Then, students could work together to make a table of all animals observed by members of the class.

After students have completed their surveys and Worksheet 1, distribute copies of Project Worksheet 2. Advise pairs or groups to choose two of the animals observed for further research on body systems. Tell students that their choices cannot be the same kind of animal, such as two mammals or two birds. You may want to prepare options for students to pick out of a hat so that a variety of animal types will be represented during the presentations. Discuss with students about where they can find information about animal body systems.

Materials and Preparation

Students will need research materials for information about specific animals and kinds of animals. You might borrow some biology textbooks from a high school. Encyclopedias—books or online—are also an excellent source of information about animals. Students will benefit from having access to a reliable Internet search engine.

Keep Students on Track—Task 1

Talk with students about where they can go to observe animals. Caution students again not to go out alone to make observations. Have a list on hand of safe areas close by that students might not think of. Point out that ecosystems near a stream or pond are likely to have different animals than those students see in backyards and urban areas. Point out that pets may be observed; some students may have different kinds of animals as pets, including turtles, lizards, snakes, or amphibians.

Keep Students on Track—Task 2

After students have conducted their surveys of animals, advise them where to find information about the animals' feeding habits. Students might use a biology textbook or a field guide to find out what various animals eat. They can also go online to search for the diets of specific animals.

Keep Students on Track—Task 3

Talk with students about the animals they chose to investigate. Make sure that a wide variety of animals will be covered among all students. Provide a variety of good research materials, and be prepared to field questions about the information students find. You may want to ask a high school biology teacher for a list of resources on animal body systems.

Chapter Project Wrap Up

As students create their posters, discuss with each pair or group how best to present the information they've found about the animals' systems. Review the illustrations they've made, downloaded, or copied to make their poster interesting and understandable. Talk with students about the use of cutaway views that show details of animal body systems and how best to add labels to illustrations.

Provide class time for a poster session, in which all posters are displayed and students have the opportunity to circulate and observe other groups' posters. After students have looked at all the posters, stand by each poster in turn and encourage students to ask challenging questions of its creators.

Extension

Interested students could make a bulletin board display of all the animals discussed in the presentations. The display could include labeled illustrations as well as a table that contains information about the digestive, respiratory, circulatory, and excretory systems of all the animals.

PROJECT OVERVIEW

Animals in the Neighborhood

Have you ever noticed what a great diversity of animals there are around you? If you stop to observe, you'll probably see rabbits, squirrels, mice, spiders, insects, fish, frogs, snails, and all kinds of birds. In this project, you will take the time to observe because you are going to make a survey of animals in your neighborhood. You'll also research the body systems of two of the animals you observe.

First, you will work with a partner or small group to conduct a survey of animals in your neighborhood. Second, you will classify and group each of the animals you observe. Third, you will choose two animals and learn about their digestive, respiratory, circulatory, and excretory systems. Finally, you will make a poster to display the information you've found.

Project Rules

- Conduct a survey of animals in your neighborhood. This might include animals in and around your house, in a park, in or by a stream or pond, and on the school grounds.

- List the animals you observe in the table on Project Worksheet 1. Classify each animal according to its biological classification. Do research to find out about an adaptation each animal has for feeding. Also, identify each animal as a herbivore, carnivore, or omnivore.

- You may list a pet as one of your animals, though your emphasis should be on wild animals in your area.

- After you have completed your survey of animals in the neighborhood, choose two of the animals for further research. Get your teacher's approval for the animals you choose before beginning research. Then, use research materials at the school, the library, or online to find details about the animals' digestive, respiratory, circulatory, and excretory systems.

- With your partner or group, create a poster that shows details of the two animals you researched. Your poster should include illustrations of each animal, with labels showing important parts of each body system you researched.

Suggested Materials

- Encyclopedias, biology textbooks, field guides, and the Internet
- Poster board, markers, and colored pencils; other materials approved by your teacher

Project Hints

- As you conduct your survey of animals, try to be outside in the early morning or in the evening just before dark. Some animals hide during the day or are nocturnal.

- Always make your observations of animals with at least one other student or an adult.

- Try to find animals to observe that most people don't see every day. You might look for animals in a wooded area or by a stream or pond.

- Try to list many different kinds of animals. See if you can observe at least one mammal, bird, reptile, amphibian, fish, and arthropod.

- To research feeding adaptations, first search for the diet an animal eats. For instance, a bird that eats mostly seeds will have a different kind of beak than a bird that eats insects.

- A good biology textbook will likely have most of the information you need about the body systems of different kinds of animals. You may not be able to find details about a specific animal. Instead, look for information about the group to which the animal belongs, such as birds or fish.

- Your poster should have good illustrations. Look for labeled illustrations in textbooks or online that show structures inside the type of animal you are researching. You can draw your own illustrations using those as models. You can also use illustrations downloaded from the Internet or copied from a textbook. If you use downloaded or copied illustrations, you will probably have to delete some labels and add your own. You should write in small print the source of any downloaded or copied illustration used on your poster.

Project Timeline

Task	Due Date
1. Complete survey of local animals	_____
2. Complete research of feeding adaptations	_____
3. Complete research on systems of two animals	_____
4. Complete your poster	_____

PROJECT WORKSHEET 1

Conducting a Survey of Animals

What animals do you see every day in and around your neighborhood? What animals do you think might be there that you don't see? Conduct a survey of animals that live near your home and in the surrounding area. This might include a park, a stream or pond, and the school grounds.

In the table below, list the animals you observe and where you observe them. Also, classify each animal as a mammal, bird, fish, reptile, mollusk, worm, arthropod, or amphibian. Your list may include one pet. Then, through research, try to identify an adaptation each animal has for obtaining food. Once you've identified a feeding adaptation, determine whether the animal is a carnivore, herbivore, or omnivore. Two rows of the table have been completed as examples. You may want to continue this table on another sheet of paper.

Animal	Location Observed	Classification	Adaptation to Obtain Food	Carnivore, Herbivore, or Omnivore?
Squirrel	neighbor's yard	mammal	teeth	herbivore
House fly	school cafeteria	arthropod	spongy, sucking mouthparts	omnivore

PROJECT WORKSHEET 2

A Closer Look

Choose two of the animals you observed while conducting your survey to study in detail. For each of these animals, use research sources to find out about these four systems: digestive, respiratory, circulatory, and excretory. Then, record the information you find on a separate sheet of paper. An example has been done for you.

Animal: House fly   **Classification:** Arthropod

Digestive system: The digestive system is a tube that opens at the mouth and ends at the anus.

Respiratory system: The respiratory system is a network of branching tracheal tubes throughout the body. Air enters and leaves the tubes through small openings called spiracles on the outside of the body.

Circulatory system: A house fly's circulatory system is an open system with a heart that pumps blood through the body.

Excretory system: The excretory system includes saclike organs called Malpighian tubules that extract wastes from blood and add them to the digestive tube from the mouth to the anus.

Source of information: *Biology* (Pearson, 2008) by Kenneth Miller and Joseph Levine

1. **Animal:** _____   **Classification:** _____

   Digestive system: _____

   Respiratory system: _____

   Circulatory system: _____

   Excretory system: _____

   Source of information: _____

2. **Animal:** _____   **Classification:** _____

   Digestive system: _____

   Respiratory system: _____

   Circulatory system: _____

   Excretory system: _____

   Source of information: _____

SCORING RUBRIC

Animals in the Neighborhood

In evaluating how well you complete the Chapter Project, your teacher will judge your work in four categories. In each, a score of 4 is the best rating.

	4	3	2	1
Participating in a Survey of Animals	Student takes a lead in conducting a survey of animals in the neighborhood.	Student participates in all aspects of conducting a survey of animals in the neighborhood.	Student participates in most aspects of conducting a survey of animals in the neighborhood.	Student plays a minor role in conducting a survey of animals in the neighborhood.
Classifying Animals	Student correctly classifies and groups 10 or more animals observed in the neighborhood.	Student correctly classifies and groups 7–9 animals observed in the neighborhood.	Student correctly classifies and groups 5–6 animals observed in the neighborhood.	Student correctly classifies and groups fewer than 5 animals observed in the neighborhood.
Researching the Systems of Animals	Student finds accurate and interesting information about the body systems of two animals.	Student finds accurate information about the body systems of two animals.	Student finds some accurate information about the body systems of two animals.	Student finds mostly inaccurate and/or incomplete information about the body systems of two animals.
Creating and Explaining Poster	Poster is logically organized, has appropriate and informative illustrations, and includes accurate and interesting information about the systems of two animals.	Poster is organized, has appropriate and informative illustrations, and includes accurate information about the systems of two animals.	Poster is organized, has adequate illustrations, and includes mostly accurate information about the systems of two animals.	Poster is not well organized, has inadequate illustration, and includes inaccurate information about the systems of one or two animals.

Design and Build an Animal Habitat

The following steps will walk you through the Chapter Project. Use the hints and detailed directions as you guide your students through brainstorming, designing and constructing a habitat, and giving a presentation.

Chapter Project Overview

In this project, students will select an animal and design and build a habitat that meets that animal's needs for survival. To launch the project, bring an animal into the classroom to show students. Discuss what the animal needs to live. Talk about where the animal lives and its diet. Ask students about where they could find out about how to take care of the animal. Explain what you expect students to learn by observing their animals in the habitats they design and build: the animal's physical characteristics, what it eats, when it is active, when it rests, and in what part of the habitat it spends most of its time.

Have students read the project description in the Project Overview and review the Project Rules. At this time, you may also want to hand out the Scoring Rubric that you will use in evaluating students' work. Establish a deadline for the project presentation and the different project tasks. Have students record these dates on the Timeline in the Project Overview.

Materials and Preparation

Organize the class into small groups. Make sure students understand what is expected of each member of a group. Point out that as they progress through the chapter, groups' designs will be reviewed to be sure they meet design requirements.

Next, lead a brainstorming session to get students thinking about what needs must be met by the habitat for their animal. Ask questions about the habitats regarding water and food sources, air circulation, space, and safety.

Explain that students will finalize their designs with drawings and detailed materials' lists. The use of simple building materials or existing habitats (aquariums or metal cages) is one way to simplify the building process.

Introduce a method for selecting the best design. The design/evaluation phase should include a defined set of criteria regarding the functionality of the habitat. Some criteria to consider are: the habitat must ensure that the animal has access to food, water, light, warmth, and space; it must provide a safe environment, free of any materials that might harm the animal(s). You might want to supply students with a checklist of requirements.

If possible, provide some basic materials and tools, such as aquariums, cages, 2-L plastic bottles, jar lids, mesh screening, leaves, garden trimmings, wood shavings, shredded newspaper, gravel, rocks, sticks and twigs, lightweight wood, and plexi-glass. Hammers, nails, saws, glue-guns, and wood glue should be available for students.

Keep Students on Track—Task 1

You may want to prepare a list of animals for students to choose from. Suitable animals might include anole lizards, crickets, earthworms, fruit flies, guppies, millipedes, pill bugs, slugs, snails, and spiders. Make students aware of school regulations regarding live animals, classroom space, and overnight and weekend temperatures. An alternate approach would be to have one animal for the class to observe. Groups would take turns observing the animal for one week, in the habitat they designed.

Talk with each group during its initial meeting. Guide them in developing their ideas and help them think about the materials they will use for their habitat.

Distribute Project Worksheet 1. Make sure students understand they will need to use this worksheet as they read the chapter and learn more about animals' needs and what elements in a habitat meet those needs.

Keep Students on Track—Tasks 2–3

Check to see that student groups have brainstormed and chosen a design for their animal's habitat. Review their material lists. Help students replace impractical or expensive materials by suggesting alternatives.

As you review students' sketches, direct them to talk with classmates to gain ideas. Encourage students to be imaginative.

You may want to score individual designs as well as the collaborative design. Approve the design and have students begin building their habitats.

Keep Students on Track—Task 4

Review each group's habitat by using the description and sketches they made on Worksheet 1. If any problems exist, have students work on solutions. Distribute Worksheet 2. Have students show their redesigned habitats to you for approval.

Keep Students on Track—Task 5

Ensure that students have completed their habitats with animals in place. Records of students' observations should be underway.

Chapter Project Wrap Up

As you review each group's habitat, you may wish to have the members "talk you through" the presentation. Make suggestions for organizing the presentation into a logical report.

Provide class time for group presentations. Allow each group to present its habitat and explain its features. Encourage other students to ask questions about the habitat and its features.

After presentations have been made, discuss with students which habitats seemed to meet all the animals' needs in the most effective and/or creative way.

Encourage students to evaluate how well they accomplished the assignment, including how well the final habitat matched the final design the group had agreed upon. Invite students to make suggestions about what they think would have made the project better.

Extension

Students might want to show their habitats and do their presentations for other classes in your school or take a field trip to a nearby elementary school and present a science lesson for younger students, including a question-and-answer period.

PROJECT OVERVIEW
Design and Build an Animal Habitat

How can you make a habitat that matches the environment of a living organism? In this project, you will work in a group to design and build a habitat that provides everything a specific animal needs to survive.

First, choose an animal to observe, and research what it needs to live and how to take care of it. Find out where the animal lives so you can match its environment as closely as possible in your habitat.

Then, brainstorm a design for a habitat. After your teacher approves your design, build the habitat. As your group learns more about your chosen animal, change or add features to the habitat design after your teacher approves the changes.

Finally, add your animal to the redesigned habitat and set up a log for recording observations. The log should include the animal's name, observer's name, day, date, and time observations were made. It should also have space for a brief description of the animal's behaviors, feeding times, preferred food, and play and work activities. Group members should take turns observing the animal and recording information in the log. At the end of the project, present your habitat and observation records to the class.

Project Rules

- Research what your animal needs to survive. Have your teacher approve your list before you start to design a habitat.

- List the materials you will use to build your habitat. Give your teacher your materials' list and design plan that includes safety precautions you will take.

- Construct your habitat following the safety guidelines in your book.

- Have your teacher approve your observation schedule.

Name _____ Date_____ Class_____

Project Hints

- Brainstorm with your group members about where to find information about your animal's needs.

- As soon as possible, begin collecting materials for your habitat.

- Work closely with other members of your group, and listen to their ideas. You might find that someone in your group has just the right idea to make your own design better.

- Work with other members of your group to fix any problems with your design after starting to build the habitat.

- For your presentation, make sure your habitat has signs and labels that provide information about your habitat.

Project Timeline

Task	Due Date
1. Select animal and research its needs.	_____
2. Create materials list, design sketches, and get safety precautions approved.	_____
3. Build habitat.	_____
4. Redesign habitat.	_____
5. Get observation log approved.	_____
6. Complete observations.	_____

Name _____ Date _____ Class _____

Research Your Animal's Needs

After selecting the animal you will observe, you must do research to identify what the animal needs to survive. You must research the physical characteristics of the animal as well as what it eats, where it lives in nature, and its other specific needs.

1. What is the animal you will observe?

   _____

2. Where does it live in nature?

   _____

   Average temperature

   _____

   Water, land, or air

   _____

   Natural enemies

   _____

   Plants in environment

   _____

   Other important information

   _____

   _____

   _____

3. What are its feeding habits?

   Type of food _____

   Amount it eats _____

   Feeding time _____

4. How much water does the animal need?

   _____

   _____

5. What other special needs does the animal have?

   _____

   _____

6. On a separate sheet of paper draw a sketch of your animal. Label the parts of the animal and describe what each part does for the animal.

PROJECT WORKSHEET 2
Design Your Habitat

After finding out what your animal needs to survive, you must use the information to design a habitat that the animal can live in while being observed. Problem solve with your group members to decide how your habitat will accommodate each need. Remember that your habitat should include everything the animal needs to survive and still allow you to observe the animal and easily provide food and water.

1. List the needs of the animal that will live in your habitat.

   _____   _____

   _____   _____

   _____   _____

   _____   _____

2. What features or items will you include in your habitat to accommodate each need of the animal?

   _____   _____

   _____   _____

   _____   _____

3. What features or items in your habitat help to keep the animal safe?

   _____

   _____

   _____

   _____

4. On a separate sheet of paper, sketch your habitat. Label all parts of your habitat's design and state what animal need each part satisfies.

Name _____ Date_____ Class_____

Design and Build an Animal Habitat

In evaluating how well you complete the Chapter Project, your teacher will judge your work in four categories. In each, a score of 4 is the best rating.

	4	3	2	1
Creating Individual Sketches and Designs	Student makes sketches that show a thorough understanding of an animal's needs and how they must be met in its habitat in order for the animal to survive.	Student makes sketches that show a good understanding of an animal's needs and how they must be met in its habitat in order for the animal to survive.	Student makes sketches that show understanding of an animal's needs and how they must be met in its habitat in order for the animal to survive.	Student makes sketches that show little understanding of an animal's needs and how they must be met in its habitat in order for the animal to survive.
Constructing the Habitat	Habitat is well built and includes all required features: a water source, food source, light, warmth, space, and attention to the animal's safety.	The construction is adequate and includes 5 of the 6 required features: a water source, food source, light, warmth, space, and attention to the animal's safety.	The construction is sloppy and is missing 3 of the 6 required features: a water source, food source, light, warmth, space and attention to the animal's safety.	The construction is poor and is missing 4 of the 6 required features: a water source, food source, light, warmth, space and attention to the animal's safety.
Presenting the Habitat to the Class	Student makes a thorough and interesting presentation that includes a clear, accurate explanation of what the habitat needed to provide and how it meets all the animal's needs.	Student makes a thorough presentation that includes a satisfactory explanation of what the habitat needed to provide and how it meets all the animal's needs.	Student makes a presentation that includes a partial explanation of what the habitat needed to provide and how it meets the animal's needs.	Student makes a presentation that includes an incomplete and/or inaccurate explanation of what the habitat needed to provide and how it meets the animal's needs.
Participating in the Group	Student takes a lead in planning, constructing, and presenting the habitat. Student makes thorough and complete observations on schedule.	Student participates in all aspects of planning, constructing, and presenting the habitat. Student makes adequate observations on schedule.	Student participates in most aspects of planning, constructing, and presenting the habitat. Student makes partial observations all or most of the time.	Student plays a minor role in planning, constructing, and presenting the habitat. Student makes incomplete observations either all or some of the time.

Mystery Object

The following steps will walk you through the Chapter Project. Use the hints as you guide your students through planning, object observations, and presentations.

Chapter Project Overview

Before introducing the project, bring organisms, such as a plant and a fish, into the classroom to show to the students. Talk about the characteristics that these organisms share with other living things.

Have students read the Project Overview. Review the Project Rules, and hand out the Scoring Rubric that you will use for scoring students' work. Discuss with students what will be expected of them.

Set a deadline for the project presentation and interim dates for the different project tasks. Encourage students to copy the dates in the Project Timeline.

Have students brainstorm a list of characteristics that living things possess. They should also think about some nonliving things that share one or more of these characteristics.

Distribute copies of Project Worksheet 1. Have students read over the questions they will need to answer in the preliminary stage of this project.

Give each student a mystery object (see Materials and Preparation section for suggestions) and an instruction sheet describing how they should care for their object. Stress to students that it is important that they care for their object even if they do not believe that their object is living. To maintain students' interest, be sure each student observes at least one object that undergoes visible changes or responds positively to some tests.

Project Worksheet 2 will help students through collecting data and preparing for the presentation. Remind students to refer to the hints in the Project Overview as they plan and carry out the project.

Materials and Preparation

Some possibilities for living mystery objects include baker's yeast (mix one teaspoonful each of yeast and sugar to 250 mL warm water; observe under microscope), seeds (soak lentil seeds in water overnight, then wrap in wet paper towel; place towel in plastic bag and store in dark; observe daily), brine shrimp, slime mold, bread mold, insect larvae, goldfish, and plants.

Some possibilities for nonliving mystery objects include pebbles, vermiculite, lead shot (they look like seeds), artificial plants (they look real but don't grow or have cellular structure), soluble salts in a saturated solution (crystal gardens appear to "grow"), hair (it has cellular structure, but is no longer living), and toys with microchips (they are capable of complex responses).

Students will also need to use various materials to test their mystery objects for signs of life. Such items would include a microscope, glass slides and coverslips, scissors, a plastic dropper, and a ruler. You may need to show students how to use a microscope.

Consider organizing the class in groups to do the project. You may also have students observe several different objects in the classroom. This would allow you to care for the objects, preventing students from harming living mystery objects.

Keep Students on Track—Tasks 1–4

Before you give students their mystery objects, make sure they have completed Project Worksheet 1. They should have a clear concept of the characteristics that are used to describe living organisms. They should also have thought of reasonable tests that they could use to observe these characteristics. Be sure that these tests will not harm the mystery objects.

Once students have received their objects, they should examine them carefully. If necessary, they should revise their list of life characteristics and the tests that they plan to use.

Keep Students on Track—Task 5

Give students time in class each day to care for their mystery objects. During this time, have them record their observations. Check students' observation records on a regular basis. Be sure students include diagrams that depict changes in the size and appearance of their objects.

Periodically, check the health of the objects. If the student's mystery object is an organism, be sure that it is still alive.

Keep Students on Track—Task 6

Tell students that analyzing their data means looking at their observations, summarizing them, finding patterns, and deciding what these patterns tell about their mystery object. Living organisms should be classified as completely as possible, given students' knowledge.

Remind students they will be introducing their mystery objects to the class. Let them decide how they want to make their presentations. Encourage students to be creative.

Chapter Project Wrap Up

As students give their reports, ask their classmates to take brief notes, writing down the major characteristics of each mystery object. Have the class decide whether they agree with the living/nonliving decision that the presenter made. If necessary, some students may have to defend their choice. Have them discuss the specific characteristics that led them to their decision, and ask the class whether they would have used different characteristics.

After all presentations have been made, have students evaluate their projects. Ask them to explain which characteristics of life were difficult to observe. Determine whether there were any common characteristics that all of the students had a difficult time observing. Discuss why this may be so. Have them write down advice to give to other students who might want to study characteristics of life in different objects.

Tell students about their mystery objects, including the classification groups the objects belong to (if applicable) and whether they are classified as living or not. Describe the characteristics of life, and explain why some of these may be hard to observe (e.g., they may occur at a different life stage).

Extension

In the 1970s, NASA sent a lander named *Viking* to Mars. *Viking* sent back pictures and other information describing the planet's surface, and scientists used some of this data to look for signs of life. Have students find out what characteristics scientists were most interested in looking for, and what kinds of instruments they used in order to detect them.

PROJECT OVERVIEW

Mystery Object

In this project you will be observing a mystery object to determine whether or not it is living. Sound easy? Maybe. But sometimes it is difficult to determine whether an object is indeed living. What characteristics distinguish living from nonliving? How do you test for these characteristics? What if an object has some of the distinguishing characteristics, but not others?

You will begin this project by identifying characteristics that distinguish living organisms from nonliving objects. You will then need to develop tests that will help you to observe these characteristics in your mystery object. Finally, you will spend about two weeks observing your mystery object to determine whether it is living. At the conclusion of this project, you will present your observations and conclusions in a class presentation.

Project Rules

- Write out a plan for testing your object to determine whether it is living or nonliving. Your teacher will approve your research plans before giving you your mystery object.

- Your teacher will give you an instruction sheet describing how you must care for your object. You are responsible for the well-being of your mystery object and should care for it in every possible way.

- You must observe your mystery object daily, sketching diagrams and recording observations in a data table.

- When you have finished making your observations, you will need to draw conclusions about your object. If you determine that your object is living, try to classify it into domain and kingdom.

Suggested Materials

- Your mystery object, which will be given to you by your teacher.

- Some items will be required for proper care of your object. Your teacher should include these on your instruction sheet.

- Items that you can use to observe your object include a microscope, glass slides and coverslips, scissors, a plastic dropper, and a ruler.

Project Hints

- Brainstorm a list of characteristics that living organisms share. Make sure you consider that not all organisms share every specific characteristic. For example, many living organisms move, but this characteristic alone does not describe all organisms. Trees are alive, but they do not move around. Also, some nonliving objects may share a specific characteristic. For examples, clouds and vehicles show movement.

- Before you conduct tests of your mystery objects, predict what observations will help to classify your object as living.

- When you observe your object, describe what the object looks like, what and how much it is eating, what it does, and anything else you think is important. Also, list things that may affect your object's behavior, such as the time of day, the temperature, and the weather.

- Recall that organisms in different domains and kingdoms get their food in different ways. If you think your object is alive and also think you know what domain or kingdom it belongs in, this knowledge can help you to design tests about nutrition and growth.

- There are many ways to present what you have learned. You can write a report, give a speech, draw illustrations with captions, or record a summary on videotape.

Project Timeline

Task	Due Date
1. Complete list of characteristics of living things.	_____
2. Propose a list of ways to test for characteristics of life.	_____
3. Receive mystery object.	_____
4. Revise test plans to fit specific mystery object.	_____
5. Complete observations of object.	_____
6. Make presentation of object, and describe analysisand conclusions.	_____

PROJECT WORKSHEET 1
Mystery Object

Part I

Complete the following tasks using a separate sheet of paper. When the tasks have been completed, you are ready to get your teacher's approval and obtain your mystery object.

1. What characteristics do all living things share? Write a few sentences describing these characteristics, and explain why you chose them.

2. How can you test for these characteristics? For each characteristic that you listed above, describe at least two ways in which you could test an object for the characteristic. Make sure that you predict the results of these tests. What results would classify this organism as living?

3. For the tests that you described above, create a list of materials that you would need. Are these materials available to you? Are there any tests that you described that you would be unable to do in the time allowed? Redesign your tests, if necessary.

Part II

Complete the following tasks using a separate sheet of paper. When the tasks have been completed, you are ready to begin your tests and observations.

4. Look at your mystery object, and make an initial hypothesis about whether or not it is living. Write a few sentences describing the observations that support your hypothesis.

5. Reconsider the tests that you designed, making any necessary modifications (you may need to use a microscope to observe your object).

6. Write out a plan for how you will proceed with this project. What tests will you use? How often will you conduct these tests?

PROJECT WORKSHEET 2

Mystery Object

Record your observations in a data table organized like the one below. Include a description of the test you conducted, how the object responded, and anything else you think is important, such as sketches of your object.

Date	Time	Test Used	Observation

Analyzing and Presenting

Complete the following tasks on a separate sheet of paper. When they have been completed, you are ready to put together your presentation.

1. Write several sentences summarizing your research. What tests did you conduct that were helpful in determining whether your object is living? What tests were not helpful? Why?

2. Write several sentences summarizing your observations from the data table. Do you think that your object is living? What leads you to this conclusion? If your object is living, to which classification group does it belong?

3. Decide how you want to communicate what you have learned to your classmates. Make a list of the things you will need to make this presentation.

SCORING RUBRIC

Mystery Object

In evaluating how well you complete the Chapter Project, your teacher will judge your work in the following categories. In each, a score of 4 is the best rating.

	4	3	2	1
Developing Hypothesis Based on Characteristics of Living Things	Considers several different characteristics of living things, including all those described in the textbook.	Considers several different characteristics of living things, but the list is missing one or two characteristics described in the textbook.	Considers some characteristics of living things, but the list is missing some characteristics described in the textbook.	Considers few characteristics of living things, and the list is missing many characteristics described in the textbook.
Designing Methods to Test Characteristics	Develops many feasible methods to test characteristics.	Develops many methods to test characteristics, but some are impractical.	Develops a few methods to test characteristics, some of which are unrelated to the characteristics described.	Chooses largely unreasonable methods to test the characteristics chosen.
Testing the Object and Making Observations	Tests and observes the object daily. Makes 15 complete observation entries on the object's responses.	Tests and observes the object on most days. Makes at least 12 complete observation entries on the object's responses.	Tests and observes the object several times. Makes 9 to 11 observation entries, but some may be unorganized or incomplete.	Rarely tests and observes the object. Makes six or fewer entries, which may be unorganized or incomplete.
Presenting the Project	Makes a thorough, well-organized presentation. Communicates why particular tests were chosen. Able to justify living/nonliving decision and choice of domain/kingdom.	Makes an adequate presentation. Somewhat able to communicate why particular tests were chosen. Somewhat able to justify living/nonliving decision and choice of domain/kingdom.	Makes a presentation, but it is hard to follow. Unable to communicate why particular tests were chosen. Unable to justify living/nonliving decision or choice of domain/kingdom.	Gives only a brief presentation. Unable to communicate the experimental design or justify living/nonliving decision or choice of domain/kingdom.

Design and Build an Interactive Exhibit

The following steps will walk you through the Chapter Project. Use the hints and detailed directions as you guide your students through the design, construction, presentation, and evaluation of their exhibits.

Chapter Project Overview

In this project, students will design and build an interactive exhibit to teach young children how plants can produce useful products. The purpose of this activity is for students to investigate the process through which a plant or plant part is transformed into products for human use. Students will construct an interactive museum exhibit that showcases the process and product they have studied. (If an interactive exhibit is not a realistic option for your classroom, you may assign students to prepare computer-generated visual presentations as an alternative.) Because their exhibits should be designed for young children, students will need to test their exhibit design on students in the target age group. They will use their feedback to redesign their exhibit.

After students have read the project description in the Project Overview, have them look over the expected steps and outcomes for the project. The Project Overview also includes a table, which summarizes products derived from plants. Review the Project Rules and encourage students to ask questions. You may also want to hand out the Scoring Rubric, so students will understand what is expected of them.

Set a deadline for the completion of the interactive exhibit and some interim dates for checking students' progress. Have students copy the dates in their Project Timeline.

To launch the project, organize the class into small groups. Groups of three to four students should be given the initial task of deciding which plant product they would like to investigate. Make sure students understand what is expected of each member of a group. Later in the project, each member will also be responsible for suggesting changes to improve the exhibit, even though the final interactive exhibit will be a collaborative effort.

Students will need time to ensure that sufficient information is available for the plant products they are considering. Be aware of the fact that some students may select plants or plant products that are rare and/or obscure. To reduce student frustration, monitor their research efforts and encourage them to choose topics that are well supported by information in available resources.

Once they have completed their research, lead a brainstorming session to get the students thinking about the characteristics of a successful interactive exhibit. Treat the brainstorming sessions as guided creativity. Interject ideas only when necessary. Ask students questions about how the exhibit will present information about each plant and the product(s) derived from it. Encourage students to remember the interests and limitations of their target audience (for example, students must remain aware of a young child's reading level).

Students must then build a prototype of their exhibit to test with young children in a "market study." To conduct this market study, students must present their exhibit to small groups of younger students. Help students develop criteria by which to gauge the success of the exhibit. When the test is completed, students should work to redesign their exhibit to satisfy the suggestions of the test audience. Construction of the actual exhibit can begin once the group and the teacher have agreed upon a final design.

Materials and Preparation

You may wish to give students a list of plants to choose from. Suitable plants include food plants such as grains (wheat, rice, corn), root crops (potatoes, yams, carrots, sweet potatoes, cassava, radishes, turnips, beets), legumes (beans, peas), and fruits. Students might also want to choose from among those tree species that are harvested for their wood and/or wood pulp (pine, maple, oak, mahogany, cherry, ash), or plants that are grown as a source of fibers (cotton, flax, sisal) or medicines (yew, periwinkle).

An alternative approach would be to select one plant (or one plant family) that is a source of many commercial products. This could be especially relevant to students if the plant is locally grown and plays a significant role in the regional economy.

Although the groups will decide for themselves what materials to use, you will need to provide basic materials and tools as needed. Begin collecting materials such as shoe boxes, paper towel rolls, cardboard, oak tag, colored paper, plastic wrap, and sheets of colored foam core before the project begins. Simple materials should be used to construct the prototypes. For the final interactive exhibit, a larger range of material options is possible. Steer student teams toward materials such as foam core and sturdier paper products, which are less expensive and easier to work with than materials such as wood or plastic acrylic. However, lightweight, easy-to-use wood products, such as craft sticks, balsa wood, and dowels should be on hand. Teams will also need tape, staples, and craft glue.

To represent plants and plant parts, students should consider using polystyrene foam or silk flowers rather than real plant materials.

Keep Students on Track—Tasks 1–2

While students consider which plant or plant product to research, guide them to begin by selecting at least two plants or plant products for initial consideration. If information is scarce for one of their choices, help them to be open to choosing a different plant or process. As a planning device, ask groups to mutually develop a list of four learning objectives (exhibit goals) that their completed exhibit will meet.

Distribute Project Worksheet 1. Make sure students understand they will need to use this worksheet as they plan their exhibits.

Keep Students on Track—Task 3

As students design their exhibits, have them begin by first planning the educational content. Help students decide what kinds of information should (and should not) be included in the exhibit. Have students list the kinds of items that will be labeled

in their exhibit. Ask each group to submit Worksheet 1.

Encourage students to be imaginative in developing their exhibit designs and to find ways to make the information appealing and easy to remember. Make sure that students are planning to present content at a level that is appropriate for their young audience. Distribute Project Worksheet 2.

Keep Students on Track—Tasks 4–7

After students present their exhibit to young children, discuss with students which aspects of the exhibit seemed to meet the requirements in the most effective and/or creative way. Ask each group to submit Worksheet 2.

Chapter Project Wrap Up

As you review each group's final exhibit, ask the members to "talk you through" the various portions of the exhibit. Ask students to explain the parts of the exhibit and supply a rationale explaining the structure of the exhibit. When appropriate, encourage the more reticent students to play a greater role in presenting the exhibit. Encourage other students in the class to ask questions about the exhibit and its features.

Ask students to evaluate how well they accomplished the assignment, including how well the final exhibit matched the final design the group had agreed upon. Invite students to make suggestions about what they think would have made the project better.

Extension

You may wish to assign writing exercises as a way to provide a more in-depth study of the subject matter. Students will benefit from a writing piece summarizing the preliminary "market study" and the subsequent improvements in the exhibit. A slightly more in-depth writing exercise could explore ways to improve the plant product that the student studied. This will be challenging, but might offer an opportunity for certain students to think critically about the research they have just conducted.

PROJECT OVERVIEW

Design and Build an Interactive Exhibit

In this project, you will work as a group to design and create an interactive exhibit that will teach young students how plants can be transformed into useful products. After choosing a plant, you will think about how to design your exhibit. Your group needs to consider the most effective ways to present information to a young audience. After your teacher reviews your exhibit design, you will develop a prototype. You will then test the prototype on your target audience. After you have tested your prototype, you will use the feedback to alter your exhibit as needed.

Your group will begin by researching one or more plant species. Plants serve as sources for many kinds of products. Here are some examples:

Plant Source	Examples of Products
Familiar fruits and vegetables	Food items, including grains (wheat, rice, corn), root crops (potatoes, yams, carrots), and legumes (beans and peas)
Corn	Livestock feed; Sweet corn, popcorn; Corn syrup (sweetening agent); Corn meal (corn bread, tamales, tortillas); Cornstarch (powders, cooking); Industrial products such as ceramics, explosives, construction materials, paints, ethanol
Soybeans	Tofu, soy sauce, high-protein meat substitute; Industrial products such as paint, adhesives, fertilizers
Trees	Paper products; Lumber; Cork
Cotton, flax, papyrus, sisal	Fibers used for cloth, paper, or rope
Various plant species	Medicines such as codeine, cortisone, ephedrine, taxol, vincristine

Project Rules

- After you have chosen a plant, you will need to learn how it is grown and harvested, what kinds of products are made from it, how the products are manufactured, and what parts of the plant are used.

- Once you have completed the research, your group will need to create a list of four learning objectives (exhibit goals). These learning objectives will summarize what your exhibit must do in order to be successful.

- Your group will brainstorm designs for an interactive exhibit. A successful design must meet the learning objectives that your group created. Submit your design and your materials list to your teacher in Worksheet 1.

- Build a prototype of your exhibit. Before you test your prototype, develop a brief questionnaire for the test audience to complete after viewing the exhibit. The questionnaire will help your group determine how well the exhibit achieved your objectives.

- Test your prototype with a small group of young students. Using the feedback from the questionnaire, meet with your group to brainstorm ideas for changes that could make your exhibit more effective. Discuss any design modifications with your teacher.

Suggested Materials

- Your teacher will provide you with materials such as paper, cardboard, tape, staples, and craft glue to construct the prototypes. For the final exhibit, you may consider a wider range of materials. Possibilities include shoe boxes, paper towel rolls, oak tag, colored paper, plastic wrap, or sheets of colored foam core.

- To represent plants and plant parts, use polystyrene foam or silk flowers.

- Manufacturers of some plant products may provide free samples upon request.

Project Hints

- Read reference materials to find information about your plant species and plant product. Learn how it is grown and harvested, the geographic regions in which the plant is found, its growing conditions, and its growing season. Also find out which parts of the plant are used to produce the product and how it is made.

- Begin to collect materials that you will use to build the exhibit. Your teacher may provide materials, but be prepared to bring some things from home.

- Think about the most effective ways to organize your exhibit and label its components. For example, you will want to present the information on plant structure separately from the part of the exhibit that describes the product and how it is made. If your exhibit includes sequential information (such as events that occur during manufacturing), you may wish to use numbered steps.

- Make sure that the information in your exhibit is presented at a level that your young audience can understand. Use simple language and short sentences.

Project Timeline

Task	Due Date
1. Complete your research.	_____
2. Write learning objectives (exhibit goals).	_____
3. Finish design, materials list, and sketches for Worksheet 1.	_____
4. Construct prototype.	_____
5. Write questions for market test.	_____
6. Conduct market test of prototype.	_____
7. Summarize feedback and refine exhibit design for Worksheet 2.	_____
8. Prepare final exhibit.	_____

PROJECT WORKSHEET 1

Design Your Exhibit

This worksheet will help you get started in selecting a topic and making a design for your exhibit.

What Materials Come From Plants?

1. List three plant products that you have used today.

   _____

2. Think about your most recent meal. What plant products were included in the meal?

   _____

Planning the Exhibit

3. What plant will your exhibit show?

   _____

4. What plant product will your exhibit describe? Explain how your exhibit will show how this product is made.

   _____

   _____

   _____

5. List the parts of the plant that your exhibit will label.

   _____

   _____

6. What materials will you need to build this exhibit?

   _____

   _____

   _____

7. List the four objectives (exhibit goals) that your group has agreed upon for this exhibit.

   _____

   _____

   _____

   _____

8. How will your group choose the best design?

   _____

   _____

   _____

9. On a separate sheet of paper, sketch an exhibit your group could build. Keep the sketch in your Project Folder. Take this worksheet and your sketch to your group meeting. Discuss your ideas with group members.

PROJECT WORKSHEET 2
Testing the Prototype

Now that you have designed a prototype, it is time to test it by showing it to a group of young students. This worksheet will help you organize feedback from the test and list changes that will occur as a result.

1. What part of the exhibit do the students like the most?

_____

2. What part of the exhibit do the students like the least? What don't they like about it?

_____

_____

3. Do the students understand the process being displayed?

_____

4. Do the students know what the product is used for?

_____

5. Are the students interested in the exhibit?

_____

6. What is one thing about this exhibit that the students will remember?

_____

_____

7. List the objectives that are met inadequately or not at all by the design.

_____

_____

_____

8. What modifications should be made to the design?

_____

_____

_____

9. On a separate sheet of paper, sketch the revised exhibit your group can build. Keep the sketch in your Project Folder. Take this worksheet and your sketch to your group meeting. Discuss your ideas with group members. Then construct the final exhibit.

SCORING RUBRIC

Design and Build an Interactive Exhibit

In evaluating how well you complete the Chapter Project, your teacher will judge your work in four categories. In each, a score of 4 is the best rating.

	4	3	2	1
Designing the Exhibit	Student designs show originality and a thorough understanding of plant structures and how the plant product is made. Exhibit design is completely engaging and appropriate for target audience.	Student designs show some originality and a good understanding of plant structures and how the plant product is made. Exhibit design is generally engaging and appropriate for target audience.	Student designs show some understanding of plant structures and how the plant product is made. Exhibit design is somewhat appropriate for target audience.	Student designs show an incomplete and/or inaccurate understanding of plant structures and how the plant product is made. Exhibit design is inappropriate for target audience.
Building the Prototype	Prototype is well constructed and meets all objectives. All plant structures are neatly and correctly labeled. Depiction of how plant product is made is detailed, thorough, and accurate.	Prototype is adequately constructed and meets 3 of the 4 objectives. Most plant structures are neatly and correctly labeled. Depiction of how plant product is made is generally thorough and accurate.	Prototype is somewhat sloppy and meets 2 of the 4 objectives. Some plant structures are neatly and correctly labeled. Depiction of how plant product is made includes some inaccuracies and/or is only partially complete.	Prototype is poorly constructed and meets 1 or none of the 4 objectives. Few plant structures are neatly and correctly labeled. Depiction of how plant product is made is inaccurate and incomplete.
Testing the Prototype and Building the Final Exhibit	Student effectively collects and organizes feedback from testing. Applies findings strategically to significantly improve the final exhibit.	Student satisfactorily collects and organizes feedback from testing. Applies findings appropriately to improve the final exhibit.	Student collects and organizes partial feedback from testing. Applies some of the findings to improve the final exhibit.	Student collects little feedback from testing. Organization is poor. Applies few of the findings to improve the final exhibit.
Working Cooperatively	Student takes a lead in planning and constructing the exhibit.	Student participates in all aspects of planning and constructing the exhibit.	Student participates in most aspects of planning and constructing the exhibit.	Student plays a minor role in planning and constructing the exhibit.

A Mushroom Farm

The following steps will walk you through the Chapter Project. Use the hints as you guide your students through choosing a variable, making a hypothesis, designing an experiment, analyzing the results, and preparing a poster.

Chapter Project Overview

Students often think of mushrooms as "green" plants that can get their energy from the sun. In reality, fungi such as mushrooms get their energy from decaying material. Like plants, they require certain conditions for optimal growth. In this project, students will test variables that affect mushroom growth. They will also look at the typical structures that make up a common mushroom.

To introduce the project, have students brainstorm variables they think would affect mushroom growth. List students' ideas on the chalkboard.

Have students read the Project Overview. Review the Project Rules and hand out the Scoring Rubric that you will use for scoring students' work. Discuss with students what will be expected of them.

Set a deadline for the project poster to be completed and interim dates for the different project tasks. Encourage students to copy the dates in the Project Timeline. It will take one class period to introduce the project. Allow students a day or two to design their experiments. The experiment itself will take between two and four weeks, depending on the conditions being tested. Allow one week following the end of the experiment for data analysis and poster preparation.

Discuss with students the different kinds of variables. Explain that the variable they choose to test is the manipulated variable. The results they get are represented by the responding variable. All other variables should be kept constant, and these are controlled variables. Ask: Suppose you hypothesized that mushrooms need fertilizer to grow. What variable could you manipulate? *(You could grow a container of mushrooms without fertilizer.)*

Divide the class into small groups. Have each group decide on a variable to test. In order to prevent too many groups from investigating the same variable, you may choose to assign a variable to each group. Variables that can be tested easily include light, heat, amount of water, and availability of nutrients.

Be aware that it is difficult to grow mushrooms from spores you collect. Use a mushroom growing kit for best results. If students' mushrooms fail to grow, have them join another group that has had more success.

Encourage students to examine their mushrooms frequently for signs of trouble. Make sure that students do not overwater their mushrooms. Be aware that the warmer the temperature, the faster the growth. Avoid temperatures below 5°C.

Distribute copies of Project Worksheet 1. Have students read over the questions they will need to answer in the experimental design stage of this project. Project Worksheet 2 will help students set up their experiment and collect data. Remind students to refer to the hints in the Project Overview as they plan and carry out the project.

Materials and Preparation

Mushroom growing kits are available from most biological supply companies. They provide all the materials necessary to complete a project. Read the instructions completely. You may want to make copies of the instructions for students or read aloud portions to the class.

You will probably need additional pots and peat moss. As an alternative to pots, you can use the bottoms of milk cartons, two-liter plastic bottles, or other such containers with holes cut in the bottom. A spray bottle works well for watering the containers.

For testing different variables you will need a dark location, a constant light source, a thermometer, a warm location or a source of heat, a cool location, and a substrate lacking nutrients, such as vermiculite.

If possible, provide students with the materials they will need for making their posters.

Keep Students on Track—Tasks 1–3

Students should complete Worksheet 1 and have you approve their hypothesis and experimental design. Make sure that students' experimental designs show that they know the difference between a manipulated variable and a responding variable. Students' experimental setups should also include a control, where all the variables are carefully controlled (controlled variables). In containers with a manipulated variable, make sure all variables are controlled except the one they are testing. Encourage students to check their experiments and record data every day.

Keep Students on Track—Tasks 4–5

Students may need help analyzing their data. Explain that they should use a graph to organize and display their data. Tell students that they do not have to use all of their data in a single graph. Ask: If you were making a line graph, what variable could you plot on the x-axis? *(Sample: time in days)* What variable could you plot on the y-axis? *(Samples: average height of mushrooms, average diameter of mushroom caps)*

Suggest that students show you a rough draft of their poster several days before it is due so that they can get feedback.

Chapter Project Wrap Up

Make sure that students understand the grading criteria for the poster. It is important that they include the hypothesis being tested, a description or diagram of the experimental design, and a graph of their data. They must then draw a conclusion from their results about the validity of their hypothesis. Students should also illustrate the anatomy of a common mushroom.

Have poster preparation occur during class. You may want to allow students to look at each other's posters to exchange ideas. You could also draw a poster plan on the chalkboard to help students get started. Be sure to mention that your drawing is only a plan and that students do not have to follow it as long as their poster meets all of the requirements.

Extension

At the end of the project, have a discussion about what would be the best combination of conditions for growing mushrooms. Then take your students to a local mushroom grower to learn what conditions are used to grow mushrooms commercially.

PROJECT OVERVIEW

A Mushroom Farm

Mushrooms, like all organisms, can grow only under certain conditions. In this project, you will determine how a single variable affects mushroom growth. You will also look at the typical structures that make up a common mushroom.

First, decide on a variable that you wish to test, or your teacher may assign a variable to you. Next, you will make a hypothesis about the effect that changing the variable will have on mushroom growth. Then you will plan and perform an experiment to test your hypothesis. Finally, you will analyze your observations by making a graph, infer the effect of the variable on the growth of mushrooms, and prepare a poster summarizing your experiment.

Project Rules

- If you are able to choose a variable, have your teacher approve your choice before proceeding.

- Make a hypothesis concerning the effect of the variable on mushroom growth.

- Design an experiment to test your hypothesis. Your experimental design should include two containers for growing mushrooms: one will test the manipulated variable and the other will represent the controlled variables. Complete Worksheet 1 and get your teacher's approval before beginning the experiment.

- Read the instructions that came with the mushroom kit or listen to your teacher read them aloud. Keep these instructions in mind when designing and setting up your experiment.

- Use Worksheet 2 to help you perform your experiment. Make observations of mushroom growth and record data every day of the experiment.

- Prepare a poster to summarize your findings. Your poster should include your hypothesis, a description or diagram of your experimental design, at least one graph of your results, and your conclusion. Be sure to include a labeled diagram of the parts of a mushroom as well.

- Follow the safety guidelines in your textbook. Always wash your hands thoroughly after handling soil.

Suggested Materials

- Available materials may include a mushroom growing kit, containers that can be used as pots, a spray bottle for watering, a dark location, a light source, a heat source, a cool location, a thermometer, peat moss, and vermiculite. Peat moss contains nutrients, but vermiculite does not.

- You may be provided with materials for making your poster, or you may bring your own materials from home.

Project Hints

- Think about the growing requirements of other organisms to get ideas about what variable to test.

- To make a hypothesis, think about where you see mushrooms growing in nature. Use these observations to make a prediction about whether changing your variable in a specific way will increase or decrease mushroom growth.

- When getting ready to design an experiment, review what you know about controlling variables. Decide what variables need to be controlled in your experiment.

- Decide what observations you will record during the experiment, and how you will analyze the results. See Worksheet 2.

- Do not overwater your mushrooms. The substrate, or the substance in which the mushrooms are growing, should be moist but not soaked. Avoid temperatures below 5°C.

- You can find books about mushrooms in the library or information about mushrooms on the Internet to help you draw and label your diagram of a mushroom.

Project Timeline

Task	Due Date
1. Variable selected and hypothesis proposed	_____
2. Experimental design approved by teacher	_____
3. Experiment and data table set up	_____
4. Experiment completed	_____
5. Final draft of survey written and presented to teacher	_____
6. Poster completed	_____

Viruses, Bacteria, Protists, and Fungi

PROJECT WORKSHEET 1

A Mushroom Farm

Answer the following questions in the space provided. When you have completed this worksheet, you will be ready to get your teacher's approval and begin your experiment.

1. What variable will you test?

   _____

2. Record a hypothesis that predicts what will happen to the growth of mushrooms when that variable is changed.

   _____

   _____

   _____

3. What treatment will you use to test your manipulated variable in the experiment? What treatment will you use with the controlled variables?

   _____

   _____

   _____

   _____

4. How will you keep other variables controlled in your experiment?

   _____

   _____

   _____

   _____

5. What results from your experiment would support your hypothesis?

   _____

   _____

   _____

6. What results from your experiment would show your hypothesis was not correct?

   _____

   _____

   _____

PROJECT WORKSHEET 2

A Mushroom Farm

Use this sheet to help set up your experiment and record your data.

1. Label one container as the manipulated variable and the other as the controlled variables (control).

2. Fill each container with substrate material provided by the mushroom kit, if appropriate for your experimental design.

3. Divide the spores into equal amounts and spread them on the surfaces of the substrate material in your manipulated variable and controlled variables containers (control).

4. Spray each container with water so that the surface is moist.

5. Place the containers in appropriate locations.

6. Record your data in a data table like the one shown below. You will need to record data for two to four weeks depending on the variable you test. For each day, record the number of mushrooms present. Then record the height of each mushroom and the diameter of each cap. You might also include any other observed changes and a sketch of each container.

Day	Container with Controlled Variables (Control)	Container with Manipulated Variable
1	Number: Heights: Diameter of caps:	Number: Heights: Diameter of caps:
2	Number: Heights: Diameter of caps:	Number: Heights: Diameter of caps:

You must decide how to analyze your observations. For example, you could compare:

- The day on which mushrooms first appeared in the two containers.
- The number of mushrooms present in each container.
- The average size (height or diameter) of the mushrooms in each container.

SCORING RUBRIC

A Mushroom Farm

In evaluating how well you complete the Chapter Project, your teacher will judge your work in the following categories. In each, a score of 4 is the best rating.

	4	3	2	1
Defining and Controlling Variables and Developing Hypothesis	Student defines the variable being tested and correctly identifies the controlled variables. Hypothesis clearly states a prediction regarding the responding variable.	Student defines the variable being tested and correctly identifies the controlled variables. Hypothesis adequately states a prediction regarding the responding variable.	Student defines the variable being tested, but incorrectly identifies the controlled variables. Hypothesis states a prediction regarding the responding variable.	Student defines the variable being tested, but incorrectly identifies the controlled variables. Student fails to state a hypothesis regarding the responding variable.
Creating Experimental Design and Making Observations	Experimental design clearly tests the effect of the manipulated variable. Student records detailed observations daily.	Experimental design tests the effect of the manipulated variable. Student records observations on all but one or two days.	Experimental design tests the effect of the manipulated variable. Student records observations on most days.	Experimental design fails to test the effect of the manipulated variable. Student records some observations.
Analyzing and Presenting Results in Poster	Poster thoroughly communicates hypothesis tested, experimental design, one or more graphs of results, and conclusion. Student rejects or accepts hypothesis based on results.	Poster adequately communicates hypothesis tested, experimental design, graph of results, and conclusion. Student rejects or accepts hypothesis based on results.	Poster fails to communicate one of the following: hypothesis tested, experimental design, graph of results, or conclusion. Student fails to reject or accept hypothesis based on results.	Poster fails to communicate two or more of the following: hypothesis tested, experimental design, graph of results, or conclusion. Student fails to reject or accept hypothesis.
Working Cooperatively (optional)	Takes a lead in group planning and in the collection of data.	Participates in all aspects of group planning and in the collection of data.	Participates in most group planning and collection of data.	Participates minimally in group planning and collection of data.

Viruses, Bacteria, Protists, and Fungi

Design and Build a Hand Prosthesis

The following steps will walk you through the Chapter Project. Use the hints and detailed directions as you guide your students through design, construction, presentation, and reflection.

Chapter Project Overview

Designing a prosthesis will allow students to see the relationship between various desired characteristics in a design and the materials available to execute it. At the same time, they should come to appreciate how difficult it is to imitate, even crudely, the functionality of the human hand.

The hand was chosen for this project because, compared to other appendages, it is relatively easy to mimic and fabricate. The choice of the hand will also make it possible to set specific and clear criteria for evaluating students' models.

This project should also provide some insight into the role that materials and fabrication play in determining the feasibility of an idea.

To introduce the project, lead a discussion about some of the technological advances that can restore certain functions: glasses, false teeth, hearing aids, implanted joints, and prosthetic limbs. Discuss the kinds of things that would be important to be able to do with a hand prosthesis, such as lifting, buttoning a coat, tying a shoe, and so on.

You may also choose to begin by showing a model of a hand prosthesis that you prepared ahead of time.

Distribute the Project Overview and review the Project Rules. You may also want to hand out the Scoring Rubric, so students will understand what is expected of them.

Organize the class into small groups. Make sure students understand what is expected of each member of a group. For example, you may want each member of a group to develop a design before meeting with other members. Point out that as they progress their design will be reviewed to be sure it meets design requirements.

Next, lead a brainstorming session to get the students thinking about what needs must be met to create a model prosthesis. Treat the brainstorming sessions as guided creativity. Interject ideas only when necessary to help guide each group along a productive path.

Once the brainstorming portion is complete, introduce a method for selecting the best design. The evaluation phase should include a defined set of criteria regarding the functionality of each model. The model prosthesis should be able to grasp, lift, and release; it must be activated by a pulled cord or string; it must spring back when the cord is released.

Set a deadline for the project presentation and some interim dates, such as at the end of each task, for checking students' progress. Have students record the dates on their Project Timeline. A sample timeline, by task, is shown below.

Examine the structure and functions of the human hand	15 minutes
Experiment with various objects and decide what type of device could best meet the design requirements	3 hours
Develop ideas for construction	3 hours
Build the device	5 hours
Prepare presentation	2 hours
Deliver presentation	10 minutes

Materials and Preparation

Tools available should include a vise; bendable coat hangers; heavy cardboard; several types of pliers, tweezers, tongs, chop sticks; cutting and bending tools for wire; wire; cord or string; sandpaper; files and saws for plastic and wood; rubber bands; spring-loaded clothespins; large clips for holding bags closed. A variety of tape products might be used, including duct tape, fiberglass reinforced packing tape, and adhesive tape. A combination of rubber bands can be used to provide the return force against the string or cord.

Troubleshooting

The most likely source of problems will be in getting the functionality that is wanted. Hinges or pivots are harder to make workable than it appears at first. If a working hinge is taken from another device, it will probably make things easier. Parts from broken toys will often be useful.

Keep Students on Track—Task 1

Talk with each group during its initial meeting. Make sure they take one another's sketches and ideas seriously. At this point, students should think about the materials they will use for their models.

Distribute Project Worksheet 1. Make sure students understand they will need to use this worksheet as they learn more about how the body works, especially the muscular system.

Keep Students on Track—Task 2

Check to see that student groups have chosen a design for their models, and review their material lists.

Look over the Project Folder to check individual designs. You may want to score individual designs as well as the collaborative design.

Keep Students on Track—Task 4

Review the prototype built by each group by using the group's checklist of criteria. Examine the model for major flaws or possible problems. If any exist, have students work on solutions to be shown to you and approved before the final build. Distribute Project Worksheet 2.

Keep Students on Track—Tasks 5–7

Models should be built and tested and any last-minute modifications made. Students should be planning their presentation/demonstration of their hand prosthesis models.

Chapter Project Wrap Up

As you review each group's final model, you may wish to have the members "talk you through" the presentation/demonstration. Make suggestions for organizing the presentation. When appropriate, encourage some students to take a greater role in presenting the model.

Provide class time for group presentations. Allow each group to present its model and explain its features. Encourage other students to ask questions about the model and its features.

After presentations have been made, discuss with students which models seemed to meet the requirements in the most effective and/or creative way.

Encourage students to evaluate how well they accomplished the assignment, including how well the final model matched the final design the group had agreed upon. Invite students to make suggestions about what they think would have made the project better.

Extension

Students might want to do more research on prosthetics and gather articles about people their age who have returned to active lives because of the prostheses available to them.

PROJECT OVERVIEW

Design and Build a Hand Prosthesis

How can you make a model that simulates the functions of a human hand? In this project, you will work in a group to design and build a prosthesis that can perform several functions of the human hand.

First, you will make sketches of your own design for a hand prosthesis. Then you will meet with your group to review all members' designs and agree on a single design for the prosthesis. As you and other group members learn more about the human body's muscular system, you may decide to modify your design. At the end of the project, your group will present your finished prosthesis to the class.

Project Rules

- Your group will begin by researching the functions of the human hand and thinking about existing devices that can be used to simulate the functions of grasping, lifting, and releasing. Your group should also review the additional design criteria: the prosthesis must be activated by a pulled cord or string; and it must spring back when the cord is released.

- Using this list of requirements, your group will brainstorm some designs for a model. Then each group member will create sketches of his or her own version of a model. Keep any sketches you make in a Project Folder. Show your sketch or sketches to your teacher and discuss your ideas for a prosthetic hand.

- With your group, review one another's ideas and sketches. Come to a consensus (agreement) on a design for the hand prosthesis model you want to build as a group.

- Choose the materials for your model—the real-life version of the design you have drawn on paper. You will be required to submit to your teacher a list of all the supplies you will need to complete this task.

- Test the completed model to find out if it meets all of the criteria for the prosthesis—it must grasp, lift, and release; it must be activated by a pulled cord or string; and it must spring back when the cord is released. Make modifications to your model if needed. Discuss any design modifications with your teacher.

- With your group, make any needed modifications to your model. Then prepare a presentation and demonstration to the class of your completed prosthetic hand. As part of the presentation, you will also explain how you chose your final design, what materials you used, any special features of your model, and how it meets the design criteria.

Project Hints

- Read reference materials to find information about prosthetic hands. Also research the structure and functions of the human hand. Observe how a human hand grasps, lifts, and releases objects.

- As soon as possible, begin collecting materials you will use to build the hand prosthesis.

- Work closely with other members of your group, and listen to their ideas. You might find that someone in your group has just the right idea to make your own design a great deal better.

- Don't be afraid to suggest changes to your group's design if it doesn't seem to function as expected after you've begun construction.

- Make sure your model meets all of the design requirements.

- Try to make your model and presentation unique as well as accurate and informative.

Project Timeline

Task	Due Date
1. Complete design and sketches for Project Worksheet 1.	_____
2. Agree on a group design for prosthetic hand.	_____
3. Collect materials.	_____
4. Construct model.	_____
5. Test model to be sure it meets requirements.	_____
6. Make any nesessary modifications to your model.	_____
7. Prepare class presentation/demonstration.	_____
8. Deliver class presentation/demonstration of model.	_____

PROJECT WORKSHEET 1

Design and Build a Hand Prosthesis

This worksheet will help you get started creating a design for your prosthetic hand.

Model Requirements

1. What activities must the model hand prosthesis perform?

   _____

   _____

2. What are some key features that must be incorporated into the design?

   _____

   _____

3. How will your group choose the best design?

   _____

   _____

Planning the Design

4. Describe the model you think your group should build.

   _____

   _____

   _____

5. What materials will you need to build this model?

   _____

   _____

   _____

6. In the space below, sketch a model of a hand prosthesis that your group could build. Keep the sketch in your Project Folder. Take this worksheet and your sketch to your group meeting. Discuss your ideas with group members.

PROJECT WORKSHEET 2
Refining the Model

Now that you have learned more about how the body works, you may want to make some changes to your model prosthesis. This worksheet will help you organize your thinking about the changes that are needed. Use a separate sheet of paper if you need more space.

1. List the functions the model can perform well and consistently.

   _____

   _____

   _____

2. List the functions the model cannot perform or performs poorly or inconsistently.

   _____

   _____

   _____

   _____

3. Are failures of the model due to the design or to the materials used?

   _____

   _____

   _____

   _____

4. What features or modifications can be used to improve the model?

   _____

   _____

   _____

   _____

5. On a separate sheet of paper, sketch a revised model that your group can build. Keep the sketch in your Project Folder. Take this worksheet and your sketch to your group meeting. Discuss your ideas with group members. Then make the necessary changes to your model.

SCORING RUBRIC

Design and Build a Hand Prosthesis

In evaluating how well you complete the Chapter Project, your teacher will judge your work in four categories. In each, a score of 4 is the best rating.

	4	3	2	1
Creating Individual Sketches and Designs	Student makes sketches that show originality of design and a thorough understanding of the criteria that the model hand prosthesis must meet: it is activated by a pulled cord or string; it springs back after cord/string is released; and it mimics three activities of the human hand—grasping, lifting, and releasing.	Student makes sketches that show some originality of design and a good understanding of the criteria that the model hand prosthesis must meet (listed in Level 4).	Student makes sketches that show adequate design and some understanding of the criteria that the model hand prosthesis must meet (listed in Level 4).	Student makes sketches that show an incomplete or inaccurate understanding of the criteria that the model hand prosthesis must meet (listed in Level 4).
Constructing Model of the Prosthesis	Model is well constructed and meets all of the required criteria (it is activated by a pulled cord or string; it springs back after cord/string is released; and it mimics three activities of the human hand—grasping, lifting, and releasing.)	Model is constructed adequately and meets at least three of the required criteria listed in Level 4.	Model is somewhat sloppily constructed and meets at least two of the required criteria listed in Level 4.	Model is poorly constructed and meets only one of the required criteria listed in Level 4.
Presenting the Model to the Class	Student makes a thorough and interesting presentation that includes a clear, accurate explanation and demonstration of how the model meets design criteria.	Student makes a thorough presentation that includes a satisfactory explanation and demonstration of how the model meets design criteria.	Student makes a presentation that includes a partial explanation and demonstration of how the model meets design criteria.	Student makes a presentation that includes an incomplete and/or inaccurate explanation of how the model meets the design criteria.
Participating in the Group	Student takes a lead in planning, constructing, and presenting the model.	Student participates in all aspects of planning, constructing, and presenting the model.	Student participates in most aspects of planning, constructing, and presenting the model.	Student plays a minor role in planning, constructing, and presenting the model.

Travels of a Red Blood Cell

The following steps will walk you through the Chapter Project. Use the hints and detailed directions as you guide your students through gathering information about the heart and circulation, planning their displays and their presentations.

Chapter Project Overview

Before introducing the project, discuss how visual and verbal communication can be used to present information. Ask students to discuss a display at a museum that caught their attention. Then, ask them to think about what it was about the display that made them interested in it.

Have students read the Project Overview. Review the Project Rules and hand out the Scoring Rubric, which you will use for scoring students' work. Discuss with students what will be expected of them.

Set a deadline for the project presentation and interim dates to check their progress. Encourage students to record the dates on the Project Timeline.

Compare blood circulation to a rural mail route. Each morning a mail carrier goes to the post office and picks up the mail much like blood picks up oxygen in the lungs. The carrier then drives to the customers' homes, delivers the incoming mail, and picks up the outgoing mail, and returns to the post office, much like blood picks up carbon dioxide and takes it to the lungs. The mail route can use roads of many sizes, but mail is usually delivered to customers on small roads. Similarly, blood travels through large arteries and veins, but oxygen is delivered in small capillaries when the blood is moving relatively slowly.

Distribute copies of Project Worksheet 1. This worksheet will help students to collect the information they will need to include on their display about the heart and blood circulation. Project Worksheet 2 will help students prepare their displays and presentations. Remind students to refer to the hints in the Project Overview as they plan and carry out the project.

Consider organizing the class in groups to do some or all phases of the project. Students can research the heart and circulation (Worksheet 1) together and can brainstorm ideas for displaying information in a group.

Materials and Preparation

Provide a wide variety of materials from which students can choose to prepare their display. Encourage students to suggest and use other materials and other media, such as videos, computers, and art media.

Whether or not some students have access to sophisticated equipment and materials, make sure that all students understand that your assessment of their projects will be based on completion of the goals of the project and the construction of an accurate and effective display.

For posters, provide poster board, colored pens, an assortment of magazines and newspapers, string, aluminum foil, and other materials that could be incorporated.

For displays involving more elaborate construction, be prepared to provide cardboard, cardboard rolls, straws, scrap wood, assorted plastic bottles, and other materials.

Keep Students on Track—Tasks 1–2

Make sure that students understand the need to plan their projects. At this point, they should have sketches that illustrate both of the circuits they want to demonstrate.

If you have time constraints, use small groups as a way to give every student an opportunity to give a progress report and discuss his or her problems and possible solutions with peers.

If some students are having difficulty deciding what to do, encourage them to discuss the project with others, or possibly modify another student's design, with his or her permission.

Keep Students on Track—Task 3

When the project is underway and students are constructing their displays, check terminology, pathways, and listed functions to be sure they are correct. You may want to list items on the board or pass out a checklist for students to go over individually or in groups. Displays should show the path of the red blood cell beginning and ending at the heart, and they should include gas exchange in the lungs and at the destination in the body.

Keep Students on Track—Task 4

Tell students to estimate how long it will take to finish their displays, based on the amount of time it has taken them to prepare the completed portion of their displays. If they have taken 4 hours to complete the first 25 percent, it will take another 12 hours to finish the remaining 75 percent.

Students who find that there is not enough time remaining will need help simplifying their projects. Encourage students to come up with solutions on their own. Help them see that the project can be simplified, but all the core information must still be expressed.

Chapter Project Wrap Up

If all of the students' projects are diagrams or posters, they can be displayed on walls or presented individually during class time. Make sure that there is adequate time for all students to present their work. If students are being evaluated on their oral presentations, make sure that they understand what you expect of them.

After all of the presentations have been made, discuss with students which styles of presentation or graphic display they thought were effective in fulfilling the goals of the project.

Leave time for students to record their own observations in their journals. Emphasize that there will be differences in opinion about the best ways to communicate information, since different people have different ways of learning.

Extension

Some students may show interest in continuing their investigation of circulation. These students might want to prepare a display with information on common circulatory problems.

PROJECT OVERVIEW

Travels of a Red Blood Cell

In this project, you will design and make an exhibit showing a complete journey that a red blood cell might take through the human body. The journey includes two loops, and starts and ends at the heart. One loop goes to the lungs, and one loop goes to a different specific part of the body.

First, you will need to make sketches of the two loops. Second, you will need to research the vocabulary and the systems involved in the two loops. Third, you will need to plan out the materials and time you will need to complete the project. Next, you will need to create your display and practice a presentation of your project to your class. Finally, you will present your project to the class. Make sure that your display provides complete information.

Project Rules

- One loop that the red blood cell travels must be from the heart to the lungs and back to the heart. The other loop must start in the heart, go to a specific body part that you choose, and then return to the heart.

- You must decide how you will display the two circuits. Your display can be still (a poster or a series of illustrations) or it can be moving (a flip-book, video animation, or similar technique). As soon as you have decided how you will present the information, obtain your teacher's approval, and then begin listing and collecting the materials you will need.

- At any stage, be prepared to report on the amount of the project you have completed and the amount that you have yet to finish.

- You must present your project to your class on the date stated by your teacher. Be prepared to answer questions from your teacher and classmates.

Suggested Materials

- Your teacher will provide some materials, but you should also consider using other materials and display methods, such as videos, computers, and art supplies.

- For posters, your teacher may provide poster board, colored pens, string, aluminum foil, an assortment of magazines and newspapers, and other materials.

- For displays involving more elaborate construction, you may need cardboard, cardboard rolls, straws, scrap wood, assorted plastic bottles, and other materials.

Project Hints

- Begin by completing Project Worksheet 1 to help you organize your research about the circulation of a red blood cell.

- Project Worksheet 2 will help you plan your display.

- Make a list of the materials you will need and collect them as soon as possible.

- Do not become discouraged if you have to simplify your display because of time limits. What's most important is to include all of the relevant information in a clear manner.

- Use Worksheet 2 to help you with your presentation. Your teacher will tell you how much time you will have to give your presentation.

Project Timeline

Task	Due Date
1. Research into blood circulation finished (Worksheet 1).	_____
2. Sketch of display and timetable completed (Worksheet 2) and approved.	_____
3. Construction of display begun, and rough draft of written description finished.	_____
4. Display finished.	_____
5. Presentation completed.	_____

PROJECT WORKSHEET 1
Researching the Heart and Circulation

Complete the following tasks on a separate sheet of paper. Use your textbook and other resources for information. When the tasks have been completed, you are ready to get your teacher's approval and begin designing your exhibit.

1. Draw a diagram showing the four chambers of the heart. Use the illustration in your textbook as a guide. Your diagram does not have to be an exact copy of the figure, but should show the relative sizes of the four chambers and the openings between chambers. Also show the main blood vessels entering and leaving the heart.

2. Label the parts of the heart and the blood vessels.

3. Show how blood flows through the heart on your diagram. In addition, show the direction of blood flow in the main blood vessels. Which of the blood vessels are veins and which are arteries?

4. For the blood vessels entering the heart, state where a red blood cell in these vessels is coming from and whether it is oxygen-rich. For the blood vessels that leave the heart, state where a red blood cell is traveling to and whether it is oxygen-rich.

From your answers to questions 1–4, you should have identified two loops, one that begins in the right atrium, leaves the heart, goes to the lungs, and then returns to the left atrium. The other begins in the left atrium, leaves the heart, goes to a specific body part, and then returns to the right atrium.

5. Choose the specific part of the body that your red blood cell will travel to on its second loop. Research the arteries and veins that the red blood cell will travel through in a loop from the heart to that part of the body.

6. Sketch the two loops and show your sketch to your teacher.

PROJECT WORKSHEET 2

Travels of a Red Blood Cell
Planning Your Display

This worksheet will help you plan your display and presentation. Write your responses on a separate sheet of paper.

1. Decide what information you wish to include in your display. In particular, how much information about the function of each part of the cardiovascular system do you wish to include? Will your display explain how the heart works, why the left ventricle is larger than the right, the structure of arteries, capillaries, and veins, and so on?

2. For each piece of information you wish to include, decide whether a written or visual display is better.

3. For information to be displayed visually, decide what the best way to present the information might be. To help you in this step, make a list of other visual displays of information that you have seen (billboards, advertisements in newspapers, commercials on televisions), and list the strengths and weaknesses of each. How will you display arteries, veins, and capillaries? How will you distinguish an oxygen-rich red blood cell from an oxygen-poor red blood cell?

4. Sketch your final display, including the materials to be used. Brainstorm ideas with other members of the class. Revise your plan, include a detailed timetable of when certain parts of the display will be completed, and then show your plan to your teacher for final approval and comments.

Presenting Your Display

1. Decide which features of your project you wish to present to the class. Will you present the details of the red blood cell's voyage around the two circuits; the features of your display that are most unusual; the problems you had to overcome during planning or construction; or examples from the written description?

2. Once you have decided what you will include, write an outline of your presentation and practice in front of a friend or relative. Make sure that your presentation is clear and the appropriate length.

3. Write a final version of your presentation and practice it a few times in front of a mirror. You are now ready to present your project to the class.

SCORING RUBRIC

Travels of a Red Blood Cell

In evaluating how well you complete the Chapter Project, your teacher will judge your work in the following categories. In each, a score of 4 is the best rating.

	4	3	2	1
Researching Heart and Circulation and Planning the Display	Plan includes a detailed sketch of final display. Materials to be used are listed. Timetable is complete and realistic. Plan followed conscientiously during display construction.	Plan includes a sketch of final display. Materials to be used are listed. Timetable is complete but unrealistic. Plan followed during display construction.	Plan is somewhat confused or sketch of final display unclear. Some materials not listed. Timetable is incomplete or unrealistic. Plan followed during display construction.	Plan inadequate. Sketch confused. Only a few materials included. Timetable incomplete. Plan not used during display construction.
Constructing Display	Display is creative and easy to understand, and includes complete and accurate information about the path of the red blood cell. Function of both loops clearly shown. Terminology used correctly.	Display is complete and easy to understand, but lacks creativity. The information on the path of the red blood cell is accurate, but somewhat incomplete. Function of both loops shown. Terminology used correctly.	Display is difficult to understand. Some information on the path of the red blood cell is lacking and not all is accurate. Function of both loops shown. Terminology incomplete but used correctly.	Display is incomplete and difficult to understand. Information on the path of the red blood cell is mostly inaccurate and also incomplete. Function of one loop missing. Terminology not used or used incorrectly.
Making Presentation	Presentation is thorough and well organized. Shows complete understanding of the transfer of oxygen and carbon dioxide in the blood flow in both circuits. Describes specifics of display construction and expresses individuality.	Good presentation. Shows basic understanding of the transfer of oxygen and carbon dioxide in the blood flow in both circuits. Describes most aspects of display construction and expresses some individuality.	Presentation unclear. Shows limited understanding of the transfer of oxygen and carbon dioxide in the blood flow in both circuits. Describes some aspects of display construction and expresses some individuality.	Presentation confused. Shows misunderstanding of the transfer of oxygen and carbon dioxide in the blood flow in both circuits. Little description of display construction or expression of individuality.

What's for Lunch?

The following steps will walk you through the Chapter Project. Use the hints and detailed directions as you guide your students through the gathering of data, converting the data into serving sizes and food groups, making suggestions to improve the diet, and preparing a written summary.

Chapter Project Overview

Begin this project by asking the students to write down what each has eaten so far today. Tell students that all of the information in their lab reports and notes will be kept confidential, so no one else will know what they have eaten. Then, using the illustration of the USDA MyPyramid Plan as a guide, ask the students to try to sort their items into food group categories. There will be questions about some foods. For instance, a sugared cereal or snack bar will be in the grains group, but the added sugar counts as discretionary calories, too. (A teaspoon of granulated sugar is the equivalent of 2.8 grams and has 11 Calories.)

Have students read the Project Overview. Review the Project Rules and hand out the Scoring Rubric, which you will use for scoring students' work. Discuss with students what will be expected of them. Explain to students that they do not need to keep track of water consumption.

Set a deadline for the project presentation and interim dates to check their progress. Encourage students to record the dates on the Project Timeline.

Since students will need to figure out serving sizes for each food item, help them visualize servings by telling them that for each dense food—such as pasta, baked beans, cooked vegetables, canned fruit, or bread—one serving would be one-half cup, about what would fit into a cupcake paper.

Since students will be using the number of servings to compare their choices with the MyPyramid Plan's recommendations, ask students for ways they might easily convert food listings into servings.

Distribute copies of Project Worksheet 1. Have students examine the sample data they will need to gather in the recording stage of this project. Remind students that thoroughness is most important in making the food log. Distribute Project Worksheet 2, which will help students to analyze the data they collected, use graphs to compare what they ate to the recommended diet, and prepare their reports. Remind students to refer to the hints in the Project Overview as they plan and carry out the project.

Remind students that food logs and written reports will be kept confidential.

Materials and Preparation

Students will need graph paper, paper, and pencils to keep the food logs and make graphs.

Since the size of many of the servings in the food groups is one-half cup, it might be helpful to have some common item on hand that will help the students visualize this size such as the paper cups used for baking cupcakes.

Keep Students on Track—Task 1

In evaluating the students' food log plans, make sure there is enough room to enter all meals, snacks, and drinks. Encourage students to come up their own systems for keeping their food logs. Remind students to record the amount of each food eaten. Help students to learn to estimate amounts.

Keep Students on Track—Tasks 2–4

Instruct students to convert the data in their food logs to servings and food groups. Students may have a hard time realizing that one dish can be in more than one food group. For example, lasagna might have one serving from the meat group, one serving from the pasta group, one serving from the milk group, and one serving from the vegetable group.

169
Digestion

Again, impress on students the importance of estimating amounts. Students may easily get bogged down if they are too exact with quantities of foods.

After putting the foods into food groups and computing numbers of servings, students will graph the number of servings of each group that they ate compared to the recommended number. A convenient way to make the comparisons would be to graph what they ate on the same grid with the recommended amounts.

Keep Students on Track—Task 5

Many students may find that their diets differ from the recommended diets. Again, remind students that the food logs and results are confidential. The purpose of this project is to help students become aware of what foods in what groups are eaten, not to pass judgment on any student's diet.

Use class time for students to work independently to make plans to improve their diets. Suggest that students pick one factor about their diets to improve. For example, a diet high in fat might be improved by substituting a complex carbohydrate snack (such as carrot sticks) for some high-fat snack foods (such as chips).

Chapter Project Wrap Up

Students should have completed written reports on significant new information they learned about eating a healthy diet. Give the class an opportunity to read or talk about some of the things they learned. The discussion will be most successful and valuable if the students feel that anything they talk about is uncritically received by the entire class. This is also an appropriate time to discuss the availability of healthy foods. Is it easy to eat a healthy diet in the school cafeteria? How prevalent are healthy foods at fast food restaurants?

Extension

- Students may wish to keep track of Calories eaten (apart from their discretionary calories) as well as which food groups are eaten. If students wish to do this, they can add an additional column to the food analysis chart. Provide Calorie charts for students to use.

- Students could design special diets, such as a low-cholesterol diet for heart patients or a diet for diabetics that limits sugars.

- Assign students the task of designing a healthy diet without meat. This exercise may help to overcome preconceived notions students may have about the necessity of meat in the diet. It is also good way to reinforce the concept of complete and incomplete proteins.

PROJECT OVERVIEW

What's for Lunch?

In this project, you will examine your diet to see if it is balanced for good health. To do this, you will keep track of the foods you eat over a three-day period. Then you will use the USDA MyPyramid Plan to determine how many servings you ate from each of the food groups. You will judge whether you ate a healthy diet for those three days. You will decide how you can improve your diet, and make another three-day food log, attempting to eat better. Finally, you will prepare a report on your experiences.

Project Rules

- You must keep a three-day log of everything you eat. You must record all your meals, and any snacks and drinks, except for water.

- Your teacher will approve your food log design before you begin.

- If possible, the three-day period for keeping your food log should span two weekdays and one weekend day.

- You must understand how to convert the foods you ate into a number of servings or discretionary calories and classify the foods into the food groups in the MyPyramid Plan.

- You must make graphs and compare the number of servings and discretionary calories you ate with the recommended numbers.

- You must make written recommendations of ways to improve your diet.

- You must keep another three-day log of everything you eat, trying to follow your recommendations of ways to improve your diet.

- You must prepare a report of your experiences of keeping the food logs and your attempt to improve your diet.

Suggested Materials

- Graph paper, paper, and pencil are the only required materials. However, you may want to gather information on food, diet, and even recipes for ensuring that healthful foods also taste good.

Project Hints

- The challenge in this project is not to eliminate treats but to balance them with satisfying amounts from the food groups your body needs for good health. You will find that an adequate daily consumption of grains, fruits, and vegetables will minimize a craving for sweets and fats.

- This project will be of greatest value to you if keep an accurate account of all the foods you eat. Don't forget to record what you consume at times other than meals. A soda, glass of juice, or snack is also food.

- Using the USDA Web site at www.MyPyramid.gov is one way to balance your diet over the course of a day. Remember, not every meal has to be completely balanced, but eating a variety of foods at different meals is the easiest way to eat a well-balanced diet.

- Prepackaged foods have labels that give you nutritional information about that food. For nonprocessed foods, you may want to find a chart of foods and their nutritional content.

- A good way to learn how many servings you eat is to become familiar with the size of a half cup. To do this, examine a half-cup measuring cup. Also, to learn to estimate how much of a food weighs one ounce, look at foods that are sold by the ounce, such as cheese.

- Foods that count as discretionary calories may be listed on nutrition labels in grams. Use print or electronic resources to find out the number of calories these servings contain.

Project Timeline

Task	Due Date
1. Three-day food log designed and approved	_____
2. Three-day food log completed	_____
3. Three-day food log converted to servings and food groups	_____
4. Servings of three-day food log items graphed and compared to recommended amounts	_____
5. Diet improvements specified	_____
6. Second three-day food log completed	_____
7. Second three-day food log compared with the first	_____
8. Report summarizing what you've learned completed	_____

PROJECT WORKSHEET 1
Starting Your Food Log

A key to doing well in this project is to keep an accurate food log. Use the table below as a guide to creating your own system for recording what you eat. An important part of keeping records is to make it easy. One option is to carry a small notebook to make your notes throughout the day, and transfer the data later into a data sheet. Or you could carry the data sheet itself and record your data directly.

You don't need to convert what you eat to portions of food groups until the first three-day period is over. Don't forget to record how much of each food you eat. When necessary, record estimated portion sizes, such as large hamburger, large glass of milk, or two handfuls of trail mix.

In the table below, the first day is completed as a sample.

Sample Food Log

Day	Breakfast Food	Amount	Lunch Food	Amount	Dinner Food	Amount	Dessert, Snacks, and Drinks Food	Amount
Thursday	whole milk	1 glass	pizza	one slice	spaghetti and sauce	large plate	soda	2 cans
	cereal	1 bowl	chocolate milkshake	medium glass	salad	medium	ice cream	1 scoop
	orange juice	small glass	French fries	2 handfuls	garlic bread	1 slice	potato chips	1 bag
			soda	1 can			energy bar	1 bar
Friday								
Saturday								

PROJECT WORKSHEET 2

Analyzing Your Food Log

1. After keeping a food log for three days, determine what food group or groups each food belongs in, and how many servings you ate. You probably won't be able to be exact about this—you will have to estimate and use your best judgment. The results will still be useful. The chart below is a suggestion for how you might record this data. The food recorded for the sample day's breakfast from Worksheet 1 has been converted into food groups and servings. Complete a similar chart for the foods you recorded in your three-day food log.

Sample Food Analysis

Day	Meal/Food	Food Group or Groups	Number of Servings
Thursday	Breakfast		
	1 glass whole milk	Milk, Yogurt, and Cheese	1
	1 bowl cereal	Bread, Cereal, Rice, and pasta	1
	1 small glass orange juice	Fruit	1

Answer the following on a separate sheet of paper.

2. After figuring out the food groups and servings for each food item you recorded in your food log, find the total number of servings of each food group that you ate. In order to compare what you ate to the recommended amounts, you will need to multiply the recommended daily amounts by three days. Make bar graphs showing how much you ate from each group and how much is recommended for three days.

3. Write a plan for improving your diet, based on the MyPyramid Plan recommendations.

4. Keep another three-day food log, following your diet-improvement plan.

5. Write a summary of your results. Did you eat a healthy diet in the first three-day period? Why or why not? What was the easiest way to improve your diet? What was most difficult thing to change?

SCORING RUBRIC

What's for Lunch?

In evaluating how well you complete the Chapter Project, your teacher will judge your work in four categories. In each, a score of 4 is the best rating.

	4	3	2	1
Keeping the Food Log	Food log is complete. Shows necessary detail of types and quantities of foods eaten for three days.	Food log is nearly complete. Shows most details of types and quantities of foods eaten for three days.	Food log has some gaps in types and quantities of foods eaten for three days.	Food log has major gaps in types and quantities of foods eaten.
Analyzing Foods Eaten	Conversion to food group and number of servings complete and accurate. Excellent use of graphs to compare actual diet with recommended diet.	Conversion to food group and number of servings mostly complete and accurate. Good use of graphs to compare actual diet with recommended diet.	Conversion to food group and number of servings fairly complete and accurate. Fair use of graphs to compare actual diet with recommended diet.	Conversion to food group and number of servings is consistently incomplete and inaccurate. Graphs do not accurately compare actual diet with recommended diet.
Revising the Diet	Student uses MyPyramid Plan recommendations to make a sensible revision to diet, if applicable.	Student uses MyPyramid Plan recommendations to make a fairly sensible revision to diet, if applicable.	Student uses MyPyramid Plan recommendations to make a minor revision to diet, if applicable.	Student's revision to diet is not based on MyPyramid Plan recommendations or is unrealistic.
Preparing the Final Report	Report is a thoughtful, thorough, and accurate summary of the project.	Report is a good summary of the project.	Report is a somewhat thoughtful, but incomplete, summary of the project.	Report is a cursory, inaccurate summary of the project.

175

Digestion

A Precious Bundle

The following steps will walk you through the Chapter Project. Use the hints and detailed directions as you guide your students through the gathering of information, presentation, and reflection.

Chapter Project Overview

As you introduce the project, ask students to brainstorm a list of examples of child-care procedures and activities. Since babies often communicate their needs by crying, students might come up with ideas in response to "Why do babies cry?" Include considerations for preparation of baby food, changing diapers, bathing, dressing, and medical checkups. Also, include child-care activities that meet infants' needs to learn to feel loved, observe and interact with their surroundings, and gain confidence that their needs will be met.

Distribute the Project Overview. Describe the project and explain that the purpose is to give students an opportunity to explore the effects of a situation by designing a model, running an investigation (on themselves!), and recording and analyzing results.

Review the Project Rules and hand out the Scoring Rubric that you will use for scoring students' work. Discuss with students what will be expected of them.

Hand out Project Worksheet 1 and Project Worksheet 2. Set a deadline for the project presentation and interim dates to check their progress. Encourage students to record the dates on the Project Timeline.

Materials and Preparation

At the launching of the project, students will need Worksheet 1 and paper or a notebook for their diary writing. Worksheet 2 should be completed before students begin their modeling experience. When the child-care phase begins, each student should have a 5-lb bag of flour and a plastic bag that encloses the flour and is sealed with either a wire twist or a zip-up lock. Tissues or paper towels should be available for "cleaning" the bag (you may prefer to use a suitable substitute).

Keep Students on Track—Tasks 2–3

Check students' completed Worksheet 1. They should reflect what will be involved in their modeling of baby care for the five day period. As you review students' child-care plans, make sure that each student understands how to create a model of an authentic situation. Each child-care task should have related steps listed for each flour-bag care task. Their planning sheet should include all the essential child-care tasks that were listed on the board and a backup plan for child care when they have other obligations.

Check that students have a journal ready in which they will make twice-daily entries of their care-giving experiences.

Keep Students on Track—Task 4

Before beginning their modeling experience, students should fill out and turn in Worksheet 2. You may find that students give more sincere answers by working alone, either as a homework assignment or in a quiet class time. Allow a class discussion of answers on a volunteer basis, since the most thoughtful responses may be personal and private.

Keep Students on Track—Tasks 5–6

Check that students have completed their journal entries. Be sure they have insights and feelings listed so that some of the problems individual students encountered can be discussed in class. Remind students that the bags of flour can model a baby, but that what is missing is the living response and interaction with a real baby.

If there is time, have students exchange information about some of the problems they encountered. Begin a discussion that supplies some possible solutions to these problems. Help students realize that community support is often available to new parents, but that the parents remain responsible for the child's care.

Chapter Project Wrap Up

In preparing students to discuss their projects, you might write several questions on the board to help them choose appropriate journal entries and data. Write questions focused on changes of attitude, frustrations, insights, and observations about the reactions of others. Ask students to hypothesize how these behaviors would affect their own or their babies' lives in actual parenting situations. Let students know they are being evaluated on how well they carried out the assignment and gathered data based on a completed project, but that a greater value can be obtained by a thoughtful assessment of their own responses as a guide for future behaviors.

Extension

After the discussion, ask everyone to expand on their insights by writing up their assignments. Encourage students to describe their own experiences as they experienced them, using their notes as a basis. Have them hypothesize how the situation would change if a real baby were involved.

PROJECT OVERVIEW

A Precious Bundle

In this project, you will be investigating the job of caring for a baby, using a model instead of a real infant. You will be expected to carry out models of actual child-care tasks such as feeding, changing, cuddling, and making sure your "baby" is never without responsible caregivers.

You must first decide what the essential tasks are and then translate the tasks into operations involving your model. To make the investigation richer in information, you will be asked to write down your feelings and insights as you complete the daily child-care tasks. At the end of the project, you will use your data and diary entries to discuss the problems and solutions that are typical of parenting.

As preparation for the discussion at the end of the project, you will prepare
- a list of essential tasks you identified at the beginning of the project;
- a summary of your journal entries and insights;
- identifications of any unanticipated problems you had in caring for the "baby";
- your thoughts about whether caring for a baby is easier or more difficult than you anticipated;
- your rating of the overall success of your plan.

Project Rules

- You must make a list of all important child-care tasks and modify them to your experimental model.
- You must make journal entries two times a day for the five days of the project.
- You must be prepared to answer questions about parenting and participate in a class discussion using both data and journal entries to support your answers.

Suggested Materials

You will be using two student worksheets to help you plan and prepare for the project. You will be given a bag of flour or a substitute that represents the infant, as well as a plastic bag and cleaning tissues. You may wish to include equipment of your own to help you model the tasks of feeding, clothing, and transport that are typical of child-care situations.

Project Hints

- The more research you do to learn about baby care and the more you enter into the modeling of the role, the more you will learn about being a parent. You will have several opportunities to discuss your experience with others, and your willingness to treat this project realistically will provide you with a rich source of data for your ideas about parenting.

- Libraries and family health facilities have literature on baby care that will help you learn about accurate procedures, as well as problems with real babies that may not come up with your flour model.

- Talking with people who have experience with baby care is a good way to prepare for this project.

Project Timeline

Task	Due Date
1. List essential tasks	_____
2. Complete research of procedures	_____
3. Complete Project Worksheet 1	_____
4. Carry out modeling investigation	_____
5. Journal entries reviewed	_____
6. Preparation for discussion	_____
7. Class discussion	_____

PROJECT WORKSHEET 1

Planning for Your Precious Bundle

Using the list of child-care tasks compiled during class discussion, convert each task to specific steps for caring for the "bag-of-flour baby." You will need to make your own version of the table below. Complete the table by providing spaces to check off the tasks for each of the five days.

Task Table

Task	Detailed Steps	How Often Each Day
Feeding		(suggested time: every 4 hr for 20 minutes)
Changing the diaper		(suggested time: every 3 hr for 5 minutes)
Social interaction		(suggested time: twice a day for 15 minutes)
Quiet nap		
Daily bath		
2:00 A.M. feeding and changing		
Evaluating a responsible baby sitter		
Diary entries		(twice a day, 15 minutes)
Others		

Diary Suggestions You will need to write about your experience as if you were responsible for the life of a helpless, demanding infant. It might be helpful to talk with parents or baby sitters, or to read books on caring for young infants. Write about behaviors that are typical of children less than a year old. Think up growth achievements or accidents that might happen to a baby. Write about how other people react to you. Record your own feelings as accurately as possible.

PROJECT WORKSHEET 2

A Precious Bundle
Recording Data

A data table like the one below can be used to record information about your tasks and how you responded to performing them. Be sure to include a thoughtful response to each major situation. The first two rows of the table have been filled in as an example. You will need to make your own longer version of this data table, since you will be performing many more tasks than there is space to show here.

Date	Time	Essential Task	Your Response
October 13	6:00 A.M.	Baby cried and needed to be fed	I am still tired. I didn't want to get up and feed baby.
October 13	9:03 A.M.	Baby needed bathing	This is a lot of trouble to go through. The baby smells clean and seems happy. It was worth it.

Getting Ready for the Class Discussion

Answer the following questions on a separate sheet of paper. Your answers, your journal entries, and the other data you recorded during the modeling investigation will be your notes for the class discussion.

1. What tasks took the least time to perform? Which were the most time-consuming?

2. What tasks were easier to perform than you had expected? Which were harder?

3. Did you find that performing some of the tasks was satisfying? Were some of the tasks not very satisfying to do?

4. What problems did you encounter that you would want help with if you were caring for a real baby?

5. How would having a baby change the life of a person your age?

Name _____ Date _____ Class _____

SCORING RUBRIC
A Precious Bundle

In evaluating how well you complete the Chapter Project, your teacher will judge your work in four categories. In each, a score of 4 is the best rating.

	4	3	2	1
Preparing for Baby Care	Task table and discussion indicate ample, detailed, and accurate research into child-care practices and issues.	Task table and discussion indicate fairly detailed and accurate research into child-care practices and issues.	Task table and discussion indicate some research into child-care practices and issues. Information is mostly accurate.	Task table and discussion indicate minimal research into child-care practices and issues. Information is very general or has significant errors.
Completing Child-Care Tasks	All tasks, responses, and diary entries completed thoroughly and on time.	Most tasks, responses, and diary entries completed thoroughly and on time.	Most tasks, responses, and diary entries completed, but some lack detail.	Only a few tasks, responses, and diary entries completed thoroughly and on time.
Taking the Role Seriously	Task table and discussion indicate complete willingness to take the role seriously. Data clearly show results of problem solving.	Task table and discussion indicate some willingness to take the role seriously. Data show results of problem solving.	Task table and discussion indicate some willingness to take the role seriously. Data show minimal evidence of problem solving.	Task table, discussion, and data show little willingness to take the project seriously or problem solve.
Participating in Class Discussion	Actively communicates well in class discussion. Written work is fairly thorough and clear.	Communicates in class discussion. Written work is fairly thorough and clear.	Participates somewhat in class discussion. Written work is somewhat clear.	Minimally participates in class discussion. Written work is unclear.

Working Together

The following steps will walk you through the Chapter Project. Use the hints and detailed directions as you guide your students through the writing and illustrating of a magazine article that makes an extended analogy between the organ systems in the human body and the structures and functions of a modern city.

Chapter Project Overview

To introduce this project, sit on a chair or lean against a desk and model reading a book. Ask students whether they think any systems in the body are at work while you're simply reading. If students can't think of any activities the body is carrying out, ask: How am I able to hold this book in place? Is anything happening inside my body to the food I ate for breakfast or lunch? Are my lungs doing anything? What is happening to the blood in my body? Am I using any senses while reading? How is my body maintaining a normal body temperature? Accept all reasonable answers, depending on how much of the chapter students have read.

After discussing how various body systems work together to carry out simple activities, make an analogy with a modern city. Ask: What are the eyes and ears of a city? Is the electrical system of a city similar to anything in the body? What "excretory system" does a city have to get rid of its wastes? Explain that, in this Chapter Project, students will work in small groups to write and illustrate a magazine article that makes such analogies between human body systems and a city.

Have students read the Project Overview, and answer any questions students have about writing and illustrating the article. Also hand out the Scoring Rubric, which you will use for scoring students' work. Discuss what will be expected in this project. Point out that unlike a test, the final product in this project has no absolute correct answers. Students should create an article that is both imaginative and accurate. Remind them to refer to the hints in the Project Overview as they complete their articles.

Set a deadline for the completion of the article. Also set interim dates for the completion of the worksheets and the rough draft of the magazine article. Encourage students to record these dates on the Project Timeline.

Divide the class into small groups. Distribute copies of Project Worksheet 1. This worksheet will help students start thinking about how body systems work together. Point out that students should finish the worksheets on their own. Warn them that their examples should be appropriate for classroom use. Then, hand out copies of Project Worksheet 2. Students should complete the worksheet individually and then discuss in their groups which analogy to use for each body system.

Materials and Preparation

Students will need access to computers to write and edit their article. You might also want to provide colored pencils or markers for students to use for creating their illustrations. Alternatively, students can import pictures from the Internet into their articles.

Keep Students on Track—Task 1

Collect and review Worksheet 1. There are no absolutely correct answers for which body systems are involved in an activity. An argument could be made for the involvement of almost every body system in an activity because the body functions as a whole. The purpose of Worksheet 1 is to help focus students' thinking on interactions among the body systems. Review this worksheet to make sure each student has provided reasonable choices.

Keep Students on Track—Task 2

Make sure all students complete Worksheet 2, though you do not need to review their completed worksheets. The purpose of this worksheet is to help students generate analogies to contribute to group planning of their magazine article.

Keep Students on Track—Task 3

As each group completes a rough draft of its article, review what students have written. Emphasize to students that editing and revising are essential steps in creating a well-written final product. Remind them that they should tie the article together with a thoughtful introduction and conclusion. They should also discuss interactions among systems, as well as the maintenance of homeostasis, in either the introductory or closing paragraph.

Chapter Project Wrap Up

As groups finish their articles, either post them in the classroom or make a few copies to distribute among the class. Encourage all students to read each article.

You may want to use class time to discuss the articles. You might address each article by having a group member mention a few analogies from the article. Then, encourage other students to ask questions and evaluate the analogies.

Extension

As students learn more about the different body systems through reading subsequent chapters, each student could expand on his or her group's article by adding an extra page that concentrates on one of the systems. This could be like a sidebar feature in a magazine that focuses on something mentioned in the main article in more detail. For example, a student could extend an analogy between the police and fire departments and the integumentary system.

PROJECT OVERVIEW

Working Together

In this project, you will explore the interactions of body systems in the human body. One way to think about these interactions is to make an analogy. An analogy is a similarity between two things that are otherwise not much alike. Analogies are useful in helping us to understand new material by comparing new concepts to more familiar ones. Here you will consider the interactions of a modern city that allow the city to function in a way that benefits its citizens.

The form your extended analogy will take will be a magazine article. In this article, you will make individual analogies between each system in the human body and the systems, structures, or functions of a city. That is, you will describe a part of a city that is similar to the structure or function of each body system. Like most magazine articles, you'll need to provide illustrations to help the reader understand what you write.

Project Rules

- Complete Project Worksheets 1 and 2 on your own. These worksheets will help in the planning and development of your group's magazine article.

- With your group, decide on an analogy for each body system. Then, as a group you should agree on who will write and illustrate each of the analogies. Group members may work individually or in pairs to write and illustrate each analogy.

- You should begin by writing a rough draft and making illustrations. Once you have written the rough draft, work together to finish the article. This involves editing the rough draft, revising illustrations, and writing introductory and concluding paragraphs.

- At the beginning or end of the article, make an analogy about how the body keeps a stable internal environment and how the city maintains a safe and stable environment—in other words, how each maintains homeostasis. Make the point that systems in both the body and a city interact in multiple ways to carry out different activities.

- Your final product should look like a magazine article, with a title and well-designed pages.

Suggested Materials

- Colored pencils or markers to create illustrations for your article. You could also use images you find on the Internet or in magazines.

Hints for Making Good Analogies

- The challenge of this project is to make strong analogies between the various body systems and the systems, structures, or functions of a city. There are no absolutely correct answers, but your group will be able to sense how strong the analogy is.

- A good analogy doesn't have to be completely serious. You can make humorous, ironic, or even goofy analogies as long as you show an accurate comparison between a body system and a city's system, structure, or function.

- The right illustrations can really enhance a magazine article. In this case, consider drawing cartoons for some or all of the illustrations. You might also find images on the Internet or in magazines to help emphasize a point made in the text or maybe to add humor to the article.

- In editing the rough draft, try to make all contributions consistent, so that the article holds together as one piece.

- Pay careful attention to writing the opening and closing paragraphs of your article. The opening paragraph should let the reader know what the entire article is about and introduce the idea of an analogy between human body systems and a city's systems, structures, and functions. The closing paragraph should summarize the main points of the article.

- Either at the beginning or the end of the article, make a strong point that systems work together, whether in a body or in a city.

- You may find it is easiest to "cut and paste" your article together. You can cut up the contributions from the different group members and paste them onto sheets of paper to make an attractive magazine article. Combine text and illustrations to make your article more interesting.

Project Timeline

Task	Due Date
1. Complete Project Worksheet 1	_____
2. Complete Project Worksheet 2	_____
3. Complete rough draft of magazine article	_____
4. Finish final version of article	_____

PROJECT WORKSHEET 1

What Body System Is Responsible?

Every activity you do involves the interaction of many body systems. For example, think of when you ate lunch yesterday. The main body system involved in eating is your digestive system. The organs of your digestive system processed the food you ate, but other systems were involved. Your skeletal system allowed you to move your fork to your mouth, and your muscular system helped move food through your digestive system. Your nervous system sent a signal to let you know when you were full, and your excretory system removed any waste from the food you had eaten. Can you think of other systems involved in eating?

Think of the various activities you've done in the last 24 hours. This worksheet will help you start thinking about the interaction of body systems. For each of the three activities, identify the main body system involved in the activity, and then explain how two other body systems were also involved. Make sure your activities are appropriate for the classroom. An example has been done for you.

Activity: Eating lunch

Main Body System: The digestive system breaks down food and absorbs nutrients.

Interacting Body System: The nervous system alerts your brain when your stomach is full.

Interacting Body System: The excretory system removed waste products from the body.

1. Activity: _____

   Main Body System: _____

   Interacting Body System: _____

   Interacting Body System: _____

2. Activity: _____

   Main Body System: _____

   Interacting Body System: _____

   Interacting Body System: _____

3. Activity: _____

   Main Body System: _____

   Interacting Body System: _____

   Interacting Body System: _____

PROJECT WORKSHEET 2

Like a City

Your group's illustrated magazine article will make detailed analogies between the interaction of systems in your body and the interaction among various departments, structures, and agencies within a city. Before beginning to write your article, think about a system, structure, or function of a city you could compare to a system in the human body. Write your analogies below. Two examples are shown.

1. Skeletal System

_____

_____

2. Integumentary System A city's fire and police departments guard against injuries to the people and structures of a city.

3. Muscular System

_____

_____

4. Circulatory System

_____

_____

5. Respiratory System

_____

_____

6. Digestive System

_____

_____

7. Excretory System A city's trash pickup and waste treatment system remove wastes from the city.

8. Nervous System

_____

_____

9. Endocrine System

_____

_____

10. Reproductive System

_____

_____

188
Human Body

Name _____ Date_____ Class_____

SCORING RUBRIC
Working Together

In evaluating how well you complete the Chapter Project, your teacher will judge your work in four categories. In each, a score of 4 is the best rating.

	4	3	2	1
Identifying Body Systems Involved in Activities	Student thoroughly and insightfully describes body systems involved in three activities.	Student adequately describes body systems involved in three activities.	Student accurately describes body systems involved in two activities.	Student inaccurately or incompletely describes body systems involved in only one or two activities.
Writing Rough Drafts and Illustrating	Student advances good ideas, helps write and edit the rough draft, and contributes several illustrations.	Student advances some ideas, helps write and edit the rough draft, and contributes one or two illustrations.	Student advances few ideas, helps somewhat write and edit the rough draft, and contributes an illustration.	Student advances few ideas, plays little or no role in writing and editing the rough draft, and contributes no illustrations.
Producing Final Article on How Body Systems Work Together	Article is interestingly written and effectively illustrated and makes good analogies between all body systems and functions of a city.	Article is fairly well written and illustrated and makes good analogies between all body systems and functions of a city.	Article is adequately written and illustrated and makes fair analogies between most body systems and functions of a city.	Article is not well written and/or illustrated and makes poor analogies between some body systems and functions of a city.
Participating in the Group	Student takes a lead in planning, writing, and illustrating.	Student participates in all aspects of planning, writing, and illustrating.	Student participates in most aspects of planning, writing, and illustrating.	Student plays a minor role in planning, writing, and illustrating.

189
Human Body

Stop the Invasion!

The following steps will walk you through the Chapter Project. Use the hints and detailed directions as you guide your students through the gathering of information and the planning and presentation of their reports.

Chapter Project Overview

As you introduce the project, ask students what it is like to be sick with a bad cold. Ask them how they knew they were getting sick, and make a list of the physical symptoms that students name on one side of the board. Then go on to successive stages of the cold, such as worsening or additional symptoms and gradual recovery. Use the other side of the board to show how each stage of the cold can be compared to the battles of a war. Once you have begun the process of comparison, encourage students to contribute their own ideas.

Discuss ways students can begin to research their chosen infectious diseases, emphasizing the need to define scientific terms for a general audience. Encourage students to be creative with their ideas: their news reports should be entertaining, yet the material must be accurate.

Have students read the Project Overview. Review the Project Rules and hand out the Scoring Rubric that you will use for scoring students' work. Discuss with students what will be expected of them.

Set a deadline for the project presentation and interim dates to check their progress. Encourage students to record the dates on the Project Timeline.

If you will not have time for each student to research and present a project, you might ask students to work in small groups so they can pool their knowledge of diseases as well as their verbal and artistic abilities. A group format that treats the students as a news team would allow time for student specialization and the creation of more elaborate graphic elements or sound effects.

Materials and Preparation

If students' presentations will only be verbal, they should need only paper and pencils. If the presentations will include oral aids or sound effects, you will need to make available tape recorders and art materials such as markers and poster board.

Keep Students on Track—Tasks 1–2

Make sure that students have chosen which disease they will feature in their news reports. To help students compare the stages of illness to battle terminology, ask them to group their information into sequences such as these: the way the disease organism enters the body, the first signs of the disease, the spread of the disease in the body, and the body's three lines of defense.

Hand out Project Worksheet 1. Tell students that they need to watch or listen to three newscasts, or read three newspaper articles, and think about the steps involved in presenting a complicated news story. Go over the worksheet to make sure that students understand the questions.

Keep Students on Track—Tasks 3–4

Hand out Project Worksheet 2. Then, check to see that students have completed researching the stages of infection of their chosen disease from first contact to recovery.

Use class time to demonstrate how to generate words and phrases that convey vivid images, such as those used in actual news reports. Remind students that news reporting requires brevity as well as exactness. The audience must be able to visualize the actions described. Ask students to read passages of their first drafts that they think are good examples of news reporting. Show appreciation for the variety of qualities expressed by students' efforts, such as humor, clarity, vividness, mood, or brevity.

Keep Students on Track—Tasks 5–6

Check that students have completed first drafts of their news stories. You might have students work in groups at this stage, evaluating each other's work for accuracy as well as coherence. Ask students to help each other by pointing out which passages are especially clear as well as sections where the audience loses track of the story.

If there are to be visual aids or sound effects, make sure that students have access to materials and equipment, and have scheduled enough time to complete their projects.

Chapter Project Wrap Up

Before the day of the presentations, go over the logistics of how students will present their stories, and discuss any specific space or equipment requirements students might have. In the process of practicing their news reports, students should time their presentations. This information will let you create a schedule for the "broadcasts" and ensure that there is sufficient class time for all presentations (including questions from the audience). Students who are presenting a television broadcast will need a central area to stand and set up their visual displays.

After all of the reports have been presented, give students time to comment on memorable images or descriptions used in the various presentations. Ask students to record some of their observations in their journals and to write about what it was like for them to explore the stages of infection caused by a microscopic organism. Encourage them to write about other ways they could use their imaginations to help learn complicated material.

Extension

This project is firmly rooted in the tradition of science fiction literature. If students are interested in how scientific information can be used to create fictional stories, you might encourage their interest by suggesting some science fiction books and giving students class time to critique the stories they read. A good example, and one that would tie into this chapter project, is the radio script for H. G. Wells's *The War of the Worlds*. Not only is it an exciting example of news broadcasting, but the dramatic climax hinges on germs and immune responses.

PROJECT OVERVIEW

Stop the Invasion!

Imagine yourself reporting the battles of an intense conflict. This is not a war between countries, however, but an invasion of a human body by disease-causing organisms. Your job is to report the progress of the invaders, their effects on the body, and the body's responses as it defends itself against the disease. As you will learn how the body fights off infectious diseases, you will be able to apply this information to common diseases such as colds and flu.

In this project, you will choose a specific infectious disease and determine the sequence of events that occur as it attacks the body and the body defends itself. You will then compare these events to a war between two armies. Finally, you will present these battles to the class in at least three news reports. Before working on your reports, you will need to analyze several newscasts or newspaper articles to determine methods used to capture the audience's attention, present a clear description of events, and communicate information accurately.

Your reports may be in the form of radio or television broadcasts or newspaper articles. They must include these topics:

- How the disease organism comes in contact with the body

- A description of the first symptoms of the disease and the first defense response of the body

- A description of further symptoms and immune responses as the disease moves to different sites within the body

- The final results of the disease conflict

- Any long-term effects on the body from the disease

Project Rules

- Choose a specific disease and research its causes and its effects on the body.

- Watch or listen to news broadcasts or read newspaper articles to study how reporters present information.

- Plan your presentation by finding parallels between the stages of the disease and the battles between two armies.

- Write first drafts of your three reports using the information you learned about the body's immune response to the disease.

- Assemble any additional materials you need for your broadcasts or articles, such as sound effects, visual aids, or illustrations.

- Practice your presentation in front of some classmates.

- Revise your reports and present your "live" broadcasts or articles to the class.

Suggested Materials

Your teacher will provide you with materials such as colored pencils, poster board, or a tape recorder for making sound effects.

Project Hints

- Brainstorm a list of infectious diseases that interest you. Choose a disease that you have had before or that you already know something about. You can find more information about the disease at the library, on the Internet, or by interviewing a doctor or nurse.
- Write down as many symptoms of the disease as you can remember. Describe the symptoms as vividly as you can.
- As you listen to, watch, or read news reports, write down any methods you notice for writing an exciting broadcast script or article.

Project Timeline

Task	Due Date
1. Select the disease.	_____
2. Complete Project Worksheet 1.	_____
3. Complete research of the disease.	_____
4. Complete Project Worksheet 2.	_____
5. Complete rough drafts of news reports.	_____
6. Prepare any sound effects, visual aids, or illustration.	_____
7. Practice and time the presentation.	_____
8. Revise news reports as necessary.	_____
9. Make presentation to the class.	_____

PROJECT WORKSHEET 1
Stop the Invasion!
Planning

An excellent project must have some of the same qualities of an excellent news broadcast. Listen to, watch, or read at least three news stories to help you answer the following questions about presenting information effectively. Read all of the questions before you begin writing your draft. Use a separate sheet of paper if you need more room.

1. **Lead-ins:** How does a reporter introduce the story? Describe the characteristics of an opening sentence that makes the audience or reader want to know more. Write down a sample of at least one opening sentence that "leads in" to the story by catching people's attention.

   _____

   _____

2. **Organization:** What patterns do you notice in the ways the stories are organized? Look for stories that are organized by sequence of events, by human interest level (the degree to which you sympathize with the events), by the different viewpoints involved, or by relating the story to other events.

   _____

   _____

3. **Unfamiliar terms:** How does the story help the audience to understand terms that may not be familiar?

   _____

   _____

4. **Putting the story in context:** If the news report is an episode of an ongoing story, what methods are used to connect it to previous reports?

   _____

   _____

5. **Endings:** Write down some ways that news stories end. Listen or read for endings that use general comments, thoughtful predictions, or "hooks" that make the audience want to follow the story in the next day's news.

   _____

   _____

   _____

6. **Visuals and sound effects:** Look and listen for ways that maps, still pictures, film clips, and sound effects are used to enhance the effect of the news story. How is it helpful to include actual interviews with the people involved? Do sound effects or visual images help to communicate the story?

   _____

   _____

PROJECT WORKSHEET 2

Stop the Invasion!

Recording Data

Record information about your chosen disease and the body's response to it in a data table like the one below. Include a description of how the disease-causing organisms invade and attack the body and how the body defends itself against these attacks. Use the Date and Time columns to indicate the sequence of events. The first two rows of the table have been filled in as an example.

Date	Time	Action of Disease	Reaction of Body
October 13	9:00 A.M.	Mr. Smith turns a doorknob and picks up cold viruses on his hand.	Mr. Smith's skin acts as a barrier to the virus.
October 13	9:03 A.M.	Mr. Smith eats a doughnut and licks his fingers, swallowing some of the viruses on his hand.	Mr. Smith's saliva destroys some of the cold viruses.

Analyzing and Presenting

Complete the following items on a separate sheet of paper. When you are finished, you will be ready to write the first drafts of your scripts or articles.

1. Decide how you want to communicate to your classmates what you have learned: in radio news broadcasts, television news broadcasts, or newspaper articles.

2. Decide how you will divide the information into three or more separate news reports.

3. Decide what visual aids or sound effects you want to include in your presentation to help your audience understand the story.

SCORING RUBRIC

Stop the Invasion!

In evaluating how well you complete the Chapter Project, your teacher will judge your work in the following categories. In each, a score of 4 is the best rating.

	4	3	2	1
Researching the Disease	Thoroughly researches the disease, including transmission, symptoms, and the body's responses.	Adequately researches the disease, including transmission, symptoms, and the body's responses.	Does some research on the disease. Research includes only two of the following: transmission, symptoms, and the body's responses.	Does minimal research on the disease. Research includes only one of the following: transmission, symptoms, and the body's responses.
Writing Scripts or Articles	Prepares three news reports that accurately compare the course of the disease to an ongoing battle. Reports are creative, organized, and thorough.	Prepares three news reports that compare the course of the disease to an ongoing battle. Reports are fairly creative, organized, and complete, but may contain a minor error.	Prepares three news reports about the disease. Reports are somewhat organized and mostly complete, but may contain a minor errors.	Prepares one or two news reports about the disease. Reports are unorganized, incomplete, and contain more than one major error.
Presenting the News Reports	Presentation is thorough and easy to follow. Student effectively makes use of visual aids or sound effects.	Presentation is adequate and easy to follow. Student makes use of visual aids or sound effects.	Parts of presentation are hard to follow. Student makes use of only a single visual aid or sound effect.	Most of presentation is hard to follow. Student does not make use of visual aids or sound effects.
Working Cooperatively (if project done in groups)	Takes a lead in the group's research, planning, and presentation of the project.	Actively participates in the group's research, planning, and presentation of the project.	Takes a limited role in the group's research, planning, and presentation of the project.	Participates minimally in the group's research, planning, and presentation of the project.

Tricks and Illusions

The following steps will walk you through the Chapter Project. Use the hints and detailed instructions as you guide your students through the planning and assembly of their science fair booths, the gathering of data, and the presentation of results.

Chapter Project Overview

In this project, students will use a variety of illusions to consider how their senses work. They will also learn that, despite variations, people experience a shared sensory world.

To introduce the project and to demonstrate how sensory data can be distorted through interpretation, have the class play the game of "gossip." Ask one student to start the gossip line by reading in a whisper the following message to the second student: "If a rabbit runs twice around the school, then puts butter on its ears, it will grow green fur." The second student whispers what was heard to a third, and so on throughout the class. Have every fifth student write down what the message sounded like so the class can later see what changes occurred as the message was passed around the room. After the last student says the message aloud and it is compared with the original and with successive versions, discuss with students how the brain uses information gathered by the senses and then "makes sense" of it.

Tell students they will be trying out and selecting illusions that demonstrate how the brain can be fooled. Have students read the Project Overview. Review the Project Rules and hand out the Scoring Rubric that you will use for scoring students' work. Discuss with students what will be expected of them.

Set a deadline for the project presentation and interim dates to check their progress. Encourage students to record the dates on the Project Timeline. The project will require at least two weeks to complete: one week to research and try out illusions and one week to hold the science fair, gather data, and present the results.

Hand out Project Worksheet 1. This activity describes three simple illusions that students can try themselves. Students will answer questions about their responses to these illusions. These questions are similar to those they can use at their science fair booths.

After students have selected or have been assigned an illusion to use at the science fair, hand out Project Worksheet 2. Students can use this worksheet to help decide which responses they will use as data and to design a table to collect these data.

Materials and Preparation

Materials will depend on the illusions students select. You could minimize the need for complicated materials by preselecting simple activities. This would also ensure that illusions involving a variety of senses are included in the science fair. Alternatively, have students obtain their own materials as part of a successful project.

The following book is a good reference for detailed descriptions of sensory illusions: *How to Really Fool Yourself: Illusions for All Your Senses* by Vicki Cobb.

To complete the illusions presented on Worksheet 1, students will need a coin, a tissue, a hand lens, a rubber glove, a bowl of warm water, a bowl of cool water, and a meter stick.

Keep Students on Track—Task 2

If students will be selecting their own illusions to present, be sure to check the activities for safety.

Students should present their illusion to several people and record their responses. Next, they should use these data to write a set of typical responses. Then, students can present the illusion to several more people and see if the subjects' answers match the predicted responses, or if the student needs to broaden his or her criteria.

Keep Students on Track—Task 5

Students may be able to set up their science fair booths at their desks. You may want to have classmates try out each other's illusions or invite a class of younger students to be the participants in the science fair. In the former case, you can divide the class into two groups. One group can present its illusions, and the other can be the participants. After each student in the second group has tried the first group's illusions, the groups can switch roles.

Keep Students on Track—Tasks 6–7

Students will need to know whether you want them to present their data in any specific form. You might have them create tables or graphs that show the compiled responses of all of the participants, or you could ask them to write a description of the illusion and what they concluded from their tests. You may also want students to present their results as an oral report followed by questions from the class.

Chapter Project Wrap Up

Help students try to explain how the illusions worked. Be aware that some of the illusions will probably be too complicated for students to explain.

Conclude the presentations with a discussion of what students learned about how their nervous system allows them to make sense of their environment. You might start the discussion by asking students whether they think they should always believe their senses.

Extension

If you will not have time for your class to complete the entire project, you could simplify it by setting up a variety of illusions at stations around the classroom. Students could try out the illusions themselves during one class period and report on their findings during another.

PROJECT OVERVIEW
Tricks and Illusions

In this project, you will be exploring a variety of illusions that can fool your senses. You will examine your own responses to these illusions, as well as the responses of other students. Sometimes you may want to describe how people first respond to an illusion, then how they figure out the way the illusion has tricked them.

For example, look at the two lines below. Which line seems longer? Next, measure the two lines with a ruler. This illusion tricks you into thinking that line B is longer than line A. Once you measure the lines, however, you realize that the lines are the same length. You may be able to find out how some illusions fool the senses. Others may be too complicated to actually explain.

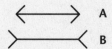

You will set up a science fair booth to test and record other students' responses to the illusion that you select. Afterward, you will make a presentation to the class that will show and explain the results of your tests. You will be using your illusions to demonstrate how different people react to the same experience. Depending on the illusion, you may also try to explain how the illusion works.

Project Rules

- Investigate at least five illusions and choose one or more illusions for your tests. Try to include some illusions that involve the senses of hearing or touch, as well as sight.

- Get your teacher's approval of the illusions you plan to present in your science fair booth.

- Try out several ways to present the illusions to others. Choose the one that seems to work best.

- Decide what responses you will need to record and what materials you will need.

- Present your illusions to several people who have never experienced them before.

- Create a summary of your findings and present them to your class.

- Either your teacher will provide you with a selection of illusions to choose from, or you will need to do research to find examples of illusions.

Suggested Materials

- You will need paper and a pencil to record responses. You will probably also need to collect other materials to carry out your illusions.

Project Hints

- Project Worksheet 1 will allow you to try several illusions and observe your responses to them.

- Pay close attention to your own responses when you try the illusions. This will help you to decide what questions to ask and what responses to look for when you conduct your tests. Once you have chosen an illusion, present it to several people. Record their responses to see if they were the same as yours. This will help to plan your data sheets. Project Worksheet 2 will help you to design a way to record your data during your tests.

Project Timeline

Task	Due Date
1. Project Worksheet 1 completed.	_____
2. At least five illusions tried.	_____
3. One or more illusions selected and approved.	_____
4. Project Worksheet 2 completed.	_____
5. Data sheet designed and booth set up.	_____
6. Tests completed and data recorded.	_____
7. Findings presented to class.	_____

PROJECT WORKSHEET 1
Fool Your Senses

Try out the illusions described below, and then answer the following questions on a separate sheet of paper.

Materials
- coin
- rubber glove
- bowl of cool water
- tissue
- bowl of warm water
- meter stick
- hand lens

The Shrinking Coin

Cover the coin with the tissue and then feel the shape of the coin through the tissue while looking at it with the hand lens. Then close your eyes and feel the coin a second time.

1. What two senses are involved in this illusion?

2. Did the coin seem to change size? Explain.

3. Why do you think you were tricked by this illusion?

Are You Wet Yet?

Put on the rubber glove. Place your gloved hand in the bowl of warm water for 5 to 10 seconds. Then move your gloved hand into the bowl of cool water.

4. In which bowl did your hand seem to be wet?

5. Was your hand really wet? How do you know?

6. What sense was involved in tricking you? What sense was involved in figuring out the illusion?

7. Why do you think you were tricked by this illusion?

Make the World Turn

Stand up and hold a meter stick so that it stands straight up from the floor. Bend over carefully so that your forehead just touches the top of the stick and walk around the stick three times, bent over. Then stand up again.

8. What happened when you stood up?

9. What senses were involved in tricking you?

PROJECT WORKSHEET 2
Designing a Data Sheet
Determining Responses

Once you have chosen the illusions you will present at your science fair booth, test your own responses to the illusions and answer the following questions. Then present your illusions to someone else and ask them to answer the same questions. Record both your own and the other person's answers on a separate sheet of paper.

1. In what way did you first interpret the illusion?

2. What did you need to do to understand how you had been tricked?

Making a Data Table

Combine both sets of answers to create a page for recording responses to the illusion quickly and easily.

You might find that the responses are similar enough that you can write down typical answers ahead of time. Then, a student's answers can be checked off as you read aloud the questions. Always leave one choice as "other" in case someone has an original response. Also, leave a space to record any interesting or unexpected ideas you may have as you do the tests. Below is a sample data sheet for the illusion described in the Project Overview. The checkmarks indicate Jacob's responses.

Name	Question	Answer Choice 1	Answer Choice 2	Answer Choice 3	Other Answer
Jacob	Which line seems longer? (before measuring)	line A	line B ✓	They are the same length.	
	Which line is longer? (after measuring)	line A	line B	They are the same length. ✓	

Once you have designed your data sheet, you or your teacher can make photocopies of it so that you can record the responses of several different students.

SCORING RUBRIC
Tricks and Illusions

In evaluating how well you complete the Chapter Project, your teacher will judge your work in four categories. In each, a score of 4 is the best rating.

	4	3	2	1
Conducting Research and Selecting Illusion(s)	Student conducts thorough research and tries out at least five illusions. Student selects one or more illusions that are appropriate to the project's goals.	Student conducts necessary research and tries out five illusions. Student selects a single illusion that is appropriate to the project's goals.	Student conducts some necessary research and tries out four illusions. Student selects a single illusion that is somewhat appropriate to the project's goals.	Student conducts little necessary research and tries out fewer than four illusions. Student fails to select any appropriate illusions.
Creating Data Sheets	Data sheets are well organized and clear. Questions are easy to understand. Student has listed a variety of typical answers.	Data sheets are organized and somewhat clear. Most questions are easy to understand. Student has listed some typical answers.	Data sheets are somewhat organized, but often unclear. Some questions are easy to understand. Student has listed a few typical answers.	Data sheets are incomplete or disorganized and unclear. Many questions are difficult to understand. Student has failed to list typical answers.
Presenting the Science Fair Booth and Gathering Data	Student has recorded responses for a large number of people. Data sheets are complete for all respondents.	Student has recorded responses for an adequate number of people. Data sheets are complete for almost all respondents.	Student has recorded responses for several people. Data sheets are complete for only some respondents.	Student has recorded responses for only a few people. Data sheets are incomplete for most respondents.
Presenting the Results	Presentation is interesting, easy to understand, creative, and includes all appropriate visual aids. Conclusions about perception are logical.	Presentation is fairly easy to understand and includes all appropriate visual aids. Conclusions about perception are mostly logical.	Presentation is somewhat difficult to understand, and some appropriate visual aids are missing. A few conclusions about perception are logical.	Presentation is incomplete and difficult to understand, and appropriate visual aids are missing. Conclusions about perception are mostly illogical.

Get the Message Out

The following steps will walk you through the Chapter Project. Use the hints and detailed directions as you guide your students through their planning, discussions, and presentations.

This chapter discusses the effects of smoking on one's health, and it touches on the reasons that people begin smoking. In this project, students will need to think about why people begin to smoke, what makes them continue to smoke, and how smoking adversely affects their health.

Before introducing the project, collect students' opinions on smoking. Why do people start to smoke or decide not to start smoking? Why do students think people continue smoking once they start? It may be interesting to record students' opinions before and after this project to see if they are influenced by what they learn.

Explain that in this project students will be playing the roles of researchers, writers, and designers for an advertisement agency. They will be creating advertisements to persuade people in three age groups not to smoke. Lead a discussion of advertising. Students may not have considered the impact that advertising has on their lives. Advertising is one of many things that influences people to start or continue to smoke. Have students give examples of how advertisers use magazine, newspaper, radio, and television ads to encourage us to buy their products. Which ads are effective? Which ads are not effective? To what age group is each ad meant to appeal? Are some ads geared primarily to men or primarily to women?

Have students read the Project Overview. Review the Project Rules and hand out the Scoring Rubric you will use for scoring students' work. Discuss with students what will be expected of them.

Set a deadline for the project presentation and interim dates to check their progress. Have students record the dates on the Project Timeline.

Distribute copies of Project Worksheet 1. This worksheet will help students work on their ads by getting them to think about what makes a good ad and how to make ads age-appropriate. After students have completed this worksheet, lead a class discussion about the effectiveness of advertising. Have students think about what elements will be important to the ads they will be making.

Distribute copies of Project Worksheet 2. This worksheet will help students begin to plan their ads. Remind students that they might want to conduct interviews of children and adults to answer questions 1 and 2. Students will learn better by hearing the answers to their questions from people they know than by reading in books or anti-smoking literature. Make sure that they make sketches of their designs and get your approval before they begin working on their final product.

Materials and Preparation

Fashion, sports, or entertainment magazines will be useful in brainstorming ideas for convincing ads. Poster board, large sheets of paper, markers, crayons, and colored pencils will be needed for designing posters.

Some students may want to write radio or television commercials, in which case they will write scripts and bring in props or costumes, and possibly materials for sound effects or accompanying music.

Keep Students on Track—Task 1

Review students' sketches, making sure that they have related what they are learning about the detrimental effects of cigarette smoking to respiratory function. Help students to understand that the various materials in tobacco smoke affect different parts of the respiratory system. For example, tar affects the proper functioning of cilia and contains chemicals that have been shown to cause cancer. Carbon monoxide decreases the ability of blood to carry oxygen. Nicotine speeds up heart and breathing rates, and is addictive.

Distribute anti-smoking materials you have collected. Have students analyze the materials to determine which audience the materials are designed to influence. Are the materials effective? Remind students to consider their own ads in the same light. Who are the target groups? Is the information presented accurately? Will the target groups be responsive to the way the information is presented?

Keep Students on Track—Tasks 3–4

Check that each sketch addresses at least three health risks associated with smoking, two pressures that encourage people to start or continue smoking, and that each is age appropriate. Make suggestions for how students can improve their designs.

Chapter Project Wrap Up

Have students present their ads to the class. In their presentations they should discuss the messages and images that are used in their ads and explain how their ads are effective in discouraging people in that particular age group from smoking.

Following the class presentations, lead a discussion on the effectiveness of advertising. Did students find any posters especially effective? Also discuss the pressures that encourage teens to begin smoking. Has this project changed their views of smoking?

Have students turn in any written work you require.

Arrange for a place for students to display their work. If it is possible, have them hang their posters in a common hallway where other students can see the ads. If students have made effective posters, perhaps they can be used to discourage other students from smoking.

Extension

- Have students interview adults that they know who either currently smoke or used to smoke. They should ask why these persons began to smoke and why they continue to smoke or why they quit. A class discussion of students' findings would be a good way to conclude this project.

- Have students take an opinion poll of their peers' views on smoking. Are any of them considering smoking? If so, why? Do other students know the consequences of smoking? Do they understand that nicotine is addictive?

PROJECT OVERVIEW

Get the Message Out

In this chapter, you will be learning about how the respiratory system works. You will also study the harmful effects that smoking has on this system. It is well established that smoking is not good for people's health. Why, then, do so many people start smoking? Peer pressure and the desire to be accepted and look more mature have a lot to do with it. Additionally, many young smokers do not realize the health risks involved in smoking.

In this project you will examine both the reasons people begin smoking and the bad effects of this habit. You will then design three ads to discourage people in three different age groups from smoking. At the end of the project, you will present your ads to the class, explaining why you chose the messages and images that you did.

Project Rules

- You must design three different ads. The first ad should convince children aged 8 to 10 years old not to start smoking. The second ad should discourage teenagers from starting to smoke. The third ad should be targeted towards adults who smoke, convincing them to stop smoking.

- Each ad must describe at least three health risks that are associated with smoking.

- Each ad must deal with at least two pressures that encourage people to start or continue smoking.

- Have your teacher approve sketches of your ads before you begin making the final product.

Suggested Materials

- Poster board, large sheets of paper, markers, crayons, and colored pencils will be needed for designing posters. If you decide to do radio or television commercials, you will need to write scripts and bring in props, costumes, or equipment for making sound effects or accompanying music.

Project Hints

- Think about the different types of ads that you come across every day—in magazines, in newspapers, on buses, on the radio, on television, etc. Choose one of these types for getting your message across to your audience. You do not have to use the same type of medium for all of your ads.

- When designing your ad, make sure that you think about your audience. The same messages or images probably won't appeal to both children and adults.

Name _____ Date_____ Class_____

- Use the chapter in the textbook as a resource to find health risks associated with smoking. You will need to understand how a healthy respiratory system works before you can comprehend how smoking adversely affects it.

- Realize that different issues are important to people of different ages. Do not attempt to guess at what these issues may be for people in other age groups. Talk to friends and family members in the different age groups to discover reasons why people start to smoke or continue to smoke.

- You may want to interview children to find out what influences tempt them to smoke.

- You may want to interview adults who continue to smoke.

- There are many ways to present what you have learned. You can write a report, give a speech, draw illustrations with captions, or record a summary on videotape.

Project Timeline

Task	Due Date
1. Project Worksheet 1 completed.	_____
2. Interviews of people in the different age groups completed.	_____
3. Project Worksheet 2 completed.	_____
4. Sketches of all three ads approved.	_____
5. Final product completed.	_____
6. Class presentation and discussion prepared.	_____

Respiration and Excretion
Copyright © Pearson Education, Inc., or its affiliates. All rights reserved.

PROJECT WORKSHEET 1

What Makes an Ad Appealing?

The following tasks should help you begin to think about how you can create a convincing ad.

1. Search through printed ads in magazines or newspapers, or examine ads on radio or television. Find at least two ads for any product that you think would appeal to each of the age groups. You may want to ask a friend or family member in each age group to help you select the ads.

2. Use your ads to complete the following table.

Ad Analysis

Product Advertised	Brief Description of the Ad	Target Age Group	Why does this ad appeal to this age group?
		Children	
		Children	
		Teenagers	
		Teenagers	
		Adults	
		Adults	

PROJECT WORKSHEET 2

Designing Your Ads

Complete the following tasks. When your teacher has approved your sketches, you are ready to create your advertisements.

1. If you conducted interviews, what did you find out influences children ages 8 to 10 years old to begin smoking? What influences teenagers?

2. From your interviews, what did you find out are the reasons adults continue to smoke?

3. List six health risks that are associated with smoking. Which of these health risks do children think is most important? Which do teenagers think is most important? Which do adults think is most important?

4. What type of ad do you plan to create for each of the three age groups (poster, magazine, newspaper, radio, television, etc.)?

5. Sketch your layouts for each of your ads on another sheet of paper, including brief descriptions of the words and images that you will use.

6. Refer to your sketches and write a few sentences that describe why you have selected particular words and images. Explain why you think each ad will appeal to that particular age group.

SCORING RUBRIC

Get the Message Out

In evaluating how well you complete the Chapter Project, your teacher will judge your work in the following categories. In each, a score of 4 is the best rating.

	4	3	2	1
Planning Appropriate Ads for Specific Age Groups	Research of each age group is thorough and complete and reveals important differences between groups that are applied in the ads.	Research of each age group is fairly complete and reveals differences between groups that are applied in the ads.	Research is not thorough but does reveal some differences between groups that are applied in the ads.	Research about age group is scanty.
Creating Informative Ads	Each ad describes at least three health risks associated with smoking and addresses at least two pressures that encourage people in that age group to smoke. Information is clear and accurate and goes beyond the textbook.	Each ad describes three health risks associated with smoking and addresses at least two pressures that encourage people in that age gourp to smoke. Information is mostly clear and accurate.	Two of the three ads describe at least three health risks associated with smoking and addresses at least two pressures that encourage people in that age group to smoke. Information is accurate.	One ad meets minimum requirements but two lack health risks or pressures. Some information given is inaccurate. Student does not go beyond the textbook.
Presenting the Ads	Makes a thorough, well-organized presentation. For each ad, student explains why images and messages were chosen and why the ad would appeal to the age group.	Makes a good presentation. For each ad, student mostly explains why particular images and messages were chosen and why the ad would appeal to the specific age group.	Makes a fair presentation that is somewhat hard to follow. Student explains why some images and messages were chosen for the ads.	Presentation is hard to follow and has major gaps in explanation of why images and messages were chosen.

Make a Model of Earth

The following steps will walk you through the Chapter Project. Use the hints and detailed directions as you guide your students through design, construction, presentation, and reflection.

Chapter Project Overview

In this project, students will work in groups to make a scale model of Earth's interior, with features associated with plate tectonics added to the surface. The model should show the layers of Earth, plates and plate boundaries, sea-floor spreading, subduction, continents, and a rift valley.

In introducing the project, do the following demonstration.

1. Cut a whole melon in half, and display to the class the insides of one half. Ask students what materials they could use to make a model of the melon.

2. Then cut a quarter out of another whole melon by cutting down to the core from the top and from the side. Have students compare the quarter melon with the half melon. Ask: Which perspective gives a better view of what's inside a melon? Point out that models likewise can be of different perspectives, and in this project each group has the choice to develop its own type of model.

Distribute Project Overview. Review the Project Rules. You may also want to hand out the Scoring Rubric so students will understand what is expected of them.

Organize the class into small groups. Make sure students understand that each member will make sketches and develop a design for a model before meeting with other members. Members will then collaborate in creating the final design. Point out that as they progress through the chapter, they will add to the design of the group's model. Each student will also make sketches to revise the group's model.

Set a deadline for the project presentation and some interim dates for the different tasks, and have students copy the dates in their Project Timeline.

Distribute Project Worksheet 1. After students have read the worksheet, ask if they have any questions.

Review scales used on maps and models. Explain that a scale is the proportion used in determining the relationship of a model to the object it represents.

1. Point out scales on maps and globes. To help students who have trouble with the concept, have them use a map and its scale to calculate the distance between their home town and other cities.

2. Display various three-dimensional models, such as model airplanes or boats, and invite students' opinions on whether they were "made to scale," that is, whether the parts of the models are in proportion to the things they represent.

Point out that in their models students will make the interior layers of Earth to a scale. The surface features, though, should not be made to the same scale, because they would be too small.

Materials and Preparation

Though groups will decide for themselves what materials to use to make their models, you might want to provide some basic materials and tools.

Materials that could be used to make a model include papier-maché, modeling compound, chicken wire, cardboard, plywood, particle board, plastic foam, wood blocks, wire, paints, and permanent markers.

Tools that could be used in constructing the model include plastic knives, pliers, hand saws, glue guns, and paint brushes.

Keep Students on Track—Task 1

As you review the student's sketches, encourage students who lack ideas to talk with classmates about a general direction to take. Three different possibilities students might pursue are a wedge-shaped model, a sphere with a portion cut away, and a block model. You might share these ideas to help students make their sketches. Creative thinkers might imagine other ways to model Earth's interior.

Talk with each group during its initial meeting. Make sure members take each other's sketches and ideas seriously. At this point, students should think about the materials they will use for their models and begin collecting them.

Distribute Project Worksheet 2. Make sure students understand that they will need to work on this worksheet as they learn more about Earth's structure in the rest of the chapter. As in Worksheet 1, students should individually make sketches. These sketches, though, should build upon the group's design for the layers of Earth's interior.

Keep Students on Track—Task 4

Check to see that students have begun making sketches of surface features, including the mid-ocean ridge and a deep-ocean trench. Encourage students to share their sketches and ideas in their groups. Questions students should be asking themselves at this point in the project include, How can we show sea-floor spreading on the surface of the model? What new materials do we need to find?

Groups should begin building the base of their models. A base might be made of wood, plastic foam, or some other sturdy material.

Keep Students on Track—Task 5

Students' sketches should now show the full range of surface features related to plate tectonics, including three types of plate boundaries. Check students' folders to see that everyone is contributing something to the group's design process.

Encourage students to rethink their original models—there's still time to revise the design. Encourage them to review the Project Overview to make sure that their models include everything they are supposed to include.

Chapter Project Wrap Up

As you review each group's final model, you may wish to have the members "talk you through" the presentation. Make suggestions for organizing the presentation into a logical report. When appropriate, encourage some students to take a greater role in presenting the model.

Provide class time for group presentations. Allow each group to present its model and explain what the model shows. Encourage other students to ask questions about the design of the model, the materials, and the scale.

After all presentations have been made, discuss with students which models seemed to work best, that is, which were the best looking and which incorporated all the necessary features in the most instructive way.

Encourage students to evaluate how well they accomplished what they set out to do, including how well the final model matched the design that group members had agreed upon. Invite students to make suggestions about what they think would have made the project better.

Extension

Students might want to find a place in the school or in a community building to display their models. To make the models self-explanatory to those who know little about this topic, groups might prepare annotations on three-by-five cards. Another possibility is to make audio- or videotapes that provide a further explanation for what the models show.

PROJECT OVERVIEW
Make a Model of Earth

How can you make a model that shows both what's inside planet Earth and how the inside affects features on the surface? In this project, you will work in a group to design and create just such a model.

First, you will make sketches of your own design for a three-dimensional model of Earth's interior. Since your model of the interior will have to be to scale, you will need to use a scale in your sketches. Then you will meet with your group to review all members' designs and agree on a single design for a model of Earth's interior. As you and other group members learn more about plate tectonics, you will make new sketches for adding features of Earth's surface to your model. As you learn more about Earth's structure, you will want to make changes in the design of your model. At the end of the project, your group will present your finished three-dimensional model to the class.

Project Rules

- Devise a scale and make a sketch of the layers of Earth, as described in Project Worksheet 1. Keep any sketches you make in a Project Folder. You will show your sketch or sketches to your teacher and discuss your ideas for a model.

- With your group, review one another's sketches and ideas. Come to a consensus on a design for the model you want to build as a group, and begin collecting the materials you will need.

- Make sketches of surface features that you want to include on your model, including features associated with sea-floor spreading and plate boundaries as described in Project Worksheet 2. You will show your sketches to your teacher and discuss your ideas for a revised model.

- Begin building the base of your model as soon as possible. Then, as you learn new information, you can add to your design and build the model from the core out to the surface.

- With your group, revise your initial model to include surface features, including at least three plates, three plate boundaries, and two continents.

- With your group, prepare a presentation to the class of your completed model. As part of this presentation, you will explain what your model includes, what scale you used for the interior layers, and how your model shows how Earth's interior affects its surface.

Project Hints

- Look through textbooks and encyclopedias to find drawings that show Earth's interior and surface features. When you find one that looks interesting and informative, think of ways you could make that drawing into a three-dimensional model.

- As soon as possible, begin collecting the materials you will use to build your model. Your teacher may be able to provide some materials, but you will probably need to bring some materials and tools from home.

- Work closely with other members of your group, and listen to their ideas. You might find that someone in your group has just the right idea to make your own design a great deal better.

- Don't be afraid to change your group's design if it doesn't seem to come together well after you've begun construction.

- Make sure your model includes everything that is necessary to inform the viewer about plate tectonics.

- Try to make your model accurate and informative, but also try to make it as artistically pleasing as possible. Encourage members of your group who have artistic talents to put finishing touches on the model.

Project Timeline

Task	Due Date
1. Complete design and sketches for Worksheet 1	_____
2. Agree on a group design for model	_____
3. Collect and test materials	_____
4. Agree on how group will show surface features on model	_____
5. Finish collecting materials	_____
6. Construct final model	_____
7. Prepare class presentation	_____
8. Present the model to the class	_____

PROJECT WORKSHEET 1

A Scale Model of Earth's Interior

This worksheet will help you get started making a design for your model of Earth's interior.

Making Layers to Scale

1. What is the distance from the surface of Earth to the center?

_____ km

2. How large will your model be, from the outside to the center?

_____ cm

3. Divide your answer to Question 1 by the answer to Question 2 to calculate the scale you will use when building your model.

1 cm = _____ km

4. Name the layers of Earth that you will include in your model, and write how thick each one is. Then use another sheet of paper to compute the thickness of each layer to the scale you will be using.

Layer	Thickness	Thickness to Scale
	km	cm
	km	cm
	km	cm

Planning a Model of Earth

5. Write a description of the model you think your group should build.

_____

_____

_____

6. What materials will you need to build this model?

_____

_____

_____

7. On a separate sheet of paper, make a sketch of a model your group could build. Keep the sketch in your Project Folder. Take this worksheet and your sketch to your group meeting. Talk over your ideas with group members.

PROJECT WORKSHEET 2

Adding Surface Features to the Model

Now that you've learned more about the structure of Earth, you will want to make some changes to your model design. This worksheet will help you organize these changes. Use the back of this sheet if you need more space.

Sea-Floor Spreading

1. What features must be added to show sea-floor spreading on the model?

   _____

   _____

2. What features must be added to show the process of subduction?

   _____

   _____

3. What materials could be used to add these features to the model?

   _____

   _____

Plate Tectonics

4. Briefly describe three plate boundaries that could be added to the model.

   _____

   _____

5. How could convection currents be shown in the model?

   _____

   _____

6. What other features of the surface should also be included in the model?

   _____

   _____

7. What materials could be used to add these features to the model?

   _____

   _____

8. On a separate sheet of paper, make a sketch of the revised model that your group could build. Keep the sketch in your Project Folder. Take this worksheet and your sketch to your group meeting. Talk over your ideas with group members. Then construct the final model.

SCORING RUBRIC

Make a Model of Earth

In evaluating how well you complete the Chapter Project, your teacher will judge your work in four categories. In each, a score of 4 is the best rating.

	4	3	2	1
Creating Individual Sketches and Designs	Makes sketches that show originality of design and a thorough understanding of Earth's interior and plate tectonics.	Makes sketches that show some originality of design and a good understanding of Earth's interior and plate tectonics.	Makes sketches that show an adequate design and some understanding of Earth's interior and plate tectonics.	Makes sketches that show an incomplete or inappropriate design and little understanding of Earth's interior and plate tectonics.
Constructing Model of a Cut-Away Earth	Model is well constructed and includes Earth's layers made to scale, at least three plates and plate boundaries, two continents, and clear, accurate labels of all features on the model.	Model is constructed adequately and includes Earth's layers made to scale, at least two plates and plate boundaries, two continents, and accurate labels of all features on the model.	Model construction is a little sloppy, and model is missing one or two features. Accurate labels of most features on the model are included.	Model is poorly constructed and missing two or more major features. Labels are incomplete, inaccurate, or missing.
Presenting the Model to the Class	Makes a thorough and interesting presentation that includes a clear, accurate explanation of what the model shows about Earth's layers and plate tectonics.	Makes a thorough presentation that includes a satisfactory explanation of what the model shows about Earth's layers and plate tectonics.	Makes a presentation that includes a partial explanation of what the model shows about Earth's layers and plate tectonics.	Makes a presentation that includes an incomplete and/or inaccurate explanation of what the model shows about Earth's layers and plate tectonics.
Participating in the Group	Takes a lead in planning, constructing, and presenting the model.	Participates in all aspects of planning, constructing, and presenting the model.	Participates in most aspects of planning, constructing, and presenting the model.	Plays a minor role in planning, constructing, and presenting the model.

Design and Build an Earthquake-Safe House

The following steps will walk you through the Chapter Project. Use the hints and detailed directions as you guide your students through designing, testing, revising, retesting, finalizing, and presenting their models.

Chapter Project Overview

When you introduce the project by having students build and test simple toothpick-and-tape models, ask them to suggest ways to make their models stronger. List their ideas on the board, and suggest that students copy the list for their reference when they build and improve the models for the project. Some ideas may not apply to the materials that students use for the actual models, but other ideas may be useful or at least adaptable for other materials and building designs.

After students have read the description in the textbook, distribute the Project Overview. Review and discuss each of the project goals. Identify the materials that you will provide, and ask students to suggest others. Also tell students that they can add other materials later as ideas occur to them.

Lead the class to discuss and agree on a list of specifications for the models. Such specifications could include minimum and maximum dimensions for the model (very low structures, for example, will not be susceptible to much earthquake damage), a prohibition on solid models or ones made from construction toys such as Legos™ and Tinker Toys™, and restrictions on the amount of bracing or support material that can be added to a model. Explain that the choice of materials affects how realistic the model will be, so, for example, the scale and strength of the materials should be proportional to the strength of the simulated earthquake. As students agree on specifications, list them on an overhead transparency or on the chalk board, and then make copies of the list to distribute to students.

Students will also need to agree on parameters for the simulated earthquakes so that all models will be subjected to the same stresses and so that earthquake intensity can be increased in each test. One easy way for students to determine and control earthquake strength is to tape a strip of adding-machine tape to the floor or to the table next to the one being used as the base and then mark the strip to show how far to shake the base back and forth for each earthquake intensity. Movements might range from 5 cm for a minor quake to 7.5 cm for a moderate quake and up to 12.5 cm for a major quake. Also let the class decide how long each earthquake will last—perhaps 5 back-and-forth shakes for a minor quake, 10 shakes for a moderate quake, and 15 shakes for a major quake.

Set a deadline for the project presentation and some interim dates for the different tasks. Have students record these dates in the Project Timeline of the Project Overview.

At or before the end of Task 1, distribute Project Worksheet 1, which explains how to make scale drawings and provides an example for practice. Check students' worksheet answers and practice drawings. If students had difficulty with the example, review it as a class and provide additional practice examples.

Project Worksheet 2 is designed to prompt students' thinking about ways to make their models more earthquake-resistant. Use this worksheet at any point in the project. As students experiment, encourage creativity. Afterward, give students an opportunity to share their ideas and results.

Keep Students on Track—Task 1

When students discuss their initial plans with one another, encourage them to do so in a spirit of cooperative problem solving, not competition. Also remind students that their first design is not expected to be earthquake-proof. Assure them that they will have ample opportunity to test their designs, revise them, retest them, and make improvements before they present their final models to the class.

If any students are having difficulty devising a plan, meet with them individually to offer guidance and support. Also encourage them to talk further with other students to get ideas.

Keep Students on Track—Task 2

To ensure that all models are subjected to the same earthquake intensities in the test, have students review the parameters they agreed on earlier. Let students practice the shaking movements necessary to produce a minor, a moderate, and a major quake until they are able to repeat them consistently.

Make sure that students have some idea what to look for as evidence of earthquake damage (for example, a broken pretzel "support beam," a torn tape "bracket" attaching two beams, or a torn tissue-paper "wall").

Encourage students to examine other students' models that were more successful in withstanding the earthquakes to get ideas for improving their own models.

Keep Students on Track—Tasks 3–4

If necessary, replenish the supply of construction materials you have provided so that students have a wide range of materials available for improving their models. Also be sure to provide materials suitable for modeling the base-isolation construction method described in the text. Such materials might include thin pieces of foam rubber, rubber washers, cotton batting, pieces of carpet padding, and small springs. Ask students for their ideas about other materials that could be used, and add those to the supply. Also let students use materials they have brought from home.

Remind students of the deadline for the class presentation. Also remind students that you will be rating their presentations as well as their models. Emphasize that being well prepared for the presentation is more important than devising a "perfect" model that sustains no earthquake damage at all.

Chapter Project Wrap Up

Allot sufficient time for each student to present his or her final model and to explain how and why changes were made after each test. Give each presenter positive feedback, not only on the model itself but also on the student's efforts to identify and address any weaknesses in the design as the model was tested.

After the class presentations, students might like to stage a "Quake-Off" to determine whose model is most resistant to earthquake damage. Students could begin by testing several models at a time at the lowest earthquake intensity and eliminating any models that sustain damage. In a second test, the models that survived the first round could be tested at a moderate intensity and damaged models could again be eliminated. Continue in this fashion until one or more final survivors are determined. You may want to present a "Best Earthquake-Resistant Design" to those students, but also give all students positive feedback on their efforts.

Extension

Encourage students to implement and test any ideas they have about improving their models, either ideas of their own or ideas they have gained from other students' presentations.

PROJECT OVERVIEW

Design and Build an Earthquake-Safe House

What construction methods and materials make structures stronger in an earthquake? In this project, you will try to answer that question by designing, building, and testing your own model structure. You could model a house, an apartment building, an office building, a factory, a bridge, a highway overpass, or any other real-life structure.

First, you will design a model, choose materials to build it, and discuss your plans with your classmates. After you learn more about earthquakes, you will complete your design and construct your model. You also should ask a classmate to review your model and suggest improvements. You will then test your model to see how well it withstands a simulated earthquake. After you learn about how engineers make structures earthquake-resistant, you will repair and improve your model, test it again, and make any final changes. At the end of the project, you will present your model to the class.

Project Rules

- With your classmates, decide on rules for building the models. For example, what should be the minimum and maximum size for the models? What kinds of construction materials should *not* be used? If you and your classmates make models that are *too* strong, you won't be modeling actual structures realistically.

- With your classmates, decide on a way to model earthquakes of different intensities. Remember, your model should be able to withstand minor, moderate, and major earthquakes. Practice making earthquakes until you can create the right intensities for each test.

- Design your model, and discuss your plans with your classmates. Draw your model to scale, and list the materials you plan to use.

- Construct your model. Ask a classmate to review it and suggest improvements. After you have made changes, test your model with simulated earthquakes. Make notes about how well your model survived the earthquakes. Pay particular attention to any parts of the model that did not function well and could be improved.

- Repair and improve your model. Then test it again to see whether your changes worked. If they didn't, make additional improvements.

- In a class presentation, explain how and why you changed your model. Then test your model for the last time. Make notes about how well it survived a major earthquake.

Suggested Materials

Your teacher will provide a variety of materials for constructing the models. You and your classmates may have other ideas, too. Be creative!

- **To represent beams, rafters, and support columns:** You could use popsicle sticks, straight pretzels, toothpicks, wooden dowels, drinking straws, uncooked pasta, or bread sticks.

- **To represent walls, ceilings, roofs, and other surfaces:** Use materials that can crack or break under stress, rather than strong, stiff materials such as index cards or cardboard. Try thin crackers, tissue paper, or aluminum foil.

- **To join the pieces:** You could use masking tape or clear tape, glue, rubber cement, gumdrops, small marshmallows, clay, staples, or paper clips.

- **To make a base-isolated building:** Use flexible materials such as foam rubber, rubber washers, marshmallows, cotton batting, pieces of carpet padding, or small springs.

- **To simulate an earthquake:** Attach your model to a sturdy, flat base such as a tray, a piece of plywood, or a small table. Hold the base at opposite ends and shake it back and forth. (You could ask a classmate to make the earthquake for you while you watch your model.)

Hints for Building Your Model

- Before you construct the entire model, build important parts of it to see how well your design and the materials you chose work. For example, if you think that support beams will make the walls stronger, first build just one wall to try your idea.

- As you study this chapter, you will do activities that may give you ideas about how to make your model stronger. Write down your ideas so that you don't forget them. When you test your model and are ready to improve it, review your list of ideas.

Project Timeline

Task	Due Date
1. Design model and choose building materials	_____
2. Construct, test, and improve model	_____
3. Test model again; then repair and improve it	_____
4. Present model to the class	_____

PROJECT WORKSHEET 1
Drawing Your Model to Scale

When you draw the model you plan to build, draw it to scale. "To scale" means that each measurement unit on your drawing will represent a certain measurement unit on the real model. For example, if you use a scale of 1 cm = 3 cm, each centimeter on the drawing will represent three centimeters on the real model. With a scale of 1 cm = 1 cm, your drawing would be the same size as your model.

First, make a scale drawing of your model's floor plan to show what the model will look like from above. Then make a scale drawing of the largest wall to show what the model will look like from the side. Follow the steps below to practice making scale drawings.

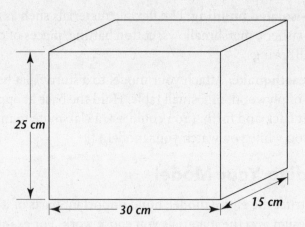

Suppose that you want to build a model with the dimensions shown in the figure above. Your graph paper is 28 centimeters long and 21.5 centimeters wide. You can't draw the model full size because it won't fit on the graph paper.

1. First decide what scale to use. What scale would let you fit both a floor plan and the largest wall drawing on the same sheet of graph paper?

_____

(*Hint:* Make the drawings as large as possible so that you can follow them easily when you build the model.)

2. With this scale, what would be the dimensions of the drawing?

Length: _____ Width: _____ Height: _____

3. Use these scale dimensions to make two scale drawings—one of the floor plan and one of the largest wall. Make both drawings on the same sheet of graph paper. Use graph paper with half-centimeter squares. Label the drawings *Floor Plan* and *Largest Wall.* At the bottom of the graph paper, write the scale you used for the drawings.

PROJECT WORKSHEET 2

Making Your Model More Earthquake-Resistant

Designers include supports in buildings to make them stronger. This activity will help you think of ways to make your model more earthquake-resistant.

Materials

- 6–8 drinking straws
- scissors
- masking tape or clear tape
- tissue paper
- glue
- 6–8 toothpicks

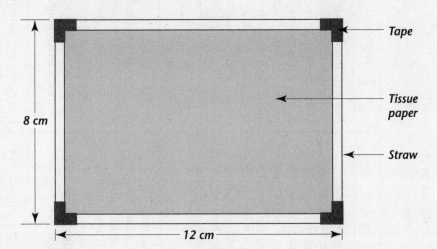

Procedure

Review the safety guidelines in your textbook.

1. Cut one straw into two pieces—one piece about 12 centimeters long and the other piece about 8 centimeters long. Cut another straw the same way.

2. Tape the four pieces of straw together to make a rectangular frame, as shown in the figure above. Use just one or two *small* pieces of tape at each corner.

3. Cut a piece of tissue paper the same size as the frame. Tape or glue the paper to the frame to make a model wall.

4. Lay the wall flat on your desk. Hold down one bottom corner with one hand. With the other hand, push the opposite top corner about 2 centimeters sideways. What happens to the straw frame? What happens to the paper?

5. Repeat Step 4, but this time keep pushing the top corner until the frame collapses. What happens to the paper?

6. Repair the wall, or make another one.

7. Now try to make the wall more "push-resistant." Use more straws and toothpicks. (You can cut them into smaller pieces if you like.) Try different ways to make the wall stronger. Which ways work best? What other materials could you use?

SCORING RUBRIC

Design and Build an Earthquake-Safe House

In evaluating how well you complete the Chapter Project, your teacher will judge your work in three categories. In each, a score of 4 is the best rating.

	4	3	2	1
Designing, Building, Testing, and Improving the Model	Makes imaginative use of construction methods and materials; carefully tests model and notes results; uses creativity in devising improvements; final model withstands a major earthquake with little or no damage.	Makes good use of construction methods and materials; tests model at all designated stages and notes results; identifies and resolves most major design flaws and weaknesses; final model withstands only a moderate earthquake.	Makes limited use of construction methods and materials; does not carefully follow project rules for testing model and makes few notes about results; makes some attempt to resolve design flaws and weaknesses; final model withstands only a minor earthquake.	Makes poor use of construction methods and materials; does not test model and/or note design flaws; makes little or no attempt to improve model; final model sustains significant damage in a minor earthquake.
Presenting the Model	Explains all construction problems identified in testing and their resolutions; presentation is interesting, clear, and well organized.	Explains most construction problems identified in testing and their resolutions; presentation is interesting and fairly well organized.	Explains some construction problems identified in testing but does not explain their resolutions clearly; presentation lacks interest, clarity, and/or organization.	Does not explain construction problems and their resolutions; presentation is unclear and disorganized.
Working Cooperatively with Classmates	Readily offers suggestions to classmates in a noncritical manner; thoughtfully considers others' suggestions for improving own model.	Offers some suggestions to classmates; accepts others' suggestions for improving own model.	Offers few suggestions to classmates; makes little attempt to implement others' suggestions for improving own model	Offers no suggestions to classmates; makes no attempt to implement others' suggestions for improving own model.

Growing a Crystal Garden

The following steps will walk you through the Chapter Project. Use the hints and detailed directions as you guide your students through the creation of their crystal gardens, data collection, presentation, and reflection.

Chapter Project Overview

In this project, students will work either individually or in small groups to design and create a crystal garden and then observe and compare growth of several types of crystals. Each garden should include an attractive garden scene using common materials as well as at least two kinds of crystals.

To introduce the project, focus students' attention on pictures of mineral crystals, either in their text or in books about minerals. Explain that in this project they will be growing similar crystals from chemicals in solutions. Then show students pictures of garden scenes, such as famous English or Japanese gardens. Point out how the shapes and colors create an attractive whole.

Distribute the Project Overview. Review the Project Rules. You may also want to hand out the Scoring Rubric so students will understand what is expected of them.

If appropriate, organize the class into pairs or small groups. The advantages of using groups include fewer materials needed and more collaboration among students of differing abilities. The advantage of individual gardens is that each student will gain more experience with growing crystals.

Set a deadline for the presentation and some interim dates for the different tasks. Have students copy the dates in their Project Timeline.

Distribute Project Worksheet 1. After students have read the worksheet, ask if they have any questions.

Materials and Preparation

Perhaps the best container for a crystal garden is a clear plastic shoe box. Gather enough of these for each student or group, or ask that students find their own containers. Any large, clear container could be appropriate.

The objects used for crystal substrates can be practically anything, though materials that are porous work best to hold the solutions and crystals. Good objects include charcoal, plastic foam, sponges, and cotton swabs. Many such materials can be made into shapes that will make attractive or representational scenes.

With Project Worksheet 2, students will create a salt solution to begin making crystals. Point out that they can do the procedure more than once, each time adding a different color of food coloring. In that way they can create a more attractive garden, though the salt crystals will always be the same shape.

Prepare ahead of time several other solutions for students' use. Various chemicals that you can purchase at a pharmacy or grocery store can be used. These include sugar (sucrose), Epsom salts, alum (aluminum potassium sulfate), and magnesium sulfate. Each chemical will produce a different crystal shape, from cubes to long, thin needles.

To prepare an alum or Epsom salts solution, follow this procedure. The resulting solution will be enough for five or six groups, depending on the size of their garden containers.

1. Heat 600 mL of water. Do not bring to boil.

2. Add 120 g of alum or 70 g of Epsom salts to warm water. Stir occasionally until the chemical has dissolved.

3. Pour the solution into a 1-L jar and seal it with a lid. Allow to cool over 24 hours. Then add a pinch of alum or Epsom salts to initiate precipitation. Shake twice a day. Add different colors of food coloring to different batches of solution.

4. When groups' gardens are ready, pour the solution (minus any precipitate) into a new jar and warm it again. Add an additional 24 g of alum or 10 g of Epsom salts to make sure the solution is saturated.

Prepare additional solutions with other chemicals in a similar way. Remember, the goal is to make saturated solutions that will readily grow crystals. Water temperature is the key to creating such a solution. Warmer water will dissolve more solute; as the solution cools, precipitation will occur.

Keep Students on Track—Tasks 1–5

As you review each student's materials list and sketches from Worksheet 1, encourage those who lack ideas to talk to classmates to gather more ideas.

Distribute Worksheet 2. Then provide each student or group with the materials needed to prepare the salt solution. An alternative to using the hot plate is to have students use hot tap water.

Demonstrate how to use the plastic dropper to add solution to an object in a garden scene.

Emphasize that students need to make an accurate map of their gardens and the places where each solution has been added. Without a map, students will forget what kind of crystal is growing where.

Provide different kinds of solutions for students to add to their scenes. Make sure each plastic dropper is used for only one kind of solution.

Keep Students on Track—Tasks 6–8

As you check the gardens, make sure students are having some success in growing crystals. Help any who are having trouble.

Make sure students are keeping a daily record of crystal growth, complete with sketches of the different kinds of crystals.

Discuss how students could compare the growth of different kinds of crystals. This might be a line or bar graph or a detailed paragraph.

Chapter Project Wrap Up

Examine each student's or group's crystal garden before their presentation. Have students "walk you through" what they will say, and make suggestions about logical sequence or any missing information in their report. If this is a group project, make sure all group members plan to participate.

Provide class time for the presentations. Allow each student or group to present the garden, with an emphasis on the materials used and the crystals grown. Encourage other students to ask questions.

After all presentations have been made, discuss with students which crystal gardens were best, both in design and results.

Encourage students to evaluate how well they created the garden they planned to create, how attractive their garden scenes were, and how well their crystals grew. Stress that they should identify in their journals ways in which they could have made their gardens better.

Extension

Have interested students draw from scenes of a variety of students or groups to make a large crystal garden in an aquarium. Then find a place in the school to display their creation.

PROJECT OVERVIEW
Growing a Crystal Garden

If you've ever seen a well-made garden, you've seen a work of art. A good gardener doesn't just plant flowers and bushes in any old place. Instead, each plant is considered for its color and shape as the gardener strives to make a pleasing whole impression. In this project, you have a chance to design and create a garden, but with crystals rather than plants.

First, you'll build a three-dimensional garden scene, using materials supplied by your teacher as well as materials you bring from home. This garden scene can be either a model of some landscape you've seen or an artistic creation of your own. Next, you'll prepare and add solutions to the objects in your garden scene, recording on a detailed map where each solution was added. From these solutions crystals will grow. You'll keep track of the growth of each kind of crystal, making sketches and recording growth data. At the end of the project, you'll present your crystal garden to the class.

Project Rules

- Complete Project Worksheet 1 by making a list of materials you could use to create a three-dimensional garden scene and by making a sketch of a possible garden.

- Collect the materials you will use to create your garden.

- Create a garden scene. This could be either a representation of a real landscape or an artistic creation using shapes and colors to make a pleasing effect.

- Follow Project Worksheet 2 to make a salt solution, and add it to your garden scene. Then add other solutions supplied by your teacher.

- Make a detailed map of your garden that includes exactly where you "planted" each kind of crystal. If your map is not accurate or doesn't include enough labels, your observations of crystal growth will be flawed.

- As your crystals grow, make sketches that accurately show the shape of each kind. At first, your sketches might be rough. Toward the end of the project, make a good sketch of each kind of crystal you've grown.

- Take and record measurements of each kind of crystal. You can do this with a metric ruler or some other measuring device. Record your measurements in a data table or a daily journal. You'll want to record when crystals begin growing, how much they grow each day, and when they stop growing.

- Make a comparison of the growth of the different crystals. You could do this in writing or with some kind of graph, depending on the data you've kept.

- Prepare a presentation to the class of your crystal garden. As part of this presentation, you will describe the materials you used to build your garden and the types of crystals grown. You will also show sketches of your crystals and present a comparison of the growth of each kind of crystal.

Project Hints

- As soon as possible, begin collecting the materials you will use to create your garden. These include a container and various objects on which your crystals will grow. Your teacher may be able to provide some materials, but you will probably want to bring some materials from home.

- Be as creative as you can in planning and building your garden scene. Remember, if your materials are unique to your garden, your garden will be different from all others in the class.

- You can make your garden scene like a realistic landscape, with mountains, rivers, forests, and so on. Or you could make an attractive scene just by using artistic shapes and colors, like a modern painting.

- Talk with your teacher and other class members about ways to take measurements of crystal growth and ways to compare those measurements.

- As you prepare for your presentation, think of what you want to say and the order in which you want to present the information. You may want to make notes on index cards to help you remember what you want to say.

Project Timeline

Task	Due Date
1. Complete Worksheet 1	_____
2. Gather materials needed for garden scene	_____
3. Create three-dimensional garden scene	_____
4. Review plans with your teacher	_____
5. Prepare solution with Worksheet 2	_____
6. Add solutions to garden, recording on map	_____
7. Prepare comparison of crystal growth rates	_____
8. Make sketches of crystals grown	_____
9. Present your crystal garden to class	_____

PROJECT WORKSHEET 1

Creating a Crystal Garden

To get started on creating a crystal garden, you need to think about the materials you will use and the garden scene you will make.

Materials

What materials can you use to make an attractive garden scene? Make a list below of possibilities of objects on which you could grow crystals. Porous materials, such as charcoal, plastic foam, and sponges will work best.

1. Possible container:

_____

_____

2. Possible materials:

_____

_____

_____

_____

Garden Scene

What will your garden scene look like when completed? Make a sketch in the space below of an attractive garden scene that you would like to create.

If you're working in a group, take this design to a group meeting and present your ideas to the other members for consideration. If you're creating your garden alone, show this design to other classmates and ask for advice and criticism. Then show it to your teacher.

Name _____ Date _____ Class _____

PROJECT WORKSHEET 2

Getting Started With Salt Crystals

Your crystal garden must contain at least two different kinds of crystals, though it may contain more. Your teacher will provide solutions to grow some kinds of crystals. The procedure here will give you a chance to prepare your own salt solution from which you can grow salt crystals.

Materials

- hot plate
- pan
- salt
- tablespoon

- food coloring
- water
- clean jar with lid
- plastic dropper

Procedure   *Review the safety guidelines in your textbook.*

1. Cover the bottom of the pan with water, and heat the water almost to boiling on the hot plate.

2. Pour salt into the hot water, stirring as you pour. Add salt until no more salt dissolves into the water.

3. Allow the salt solution to cool slightly, and then pour it into the jar and screw on the lid. Allow the water to cool for 24 hours.

4. Remove with a spoon any salt crystals that have formed overnight. Or, you can shake the jar twice a day until no more salt crystals form.

5. Pour the solution back into the pan and reheat on the hot plate. When the water is hot but not boiling, add a tablespoon of salt to the solution and stir.

6. Use a plastic dropper to add food coloring, and stir the solution.

7. Use a plastic dropper to cover objects in your garden scene with the salt solution. Add enough solution to saturate the objects, but do not add so much that you create standing puddles. Remember that you will want to cover some objects with other kinds of solutions.

8. Observe the growth of crystals within two to four days.

230
Minerals and Rocks

SCORING RUBRIC

Growing a Crystal Garden

In evaluating how well you complete the Chapter Project, your teacher will judge your work in the following categories. In each, a score of 4 is the best rating.

	4	3	2	1
Creating a Crystal Garden Scene	Garden scene is creatively designed and attractive and contains well-formed examples of at least four kinds of crystals.	Garden scene is carefully designed and attractive and contains well-formed examples of at least three kinds of crystals.	Garden scene is partially designed and fairly attractive and contains examples of at least two kinds of crystals.	Garden scene does not appear to be well planned and contains examples of only one or two kinds of crystals.
Recording Crystal Growth	Makes well-drawn sketches of each kind of crystal as well as accurate measurements and comparisons of crystal growth.	Makes sketches of each kind of crystal as well as measurements and comparisons of most crystal growth.	Makes sketches of each kind of crystal as well as some measurements and comparisons of crystal growth.	Makes sketches of some crystals; measurements and comparisons of crystal growth are incomplete.
Presenting the Crystal Garden	Makes a thorough and interesting presentation that includes a good explanation of materials used and a logical comparison of crystals grown.	Makes an adequate presentation of the system that includes a clear explanation of materials used and a comparison of crystals grown.	Makes a presentation of the system that includes a partial explanation of materials used and some comparison of crystals grown.	Makes a presentation of the system that includes a weak explanation of materials used and an incomplete comparison of crystals grown.
Participating in the Group (optional)	Takes a lead in planning, creating, and presenting the crystal garden.	Participates in all aspects of planning, creating, and presenting the crystal garden.	Participates in most aspects of planning, creating, and presenting the crystal garden.	Participates minimally in planning, creating, and presenting the crystal garden.

Plates Move!

The following steps will walk you through the Chapter Project. Use the hints and detailed directions as you guide your students through the research, design, and construction of models, and the presentation to the class.

Chapter Project Overview

In this project, students will work in small groups to identify through research specific examples of the different types of plate boundaries, make sketches of the three types, and then use their sketches to make a model of one of the three types.

To introduce this project, show students a map of the tectonic plates that make up Earth's surface. Point out the boundaries between plates. Explain that at each boundary, movement is occurring. Some plates are moving away from each other, some plates are moving into each other, and some plates are moving past each other. Tell students that these movements are the cause of many geologic features on land and under the sea, including mountains, volcanoes, and valleys. Explain that this Chapter Project will help them better understand the significance of plate boundaries.

Have students read the Project Overview. Review the Project Rules, and ask if students have any questions. Hand out the Scoring Rubric, which you will use for scoring students' work. Discuss with students what will be expected of them.

Set a deadline for the presentation of research and model. Also set interim dates for the completion of the first part of Project Worksheet 1, research and the table on Worksheet 1, student sketches, and the finished model. Encourage students to record these dates on the Project Timeline.

Divide the class into small groups. Explain to students that in this Chapter Project there are tasks they will do on their own and tasks that group members will do together. Group tasks include: conducting research to complete the table on Worksheet 1, making a model of one type of plate boundary, and presenting to the class.

Distribute copies of Project Worksheet 1. Give students time to answer the questions at the top of the worksheet using their student text. Have students answer the questions individually, but allow them to meet with their groups to compare and revise answers. Encourage students to work together to complete the table.

Distribute copies of Project Worksheet 2. Tell students they should answer the questions and make the sketches on their own. Explain that making sketches of each type of plate boundary is good preparation for creating a model of one of the boundaries.

After students have completed Worksheet 2, have each group get together to construct its model. You might assign each group the type of boundary to model so that the three types are well distributed among the groups. You can do this by having a member of each group pick a slip of paper out of a hat containing names of real-world boundaries. Ask each group what materials they plan to use before they begin making models.

Materials and Preparation

Students will need access to research materials to identify specific examples of the three different kinds of plate boundaries. Internet access will be helpful. If that is difficult for some students, provide upper-level Earth science textbooks.

Members of each group should decide what materials they will use to make the model. You may want to provide some basic materials, such as wooden boards or poster board as a base, modeling compound of different colors, papier-mâché, wooden blocks, markers, and paints. Student might need such tools as paint brushes, plastic knives, and glue guns.

Keep Students on Track—Task 1

By answering the questions on Worksheet 1, students should gain an understanding of basic information about plate boundaries before they begin their research. Tell students they can answer the questions using their text, but they should answer the questions on their own. After students have completed the questions, they can meet with their group to make sure all members understand the material.

Keep Students on Track—Task 2

As groups begin their research to the complete the table on Worksheet 1, advise students to focus not only on finding examples of each type of plate boundary but also on identifying the results of plate movement at each boundary. Results of plate movements include mountain ranges, volcanoes, earthquakes, deep-sea trenches, island arcs, and rift valleys. Examples of divergent boundaries include the boundaries at the Mid-Atlantic Ridge and Great Rift Valley in East Africa. A good example of a convergent boundary is the collision of the Indian Plate and the Eurasian Plate, which resulted in the rise of the Himalayas. The best example of a transform boundary is the San Andreas fault in California, but other examples include a boundary on New Zealand and one near the Dead Sea.

Keep Students on Track—Task 3

Before students begin Worksheet 2, point out the illustrations of each type of plate boundary in their text. You may want to provide other examples from higher-level Earth science textbooks or from Internet sources. Emphasize to students that their sketches should clearly show the type of movement occurring at each plate boundary. Suggest they use arrows to show direction of movement.

Keep Students on Track—Task 4

After students have completed Worksheet 2, either assign groups a plate boundary to model or have them choose by picking names out of a hat. Then, provide materials for groups to use for making their model, though students could also use materials they bring to class. Tell students that their model should be on a base, such as a board or poster board. Remind them to refer to their sketches as they construct their model.

Chapter Project Wrap Up

As students prepare for their presentations, visit each group to see if students have organized their talk. Make suggestions about what to emphasize or omit. Stress that all group members should participate in the presentation.

Provide class time for groups to present their research and model. After each presentation, encourage other students to ask thoughtful questions.

After all presentations have been made, discuss with students why the theory of plate tectonics is important for understanding many geologic features.

Extension

Students can research the plates, structures, and events associated with the Ring of Fire around the Pacific Ocean. The name comes from the many volcanoes that border the ocean, and these volcanoes are the result of collisions between oceanic and continental plates.

PROJECT OVERVIEW

Plates Move!

According to the theory of plate tectonics, Earth's lithosphere is broken into plates, and those plates move. As they move, they collide, spread apart, or slip past each other. These interactions between plates occur at plate boundaries. The movements of tectonic plates have resulted in many geographic features both on land and the ocean floor.

In this Chapter Project, you will work on your own and with a group to learn about the three different types of plate boundaries. First you will answer questions about plate tectonics using information from your text. Then, you will conduct research to find specific examples on Earth's surface of each type of plate boundary. You will sketch the three types of plate boundaries and use these sketches to make a model of one type of boundary using materials of your choice. Finally, you will present the results of your research and your model to the class.

Project Rules

- Answer the questions at the top of Project Worksheet 1 on your own. You can find the answers to these questions in your text.

- With your group, use library resources, other textbooks, or the Internet to find and identify examples of each of the three types of plate boundaries. Your text gives an example of each type, but you should try to find other examples. Complete the table on Worksheet 1 with the information you find.

- Complete Project Worksheet 2 on your own. You can use your text as a resource to write the definitions of the different plate boundaries and to make sketches of the boundaries.

- With your group, choose materials you will use to construct a model of a plate boundary. Your teacher will help you choose which specific boundary on Earth you'll construct. The model should accurately show the type of interactions that can occur between plates at that particular boundary. You will be asked to submit to your teacher a list of all the materials you will need to complete this task.

- With your group, make a presentation to the class of your model and the research you've done for your plate boundary. You should be able to explain in detail where it is located, what type of plate boundary it is, and the history of the area (such as major earthquakes or mountain ranges).

Name _____ Date _____ Class _____

Suggested Materials

- Modeling compound, papier-mâché, or wooden blocks are useful to make your models, but you can choose other materials with your teacher's approval.

- Use paint and paint brushes or markers to show land or deep-sea features on your models.

Hints for Doing Research and Building Your Models

- Use information and illustrations from your text to answer the questions on Worksheet 1 and make your sketches on Worksheet 2. You may need to read ahead of what you've already been assigned.

- You could start your research by looking in Earth science textbooks or books at the library about plate tectonics. The Internet might be your most valuable resource. Use an Internet search engine to find reliable websites about the following topics: plate tectonics, Earth's tectonic plates, divergent plate boundary, convergent plate boundary, transform plate boundary.

- Note the examples of each type of plate boundary given in your text. Look up those examples on the Internet to see if other examples are mentioned.

- Decide as a group what materials you will use to construct your model. Divide responsibility for bringing materials to class, if necessary.

- For your presentation, you should include detailed information about a specific example of a plate boundary than you could include in the table on Worksheet 1. Consider using a world map to show where your example is located. You can also include a timeline to show the major events that have occurred at your plate boundary.

Project Timeline

Task	Due Date
1. Answer the questions on Project Worksheet 1	_____
2. Complete the table on Project Worksheet 1	_____
3. Complete Project Worksheet 2	_____
4. Complete the model of a plate boundary	_____
5. Make the class presentation	_____

PROJECT WORKSHEET 1
Plate Tectonics

Answer the following questions on a separate sheet of paper.

1. What is the theory of plate tectonics?

2. What are the three types of tectonic plate boundaries?

3. What has caused changes in the location of Earth's continents over time?

4. What causes Earth's plates to move?

Plate Boundaries Around the World

Research Earth's tectonic plates to complete the table below.

Plate Boundaries

Type of Boundary	Example and Location	Result of Plate Movement	Source(s) of Information
Divergent Boundary			
Convergent Boundary			
Transform Boundary			

PROJECT WORKSHEET 2

Models of Plate Boundaries

Before you construct the model of a plate boundary, it is important for you to have a good understanding of what is involved with each type of boundary. You should be able to picture what happens at each type of boundary, and you should also be able to explain what happens. This worksheet will help you start thinking about your model of a plate boundary.

Three Types of Plate Boundaries

1. What happens at a divergent plate boundary? _____

_____

Make a drawing of a divergent plate boundary in the space below.

2. What happens at a convergent plate boundary? _____

_____

Make a drawing of a convergent plate boundary in the space below.

3. What happens at a transform plate boundary? _____

_____

Make a drawing of a transform plate boundary in the space below.

SCORING RUBRIC
Plates Move!

In evaluating how well you complete the Chapter Project, your teacher will judge your work in four categories. In each, a score of 4 is the best rating.

	4	3	2	1
Researching Examples of Plate Boundaries	The research is thorough, excellent examples are given for each boundary type, and reliable sources are provided.	The research is adequate, good examples are given for each boundary type, and reliable sources are provided.	The research is incomplete, fewer than three examples are given, and sources provided are not reliable.	The research is incomplete, poor or no examples are given for boundary types, and no resources are provided.
Sketching the Three Types of Plate Boundaries	Student correctly defines and accurately sketches each of the three plate boundaries.	Student correctly defines and sketches the three plate boundaries.	Student correctly defines and sketches only one or two of the three plate boundaries.	Student incorrectly defines and/or sketches all three types of plate boundaries.
Making a Model of a Plate Boundary	Model is well constructed and shows the correct type of movement between plates.	Model is adequately constructed and shows the correct type of movement between plates.	Model is poorly constructed and somewhat shows the type of movement between plates.	Model is poorly constructed and/or incorrectly shows the type of movement between plates.
Presenting Research and Model	Student takes lead in making a thorough and interesting presentation of the research and model.	Student participates fully in a thorough presentation of the research and model.	Student briefly participates in a presentation of the research and model.	Student takes little or no part in the presentation of the research and model.

Volcanoes and People

The following steps will walk you through the Chapter Project. Use the hints and detailed directions as you guide your students through the research, planning, and preparations for their documentaries about life in volcanic regions.

Chapter Project Overview

Introduce the project by having students preview some volcanoes presented in the chapter and asking them to suggest ways in which the volcanoes may have affected people living nearby. Encourage students to take notes about the effects that interest them. Suggest that they add other ideas to the list as they think of them.

Make sure students understand that they will be working in small groups to create their documentaries. Explain that group members may divide tasks among themselves any way they wish. Emphasize, though, that every group member should take part in planning the documentary and should be prepared to answer questions about the documentary's content.

After students have read the project description in their textbook, distribute the Project Overview, which presents the Project Rules, a list of possible research topics, and hints for researching information and taking notes. Also distribute Project Worksheet 1, which includes a list of volcanoes that students may want to consider for their documentaries. Explain that each group may choose any volcanic region and any topic the members wish, so long as they are able to find adequate source material for their research.

Set a deadline for the project presentations and interim dates for the different tasks. Have students record these dates in the Project Timeline section at the end of the Project Overview.

Materials and Preparation

Provide a wide variety of age-appropriate source materials for students to use in their research, including encyclopedias, nonfiction library books, magazine articles, and films on videocassette and DVD. If students have access to the Internet in school or at home, encourage them to use that source as well. One appropriate Web site is Volcano World at volcano.oregonstate.edu.

Also provide index cards for taking notes and self-sticking, removable tags for flagging appropriate information in books.

When students are ready to prepare their multimedia materials, supply a variety of materials and devices—poster paper, art supplies, acetate sheets for making overhead transparencies, videocameras, and tape recorders for taping songs, background music, or sound effects. Also encourage students to use materials and devices from home.

Keep Students on Track—Tasks 1–2

Check each group's choice of a volcanic region and topic to avoid duplication. You may want to allow two groups to choose the same region so long as the groups focus on different specific topics.

Distribute Project Worksheet 2, which provides support for helping students take notes as they do their research.

Monitor students' work as they do their research, and provide assistance as needed. In particular, make sure the members of each group focus on the specific topic they have selected and do not waste time taking notes on unrelated issues.

Keep Students on Track—Task 3

At this point, students should be ready to begin planning their documentaries based on the information they have gathered. Help the groups sift through all their information, select the points they want to include, organize the content into a logical and interesting flow, and plan audiovisual materials to accompany the narrative.

If any groups are unable to find certain information they want to include, provide or suggest additional source materials.

Review the storyboard technique with the entire class. Emphasize that the storyboard should identify the presentation's major steps—each on a separate sheet of paper—so it can serve as an outline of the documentary. If necessary, help students identify and eliminate any fine-level details that do not belong in the storyboard.

Keep Students on Track—Task 4

Remind students of the deadline for the class presentations. Advise them to finish all elements in the documentary before that date so they will have enough time to rehearse and make any final improvements.

Make students responsible for gathering or providing you with a list of any special equipment, such as extension cords, television monitors, or overhead projectors, that they will need for their presentations.

Chapter Project Wrap Up

Encourage students to practice using all the documentary elements—narrative, visuals, audiotapes, videotapes, skits, and so forth—to make sure each is placed appropriately and adds to the presentation's clarity and interest.

Tell the class how much time each group will be allowed for its presentation. Encourage groups to keep this time limit in mind as they rehearse their presentations. If group members find that their presentation is running much too long, suggest that they cut some material rather than speed up the presentation to fit the time limit.

When each group presents its documentary to the rest of the class, encourage the other students to ask questions. Make sure you and the other students give each group positive feedback on its presentation.

Allow time for students to record their evaluations and their ideas for improvements in their journals. Use the textbook's final question—"Did you see any similarities between how people in different regions live with volcanoes?"—as the basis for a whole-class discussion.

Extension

Have the members of each group count off from "one" so each student has a different number. Then let students reassemble with all the "ones" in one group, all the "twos" in another group, and so on. Suggest that each new group discuss the following questions: What was the most difficult part of creating the documentary? What was the easiest part? What was the most interesting thing my group learned about the volcano we chose?

Name _____ Date_____ Class_____

Volcanoes and People

How do volcanoes affect the people who live near them? In this project, you and the other members of your group will try to answer this question by making a documentary about life in a volcanic region.

First, your group will choose a volcano or volcanic region and one topic to research about how people nearby are affected. For example, your group could decide to find out how people have benefited from living near a volcano or the ways people show volcanoes in their art and stories. Your group may choose any volcano or volcanic region and any topic you want, so long as you are able to find enough information to create a good documentary.

Next, your group will research information about the volcanic region and topic you chose. As you do your research, you will need to take notes. Your group will use the notes to plan and then write your documentary. Some of the information can be presented by a speaker. Other information might be better as a visual—a poster, an overhead transparency, computer art, or a mural, for example. Some information could be presented in a video, a song, or a skit—either "live" or on tape.

Your group will have time to rehearse your documentary and practice using the audiovisual materials. After you have made final changes, your group will present the documentary to the class.

Project Rules

- With the other members of your group, choose a volcano or volcanic region to study. Also decide on one topic to research about how people there have been affected.

- Research the volcano or volcanic region and topic your group has chosen. Your teacher may provide some materials for your research. You can use other materials of your own choice. As you do your research, take notes on the information you find.

- Work with the other group members to plan your documentary. Decide which pieces of researched information best fit the topic you chose. Decide how to present each piece of information. Make a storyboard that shows each major step in your group's presentation. Identify the audiovisual materials you will use and where each will be included. Also identify which group member will present each step.

- Use the storyboard as an outline to write your documentary and create the audiovisual materials.

- Rehearse your group's presentation. Make sure it fits the time limit that your teacher has allowed. Make any final changes and improvements.

- With your group, present your documentary to the rest of the class. Be prepared to answer questions about any part of your group's presentation.

Topic Ideas

Here are some suggestions for topics about how volcanoes have affected people living nearby. Feel free to think of your own topic ideas, too. Your group should choose only one topic to research.

- Hot springs for recreation and health
- Tourism in a volcanic region
- Uses of and products made from volcanic materials
- Volcanic soils and agriculture
- Evacuating people from a volcanic region
- Cleaning up and rebuilding after an eruption
- Archaeological excavations in a volcanic region
- Art and literature about a volcano
- Myths and legends about a volcano
- Geothermal energy

Hints for Researching Information and Taking Notes

- Write down the topic your group has chosen on an index card. When you look through a source for information, refer back to the index card to remind yourself of the topic.

- As you examine each source, ask yourself, "Which information is directly related to my group's topic?" Take notes on only that information.

- Take notes on a separate index card or sheet of paper for each source. Also write down the name of the source.

- At the top of each index card or sheet of paper, write a key word or phrase to tell you what those notes are about. For example, if you are researching how people show volcanoes in their art and you find some information about pictures of volcanoes on pottery, write *Pottery* as the key word. Group all the *Pottery* notes together.

Project Timeline

Task	Due Date
1. Choose a volcano or volcanic region and a topic to research	_____
2. Complete your research	_____
3. Make a storyboard to plan the documentary	_____
4. Write the narrative and create the audiovisual materials	_____
5. Present the documentary to the class	_____

Name _____ Date_____ Class_____

PROJECT WORKSHEET 1

Active Volcanoes and Volcanic Regions

Country	Volcano/Region Names
Chile	Calbuco, Llullaillaco, Villarrica
Colombia	Nevado del Ruiz, Puracé
Congo	Nyamuragira, Nyiragongo
Costa Rica	Arenal, Irazú, Poás
Ecuador	Cotopaxi, Guagua Pichincha, Reventador, Sangay
El Salvador	Izalco
Ethiopia	Erta Alè
Guadeloupe	Soufrière
Guatemala	Fuego, Pacaya, Santa María
Iceland	Askja, Heimaey, Hekla, Krafla, Laki, Surtsey
Indonesia	Agung, Colo, Dieng, Galunggung, Gamalama, Kelut, Krakatau, Merapi, Papandajan, Semeru, Tambora
Italy	Etna, Solfatara, Stromboli, Vesuvius, Vulcano
Japan	Asama, Aso, Bandai, Bayonnaise Rocks, Fuji, Oshima, Sakura-jima, Tarumai, Unzen, Usu
Kamchatka (Russia)	Bezymianny, Karymsky, Kliuchevskoi, Tolbachik
Martinique	Pelée
Mexico	Colima, El Chichón, Paricutín, Popocatépetl
Montserrat	Soufrière Hills
New Zealand	Ruapehu, Tarawera, White Island
Nicaragua	Cerro Negro, Coseguina, Masaya
Papua New Guinea	Lamington, Rabaul
Peru	El Misti
Philippines	Pinatubo, Mayon, Taal
St. Vincent	La Soufrière
Tanzania	Ol Doinyo Lengai
USA: Alaska	Augustine, Katmai, Pavlof, Redoubt, Shishaldin
California	Lassen Peak
Hawaii	Kilauea, Mauna Loa
Oregon	Mount Hood
Washington	Mount Baker, Mount Rainier, Mount St. Helens
Wyoming	Yellowstone Caldera

Find each of the countries listed above on a world map. Use the map to answer the following questions on a separate sheet of paper.

1. Which countries are in Africa?

2. Which countries or states are islands or island chains?

3. Which countries or states are located around the rim of the Pacific Ocean?

PROJECT WORKSHEET 2
Taking Research Notes

Pretend that your group has decided to study the volcanic region near Naples, Italy, where Mount Vesuvius is located. Your topic is how people have used volcanoes for health benefits. Suppose you found the article below about another volcano near Naples. Follow these directions to practice being an effective notetaker.

1. **Skim the article.** Which paragraphs relate to the topic?

   _____

   _____

2. **Read the related paragraphs carefully and take notes.** On a separate sheet of paper, write notes about the information you find. You don't need to copy entire sentences from the article. Focus on the most important words and phrases. Remember to label your notes to identify the volcano.

3. **Read the entire article.** Identify three other topics for which this article would be a good source of information.

   _____

   _____

Solfatara Volcano

Solfatara volcano is located near Naples, Italy. The ancient Romans believed that Solfatara was an entrance to the underworld. The volcano was also thought to be one of Vulcan's workshops. Vulcan was the Roman god of fire, for whom volcanoes are named.

Like many other active volcanoes, Solfatara has vents that release steam and other gases between eruptions. The temperature at some vents can reach 140°C. These vents may be good sources of geothermal energy.

Besides steam, Solfatara's vents also release sulfur gas, which smells like rotten eggs. As the sulfur gas moves away from the vents, it cools and condenses to form solid crystals. Sulfur is mined for many uses, particularly in manufacturing. For example, sulfur is added to rubber to strengthen it—a process called vulcanization.

The steam and gases from Solfatara's vents are believed to have special healing powers. Since early Roman times, visitors have taken steam baths at Solfatara to treat arthritis and breathing problems and to get the supposed health benefits of "sweat baths."

At some of Solfatara's vents, sulfur gas bubbles up through mud that the gas itself has created. Sulfur is acidic. As the gas rises through cracks underground, it corrodes the rock around it, creating a large pool of hot mud at the surface. The mud in some pools is scorching hot. In other pools, the mud is cool enough for people to soak in it. Mud baths are a popular treatment for softening the skin.

SCORING RUBRIC

Volcanoes and People

In evaluating how well you complete the Chapter Project, your teacher will judge your work in three categories. In each, a score of 4 is the best rating.

	4	3	2	1
Researching Information and Taking Notes	Consults a wide variety of appropriate source materials. Research notes are well organized and focused on the topic.	Consults an adequate variety of source materials. Research notes are fairly well organized; most notes are related to the topic.	Consults more than three source materials. Research notes are somewhat unorganized and include information unrelated to the topic.	Consults only one or two source materials. Research notes are disorganized and generally unrelated to the topic.
Planning, Creating, and Presenting the Documentary	Documentary is well organized, clear, interesting, and focused on the topic. Audiovisual materials are creative and well-integrated.	Documentary is organized, fairly clear, interesting, and focused on the topic. Audiovisual materials are used effectively.	Documentary is rather disorganized and not always focused on the topic. Uses few audiovisual materials.	Documentary is disorganized and unclear, includes much unrelated information, and makes poor use of audiovisual materials.
Working Cooperatively	Takes a lead in planning, writing, and presenting the documentary, including suggesting ideas for and creating audiovisual materials. Successfully leads group to share responsibilities; helps allocate tasks based on group members' skills and interests.	Actively participates in planning, writing, and presenting the documentary, including offering ideas for audiovisual materials. Cooperates with others in sharing responsibilities; volunteers for specific tasks.	Participates in most aspects of planning, writing, and presenting the documentary but offers few ideas. Undertakes responsibilities and tasks at others' direction.	Participates marginally in planning, writing, and presenting the documentary; may create a simple audiovisual material suggested by others. Does not carry out all responsibilities and tasks assigned by others.

Design and Build a Dam

The following steps will walk you though the Chapter Project. Use the hints and detailed directions as you guide your students to design and build a dam and then to test and redesign, if time allows.

Chapter Project Overview

The purpose of this project is to introduce students to the concepts of building an earthen dam, using the engineering design process and the scientific method.

Introduce the purposes for building earthen dams:

- Dams help control floods by regulating water flow. Often the reservoirs above dams are able to absorb some of the floodwater to protect downstream locations.

- Dams are used to produce a reservoir that can be used to generate electricity or can be used recreationally.

- Dams are also used to impound a stream or river, creating a water supply area for area towns and cities.

Dams result in a human-made change to Earth's surface and require upkeep.

Students might investigate the levees along the Mississippi River, which are mainly earthen dams running along the edge of the river to keep it from overflowing its banks and flooding adjacent towns.

Distribute Project Worksheet 1. After students have read the worksheet, ask if they have any questions. Students should use the worksheet while completing the Chapter Project.

Organize students in teams of two or three to work together to investigate the project. The teams should plan their designs together, although they may decide to divide the tasks.

In conducting the permeability test, students should place the same height of soil sample in a test tube for each of the different grain sizes. A sample of water should be carefully poured onto the soil. Students should use a stopwatch to determine how long it takes

the water to travel a set distance. (This distance should be the same for each of the test tubes.) The sample with the shortest time has the highest permeability since it allows water to pass through it more quickly.

In conducting the erosion study, students should just pour water over the soil at an equal rate and determine how much material is eroded. This can be done visually if equal amounts of soil are used.

When designing the dam, students should consider the placement of material based on the materials' properties. Students should either redesign the dam or discuss approaches they would take to do so.

Materials and Preparation

Have water, test tubes, and stopwatches on hand.

The types of soil given to students need to represent three different grain sizes. This could be accomplished by using silt, sand, and gravel. If silt is difficult to obtain, cornstarch may be used. If it is difficult to obtain gravel, aquarium gravel may be used.

The permeability test may be completed in test tubes or graduated cylinders.

The dam can be constructed inside a large foil roasting pan. The dam can be built in the middle of the pan, across the short dimension. Water can be poured into one half of the tray, and students can time how long it takes to penetrate the dam.

Keep Students on Track—Tasks 3–4

Students should design a scientific experiment to determine the permeability of the soil and the ease of erosion for the different grain sizes. They need to know how rapidly water can pass through the sample and how rapidly water can remove the soil. Credit should be given for innovative approaches.

Teams should brainstorm the project to determine which construction materials to use. If possible, they should create a sketch showing the layers of the structure.

Alternate solutions should be evaluated, and teams should select the best design for the project.

Keep Students on Track—Task 5

Students should complete construction of the dam.

Keep Students on Track—Tasks 6–7

Students should test the structure, noting how well the dam performed. Allow students the opportunity to redesign their structure. Ask them to reflect on their design and make suggestions for how they would alter the construction.

Keep Students on Track—Task 8

A group presentation should be developed, explaining all the steps taken to construct the dam. How did students accomplish the design? Why did they choose a particular technique? Students should create a diagram of the dam they constructed, outlining the placement of the different soils.

Chapter Project Wrap Up

Investigating the permeability of the soils may be difficult, depending on the equipment available to students. If this is the case, tell students that the coarse-grained soils are the most permeable, which means that the soil will allow water to pass through easily, while the fine-grained soils are the least permeable, which means they will form a barrier against the water.

The soils may need to be compacted slightly in order to be more effective. They may also be more effective if they are slightly damp (sprayed with a misting bottle).

The shape of the dam should be a rough triangle for maximum integrity.

Extension

The weathering of Earth's surface accounts in part for the creation of the different grain sizes of the soil. A mountain river begins with large coarse materials, but the time that river reaches the sea, it is generally depositing very fine silts and clays. Engineers are aware of the different properties of soils and use those properties to their advantage in dam construction and other projects. In sealing off a landfill, engineers use the fine-grained clays to form an impermeable barrier above and below a landfill. This prevents water from entering the landfill and becoming contaminated. Challenge students to use this information to redesign their dams.

PROJECT OVERVIEW

Design and Build a Dam

Dams are something that we are all familiar with, yet many of us may not know why they exist. Dams have many purposes: They can be used as a means of controlling flooding, they can be used to generate power, and they are also integral in many communities for creating and maintaining a public water supply. Dams can range in height from a low of 1 to 2 meters to as high as the world's tallest dam—292 meters. Dams can be constructed from a variety of natural and synthetic materials, including wood, concrete, and soil.

Project Rules

- The purpose of this project is to introduce you to the concepts of building an earthen dam. You will use an engineering design process and the scientific method.

- You will be using soils with three different grain sizes. You will need to test the permeability of each soil to determine how readily water passes through it. You will then need to develop an experiment to test how easily water erodes each soil. When constructing the dam, you will need to combine the information from your two experiments to make the best dam. Think about which layers or combinations of materials will make the most effective dam.

- Create a chart that shows which soil eroded easily and which did not. Identify which soil was most permeable. Record your data on a single chart to make evaluation of the soil types easier. Then describe the construction process for your dam and why you chose to put each soil type where you did. Include in your description a diagram of the dam that shows the placement of the different soils.

- In your journal, please comment on the following questions: If you were able to redesign, what did you change? If you did not have an opportunity to redesign the project, what would you do differently next time? Which part of the project was most difficult for you? Can you create a relationship between how easily a material is eroded and the permeability of the object?

Project Hints

- Your class may choose to conduct the permeability experiment together, rather than in individual groups. The results would be shared as a class.

- Your class may choose to have different groups working on separate parts of the project. For example, one group might be responsible for testing the permeability of each soil. Another group might be responsible for testing how easily each soil is eroded.

- The permeability test may cause problems. If the soil is not placed in the test tubes properly, the water could run down the side of the tubes. This would make it impossible to calculate the permeability of the soil.

- Care should be taken when pouring water into the large foil pan to decrease the erosion of your work, unless that is the desired outcome.

- In redesigning your dam, you may want to consider the following:

  - Use the medium-grained materials to form the basic shape of the dam.

  - Place the fine-grained materials around the basic shape of the dam, compacting the materials as you proceed.

  - Construct the exterior of the dam of coarse-grained materials that do not erode easily. They will help keep the fine-grained materials from eroding.

  - Experiment to determine the appropriate mass of the dam needed to hold back the water from one half of the tray.

Project Timeline

Task	Due Date
1. Complete Project Worksheet 1.	_____
2. Design your dam.	_____
3. Conduct the permeability test.	_____
4. Conduct the erosion study.	_____
5. Build the dam.	_____
6. Test the structure.	_____
7. Complete Project Worksheet 2.	_____
8. Present your dam and your findings to the class.	_____

PROJECT WORKSHEET 1
Planning Your Investigation

With other members of your group, you will be designing and building a dam. To help you get started, answer the following questions and share your answers with the group.

1. What three types of soils will you use to build your dam?

   _____

   _____

   _____

2. How will you design your permeability test?

   _____

   _____

   _____

3. How will you conduct the permeability test?

   _____

   _____

   _____

4. How will you design your erosion study?

   _____

   _____

   _____

5. How will you conduct the erosion study?

   _____

   _____

   _____

6. How might these test results impact the design of your dam?

   _____

   _____

   _____

PROJECT WORKSHEET 2

Design and Build a Dam

As you conduct your project experiments and build your dam, complete this worksheet to document your findings. Upon completion of your project, use this worksheet to present your findings to the class.

Progress Checklist

Task	Notes	Completed Y/N
Conducted permeability test		
Conducted erosion test		
Created a chart listing the soil types and their relative permeability and ease of erosion		
Brainstormed dam solutions and selected the best one		
Tested the dam		
Assessed what would be done differently when redesigning the dam		

SCORING RUBRIC

Design and Build a Dam

In evaluating how well you complete the Chapter Project, your teacher will judge your work in three categories. In each, a score of 4 is the best rating.

	4	3	2	1
Conducting Permeability and Erosion Analysis	Students conducted an experiment, analyzed data, and successfully ranked the soils.	Students conducted two successful experiments, but soil ranking was incorrect.	Students conducted only one successful experiment.	Students sorted the soils without any investigation.
Constructing Dam	Students constructed a successful dam with justification for choosing particular soils.	Students constructed a successful dam but did not include justification for choosing soils.	Students constructed an unsuccessful dam and did not provide justification for soil change.	Students built the dam from nonsieved soil.
Making Final Presentation	Students tie all three parts together and state how they would improve the dam in the future.	Students state how they would improve the dam.	Students relate how the first two steps impacted their decision for construction.	Students talk about their project.

A Journey Back in Time

The following steps will walk you through the Chapter Project. Use the hints and detailed directions as you guide your students through planning, research, creation of the brochures and timeline, presentation, and reflection.

Chapter Project Overview

In the Chapter Project, students will work individually to create a "travel brochure" that describes the environment and living things during one period of Earth's history. In addition, students will collaborate on a class geologic timeline.

To introduce the project, show students travel brochures that focus on states, foreign countries, or national parks. Travel agents or state tourist bureaus can supply these materials. Give students time to examine the brochures' features, and then discuss which brochures are most informative and attractive. Explain that in the Chapter Project, each student will create a similar brochure that shows what it was like in a specific time period of Earth's geologic history.

Students' work on this project must necessarily begin before they are introduced to the geologic time scale and the brief history of Earth. As a consequence, students may have difficulty choosing a geologic time period. Therefore, you may wish to have students preview these topics to help them select a time period. As an alternative, you can assign each student a time period, thereby ensuring that all time periods are researched by at least one student.

Invite student volunteers to help you make a timeline along one wall of the classroom. Hang a long piece of butcher or table paper on the wall. Then have the volunteers mark the boundaries between eras and periods and mark the names of the time units on the timeline.

At least one student should research each of the following geologic time periods: Precambrian Time; the periods of the Paleozoic—Cambrian, Ordovician, Silurian, Devonian, Carboniferous, Permian; the periods of the Mesozoic—Triassic, Jurassic, Cretaceous; and the periods of the Cenozoic—Tertiary and Quaternary. Since the Cenozoic periods have such a detailed fossil record, you may want to have more than one student work on each of those periods.

Students should research and create their brochures individually, but they can work in small groups to illustrate the class timeline. About halfway through the project, have all students working on the same time period meet and decide how each group member will contribute to the illustrations of that period on the timeline.

Distribute the Project Overview. Review the Project Rules. You may also want to hand out the Scoring Rubric so students will understand what is expected of them.

Set a deadline for the project presentation and some interim dates for the different tasks. Have students copy the dates in the Project Timeline.

Distribute Project Worksheet 1. This worksheet will help students focus their research. After students have read the worksheet, answer any questions they have.

Materials and Preparation

For research, students will need a wide array of reference materials. Collect books and magazine articles on Earth's history from friends and local libraries. In addition, you may want to do an Internet search and make a list of helpful sites students could visit. Many natural history museums, for example, have Internet sites that provide information about various topics related to Earth's history.

To illustrate their brochures, students will need colored pencils, markers, or watercolors.

Some students may want to create their illustrations—and even the whole brochure—on a computer. Encourage computer-savvy students to work with students who lack computer skills so that every student has the opportunity to create the best possible brochure.

For the class timeline, you will need butcher or table paper and art supplies. Tape or glue will also be necessary. Some students may want to create three-dimensional illustrations for the timeline. In such cases, provide construction paper, scissors, or other necessary materials.

Keep Students on Track—Tasks 2–4

As you review each student's list of research materials, encourage students who have not yet made much of an effort to find information to do so quickly. Make suggestions about which books in the classroom could give such students a good start.

Distribute Project Worksheet 2. This worksheet will help students get organized to create their brochures and timeline illustrations. After students have read the worksheet, ask if they have any questions. Be prepared to provide each student or group with the materials needed to prepare the brochures and timeline art.

Keep Students on Track—Tasks 5, 7

By now, each student should have written at least a rough draft of the information that will appear in the final brochure. The design of the brochure should also be set, since illustrations will have to be made to fit in specific spaces.

At this point, have all students working on the same time period meet to decide who will make which illustrations. Each time period will also need some brief annotations. Advise students to work together to compose labels, sentences, or short paragraphs to use as annotations.

Keep Students on Track—Task 8

Make sure each student or group has the necessary materials to make the illustrations for the timeline.

Encourage students to critique one another's rough drafts. Advise students that they should make constructive suggestions, such as where a student might find more information or how illustrations could be improved.

Allow time for students to add their illustrations to the class timeline.

Chapter Project Wrap Up

Examine each student's brochure before presentation. Have students "talk you through" what they will say, and make suggestions about logical sequence or any missing information in their reports.

Provide class time for the presentations. Have students make their presentations in chronological order of Earth's history to reinforce how Earth has changed over time. Assess the general design and look of the brochure, the quality and scope of the information presented, and the sources used to support the information. Encourage other students to ask questions about the important events of the geologic time period covered.

After all the presentations have been made, discuss with students which brochures were best, both in design and quality of information.

Encourage students to evaluate how well they created their brochures and how they could have made the brochures better after seeing what other students did.

Extension

Have students work together to create a geologic time scale in a school hallway for students from other classes and grades to see. This could include not only the illustrations used on the classroom timeline, but also the best of the brochures that students created.

PROJECT OVERVIEW

A Journey Back in Time

Suppose you had a travel company that could take people back in time—far back in time. In fact, your time machine can take tourists back millions, and even billions, of years to times when plants, animals, and the continents themselves were much different than anything you can see today. In this Chapter Project, you will create a travel brochure that focuses on a geologic time period of Earth's past. You will also work with others in the class to create a timeline of Earth's history.

First, you will choose—with the help of your teacher—a specific time period from Earth's history. Next, you will use books and other resource materials to research that time period. Then, you will create a travel brochure for the time period that includes both written descriptions and illustrations. You will also contribute to a class timeline of Earth's history. Finally, you will use your brochure to present your geologic time period to the class.

Project Rules

- With the help of your teacher, choose a geologic time period about which you will become an expert.

- Make a list of reference materials you could use to find information to complete a travel brochure of the geologic time period you choose. Project Worksheet 1 will help you focus your research.

- Use books, magazine articles, and Internet sites to gather information about your time period.

- Create a travel brochure that gives an accurate and comprehensive picture of your geologic time period. Project Worksheet 2 will help you organize your ideas for your brochure.

- Create illustrations for the travel brochure. These can be cartoons or realistic pictures. They should be interesting, well-made, and accurate to the time period.

- Work with other students to illustrate the class timeline. You will need to create at least two illustrations for your time period.

- Use your travel brochure to present your geologic time period to the class. In this presentation, you should urge classmates to visit your time period for the reasons included in the brochure. You must support any information in the brochure with a list of books and other materials you used for reference.

Project Hints

- As soon as possible, begin making a list of the reference materials you will need to create your brochure. Read widely at first, taking notes of important points each book or article makes. Then concentrate your attention on those sources that you think can provide you with the best information about your geologic time period. Make sure, though, that you use more than one source and that you never directly copy exact sentences from those sources. Your brochure must be written in your own words.

- As you read the reference materials and look at their illustrations, do not concentrate your attention only on animals. Your brochure must be accurate. For instance, flowering plants didn't evolve until the Cretaceous period, so including such plants in illustrations for a time period before that would make your brochure inaccurate. Make sure you get an overall idea of the environment of the time period on which you are working.

- Make your brochure not only accurate, but also fun. Remember, this brochure should be designed to make people want to travel back to your time period.

- For the illustrations in your brochure, you may use colored pencils, markers, watercolors, or computer graphics. For the illustrations for the class timeline, you could also make three-dimensional illustrations. Give some thought to which materials would represent your period best, and make the brochure and timeline attractive.

- As you prepare for your presentation, think of what you want to say and the order in which you want to say it. You may want to make notes on index cards to help you remember what you want to say.

Project Timeline

Task	Due Date
1. Choose a geologic time period to research.	_____
2. Find reference materials.	_____
3. Complete Worksheet 1.	_____
4. Complete Worksheet 2.	_____
5. Complete draft of brochure copy.	_____
6. Complete final copy for brochure.	_____
7. Create illustrations for brochure.	_____
8. Create illustrations for class timeline.	_____
9. Present your geologic time period to the class.	_____

Name _____ Date _____ Class _____

PROJECT WORKSHEET 1

Researching a Geologic Time Period

As you work to become an expert on a geologic time period, you can use this worksheet to help focus your research. If you need more space, use another sheet of paper.

1. Which geologic time period will you research?

_____

2. What were the major geologic events of that time period?

_____

_____

_____

3. What did Earth's surface look like then?

_____

_____

_____

4. What was the climate like?

_____

_____

5. What were the dominant organisms living at that time?

_____

_____

6. What was the environment like, compared to the present?

_____

_____

7. What are the main things travelers might like to see?

_____

_____

8. What should travelers pack for comfort and safety?

_____

_____

9. What dangers might travelers face?

_____

_____

PROJECT WORKSHEET 2
A Travel Brochure

Use this worksheet to help you plan your travel brochure for a geologic time period and the illustrations you plan to make for the class timeline. If you need more space, use another sheet of paper.

1. What is your geologic time period?

_____

2. Describe the general design of your brochure.

_____

_____

_____

_____

3. Tell what kinds of information you will include in your brochure.

_____

_____

_____

_____

4. Tell how you will encourage people to visit your geologic time period.

_____

_____

_____

_____

5. Describe and tell the purpose of each illustration you plan to make for your brochure.

_____

_____

_____

_____

6. Describe the illustrations you plan to make for the timeline, and tell why each is important.

_____

_____

_____

_____

Name _____ Date _____ Class _____

SCORING RUBRIC

A Journey Back in Time

In evaluating how well you complete the Chapter Project, your teacher will judge your work in four categories. In each, a score of 4 is the best rating.

	4	3	2	1
Designing Brochure	The brochure is creatively designed, with attractive headings and print, and includes three to four appropriate and well-made illustrations.	The brochure is well-designed, with attractive headings and print, and includes two to three appropriate and neatly done illustrations.	The brochure is fairly well-designed and includes at least two appropriate illustrations.	The brochure is poorly designed and includes inappropriate illustrations or lacks illustrations.
Creating Brochure Copy	Information in the brochure is accurate, well-written, and interesting, includes the major events of the geologic time period, and gives a good sense of that part of Earth's history.	Information in the brochure is accurate and interesting, includes most of the major events of the geologic time period, and gives a fairly good sense of that part of Earth's history.	Information in the brochure is mostly accurate, includes some of the major events of the geologic time period, and gives a limited sense of that part of Earth's history.	Information in the brochure is mostly inaccurate, includes few of the major events of the geologic time period, and gives a poor sense of that part of Earth's history.
Creating Timeline Illustrations	Makes at least two creative, appropriate, and attractive illustrations for timeline.	Makes at least two creative, appropriate, and attractive illustrations for timeline.	Makes one or two appropriate and fairly attractive illustrations for timeline.	Illustration for timeline is inappropriate and/or poorly made.
Making Presentation	Makes a well-prepared and thorough presentation that includes an interesting description of the geologic time period through creative use of the brochure.	Makes a prepared and thorough presentation that includes a clear description of the geologic time period through good use of the brochure.	Makes a somewhat prepared but incomplete presentation that includes a description of the geologic time period through reference to the brochure.	Makes an unprepared presentation that includes an incomplete description of the geologic time period with little or no reference to the brochure.

Getting on the Map

The following steps will walk you through the Chapter Project. Use the hints and detailed directions as you guide your students through selection of a site, measuring and sketching, devising a scale, creating a map, presentation, and reflection.

Chapter Project Overview

In the Chapter Project, students will map a square or rectangular piece of land in their area.

To introduce the project, focus students' attention on a local park that is familiar to all students. Ask how they would go about making a map for that location. Emphasize that this map would not be a landscape painting or other artistic endeavor. Rather, it is a map that someone who has never been to the park could use to get around. Introduce the idea of scale and proportionality as central to this task.

Distribute the Project Overview. Review the Project Rules. You may also want to hand out the Scoring Rubric, so students will understand what is expected of them.

If appropriate, divide the class into pairs or small groups. The advantages of using groups are more collaboration among students of differing abilities and a sense of security in the field. The advantage of individuals making their own maps is that each student will gain more experience with mapmaking.

Set a deadline for the project presentation and some interim dates for the different tasks. Have students copy the dates in their Project Timeline.

Distribute Project Worksheet 1. After students have read the worksheet, ask if they have any questions. Encourage students to immediately begin looking for an appropriate site.

Distribute Project Worksheet 2. After students have read the worksheet, ask if they have any questions. It is critical that students have some way of measuring boundaries and distances between features at their sites. You may want to have student volunteers demonstrate for the class the procedure described in the worksheet.

Materials and Preparation

Although students are responsible for finding their own sites, you might make a list of appropriate sites in order to make suggestions for any students having trouble thinking of a site. Appropriate sites might include sections of local parks, vacant lots, playgrounds, and so on.

Students will not need much in the way of materials to make their maps. For measuring the site, a tape measure would be helpful, though students can count how many footsteps they take over a measured distance, thus creating a standard for themselves.

To create the map, students will need paper and a ruler. Students may want to use colored pencils to enliven their maps with various symbols or different-colored boundaries.

Students can use a compass to find north. If a compass is unavailable for every student, there are two simple ways of finding north without a compass:

- On a sunny day sometime before noon, drive a stick into the ground so that it is perpendicular to the ground. Then mark the extent of its shadow every few minutes until after noon (or after 1:00 P.M. during Daylight Savings Time). A line from the base of the stick through the shortest shadow points to true north.

- Use a watch in the afternoon. Point the hour hand of the watch directly at the sun. Then find the halfway point between the hour hand and the number 12 (number 1 during Daylight Savings Time). A line from that halfway point through the center of the watch hand points directly north.

Keep Students on Track—Tasks 1–2

Approve each student's site selection. Ask if permission is needed and has been requested. Students probably do not need permission for public parks and playgrounds. They will need permission for any privately owned spaces.

Make sure students understand the procedure involved in estimating measurements, as spelled out in Worksheet 2. If possible, demonstrate the procedure in class.

Help students understand how to find north at their sites. Either make sure students have access to a magnetic compass or can carry out one of the alternative ways of finding north.

Keep Students on Track—Tasks 3–5

As you review each student's description, measurements, list of features, and sketches from Worksheet 1, encourage students whose data are incomplete to return to the site for more work.

Help students convert their site measurements into an appropriate scale for the map. Some students may have used a common tape measure. If so, their measurements may not be metric. Advise them to make conversions before devising a scale.

Keep Students on Track—Tasks 6–7

Check that all students have begun working on the final draft of their maps. Remind them to include a scale, symbols, a legend, a north arrow, and contour lines to give some sense of topography.

Encourage students who are having trouble to try to make a finished map, assess it with your help or another student's help, and then make revisions in time for the presentation.

Chapter Project Wrap Up

Examine each student's map before presentation. Have students "talk you through" what they will say, and make suggestions about logical sequence or any missing information in their report. Make sure a student plans to talk about the features at the location as well as the processes involved in mapping the site. Encourage students to relate any difficulties they had and how they overcame them.

If this is a group project, make sure all group members plan to participate in a meaningful way in the presentation.

Provide class time for the presentations. Allow each student or group to present the map, with an emphasis on the mapping techniques used. Encourage other students to ask questions about the measuring of the site as well as the choices made for scale, symbols, and other map characteristics. As an alternative, students can present their maps in a poster-session format.

After all presentations have been made, discuss with students which maps are best, both in planning and execution.

Encourage students to evaluate how well they measured and initially sketched the site, how well they planned the map, and how accurately the final draft represented the location. Emphasize that in their journals, they should identify ways in which they could have made their maps better, especially since they have seen other students' maps.

Extension

Have interested students work together to map a larger area, such as a large city park, an industrial park, a farm, or a city or suburban block. A larger portion of this map could include contour lines, though finding elevation is impossible without special equipment. Nevertheless, students can still use contour lines to show the lay of the land.

PROJECT OVERVIEW

Getting on the Map

You've probably been in a car when the driver has gotten lost. There's more than one way to handle this situation. You can stop to ask someone, but that can be embarrassing. You can drive around until you recognize something, but that can be time-consuming. You can also use a map. But the map has to be a good one. The mapmaker has to have prepared it accurately, with enough detail so that a lost driver can figure out how to find a familiar road.

Maps are important, and in this Chapter Project you will find out how to make a map. First, you will find a site to map. Second, you will measure the site's boundaries, make a list of its features, and prepare an initial sketch. Then, you will make an accurate map of the location. At the end of the project, you will present your map to the class.

Project Rules

- Work with your teacher or an adult family member to find a good site to map. This site could be a section of a park, a playground, a vacant lot, a yard in your neighborhood, or any other place that interests you.

- The site should be square or rectangular and from 300 to 1,000 square meters. The boundaries, for example, could measure 20 meters by 30 meters, which is 600 square meters.

- Complete Project Worksheet 1 by recording all the information you can about the site. This includes details about the location, measurements, and lists of all the natural and human-made features.

- Make measurements using the procedure outlined in Project Worksheet 2. Mark the corners of the boundaries with stakes or stones, and then measure the distances in between them. Measure other distances at the site as well.

- Make a sketch of the site, including all the details you can. Find which direction is north, and include that on your sketch.

- Use your sketch and all the other information you have collected to prepare a final draft of your map. Your map should contain the following: a scale, a north arrow, all natural and human-made features of the site, symbols, a symbol legend, and contour lines showing the topography of some part of the site.

- Prepare a presentation of your map for the class. Explain what your map shows and how you made it accurate and interesting.

Name _____ Date_____ Class_____

Project Hints

- As soon as possible, begin looking for a site. You want one that has interesting features—there's no sense in mapping a flat field of grass. Look for a location with playground equipment, a small building or two, a hill or stream, trees and bushes, and so on. The more features you include on your map, the more interesting the map will be.

- Be as accurate as you can in measuring the boundaries of your site. In addition, measure as many other distances as possible, such as the distance of a small building or swingset from a boundary or the distance between large trees.

- If you have a compass, use it to find north. If you don't have a compass, ask your teacher for another way to find where north is at your site.

- Devising a scale is essential for making your map accurate. First, convert any measurements you've made into metric measurements. Then, find a scale that works on the paper you will use for your map. If your site is 40 meters by 40 meters, for example, a good scale might be 1 centimeter = 2 meters.

- Use as many symbols as you can on your map. This will make the map more interesting.

- Choose a hill, a depression, or some other striking natural feature to show with contour lines. You don't have to use contour lines for the whole map, though you may. You don't have to show elevation on your lines.

- As you prepare for your presentation, think of what you want to say and the order in which you want to present the information. You may want to make notes on index cards to help you remember what you want to say.

Project Timeline

Task	Due Date
1. Select a site to map.	_____
2. Measure the site's boundaries.	_____
3. Make a detailed sketch of the site.	_____
4. Complete Worksheet 1.	_____
5. Create a scale to use on your map.	_____
6. Brainstorm a list of symbols to use.	_____
7. Prepare a final draft of your map.	_____
8. Present your map to the class.	_____

PROJECT WORKSHEET 1

Planning a Map of a Local Area

After you have found and selected a site to map, you need to collect as much information as you can. Use this sheet to record that information. Attach additional sheets of paper if you run out of space here.

Name of site _____

Location _____

General description _____

_____

_____

Direction of north _____

Natural features _____

_____

_____

Human-made features _____

_____

_____

Measurement of boundaries _____

_____

_____

Other measurements _____

_____

_____

Symbols useful for making map _____

_____

_____

On a separate sheet of paper, make a sketch of your site. Stand at a place where you have a good view, and sketch as many features as possible.

PROJECT WORKSHEET 2
Estimating Distances

You need to make measurements of the boundaries of your site, as well as measurements of distances between features. Making such measurements is the only way to make an accurate map. You can use a tape measure if you have one. If you don't, then measure the distances with the procedure described below.

Materials
- yardstick
- chalk

Procedure

1. Find a sidewalk or parking lot where you can measure a distance and mark that distance with chalk.

2. Mark a starting line with chalk.

3. Use a yardstick to measure 20 yards down the sidewalk or through the parking lot. (*Hint:* When using a yardstick to measure, place it on the ground, flip it lengthwise for another yard, and so on.) At 20 yards, mark a finish line.

4. Walk down the sidewalk or through the parking lot, from starting line to finish line. Take normal-sized steps. Count your steps as you go.

5. Write the number of steps you walked in 20 yards here: _____

6. Convert the number of yards you walked to meters by multiplying the number of yards by 0.91: 20 yards × 0.91 = 18.2 meters, rounded to 18 meters.

   Write the number of steps you walk in 18 meters here: _____

7. Make measurements at your site by recording how many steps you take. Then use this formula to determine that distance in meters:

   Distance = (18 meters × Steps you take at site) ÷ Steps you take in 20 yards

   Example: Suppose you take 25 steps in 20 yards. Then, at your site you take 40 steps to walk a boundary line. Find that length in meters by using the formula:

   Distance = (18 meters × 40) ÷ 25

   Distance = 720 ÷ 25

   Distance = 28.8 meters, rounded to 29 meters

SCORING RUBRIC
Getting on the Map

In evaluating how well you complete the Chapter Project, your teacher will judge your work in four categories. In each, a score of 4 is the best rating.

	4	3	2	1
Measuring the Site and Using a Scale	Creates an excellent scale for the map and employs it accurately and consistently in portraying measured distances and sizes of features.	Creates an appropriate scale for the map and employs it accurately and consistently with a few minor exceptions in portraying measured distances and sizes of features.	Creates an adequate scale for the map, but employs it inconsistently, and in some cases inaccurately, in portraying measured distances and sizes of features.	Creates a scale for the map, but employs it inconsistently and mostly inaccurately in portraying measured distances and sizes of features, or creates a scale that is inappropriate.
Including Features of the Site and Using Symbols	Includes 8–10 natural and human-made features of the site and uses symbols accurately and creatively, including contour lines.	Includes 5–7 natural and human-made features of the site and uses symbols accurately, including contour lines.	Includes 3–4 natural and human-made features of the site and uses symbols fairly accurately, but uses few contour lines.	Includes 1–2 natural and human-made features of the site; use of symbols is inconsistent and has no contour lines.
Making an Interesting and Accurate Map	Makes a well-drawn and interesting map with a creative use of symbols and an accurate placement of boundaries and features.	Makes a well-drawn map with a good use of symbols and an accurate placement of boundaries and features.	Makes a fairly well-drawn map with an adequate use of symbols and a fairly accurate placement of boundaries and features.	Makes a poorly drawn map with an inaccurate use of symbols and a mostly inaccurate placement of boundaries and features.
Presenting the Map	Makes a well-organized and interesting presentation that includes a thorough explanation of the map and the processes used in making the map.	Makes an organized presentation that includes a clear explanation of the map and the processes used in making the map.	Makes a somewhat organized presentation that includes only a partial explanation of the map and some details about the processes used in making the map.	Makes an unorganized presentation that includes a weak explanation of the map and an incomplete explanation of the processes used in making the map.

Soils for Seeds

The following steps will walk you through the Chapter Project. Use the hints and detailed directions as you guide your students through planning, setup, observation, presentation, and reflection.

Chapter Project Overview

In the Chapter Project, students will work in small groups to investigate the effect that soil or other growing materials have on the growth and health of bean plants.

To introduce the project, show students a healthy potted plant. Guide students in generating a list of variables that could affect the health of the plant, including soil, sunlight, temperature, water, and type of plant.

Distribute the Project Overview. Review the Project Rules with students. You may also want to hand out the Scoring Rubric so that students will know what is expected of them.

Divide the class into small groups of three or four students. The advantages of using groups include fewer materials needed and more collaboration among students of differing abilities. If a group includes three students, for example, the group might investigate three different soils. Each student can then be primarily responsible for recording data about the growth of one pot of plants, although all group members should observe all plants. At the conclusion of the project, group members can collaborate on creating a compare/contrast table and/or line graphs showing growth rates.

Set a deadline for the project presentation and some interim dates for the different tasks. Have students copy the dates in their Project Timeline.

Distribute Project Worksheet 1. After students have read the worksheet, ask if they have any questions.

Provide each group with the materials needed to carry out the project, including various growing materials and pinto bean seeds. Display the different types of soil, and allow students to examine each type. Encourage groups to immediately choose the soils they will use and collect local topsoil

from their neighborhood. Because the project involves observing plant growth, it is essential that students plant the bean seeds as soon as possible.

Distribute Project Worksheet 2. After students have read the worksheet, ask if they have any questions. Make sure students understand that each group member is responsible for making a data table, observing plant growth, and recording data in the table.

Materials and Preparation

The soils that groups can choose for their investigations include commercial potting soil, vermiculite, sand, gravel, and local topsoil. Both potting soil and vermiculite are sold at garden and large hardware stores. Vermiculite is a water-absorbing mineral product derived from mica. Sand and gravel can be purchased at a major garden, hardware, or building supply store. In addition, each group will need three to five small plastic pots, depending on how many soils they investigate.

For groups who choose to investigate local topsoil, have them collect it themselves. Since different groups will use soil from different areas of the community, this will add another variable to the project. The beans may do well in one group's soil but not in another's, simply because the soils were collected from different spots.

Students will need a metric ruler to measure the growth of their plants. Some students may want to use a hand lens to examine plants closely, especially as the seeds begin to sprout.

Since the project is relatively short for observing plant growth, groups could plant bean seedlings rather than starting from seeds. If you wish to have them do this, you should purchase pinto beans about a week in advance of the project and prepare them in the following way:

- Soak the bean seeds overnight in water.
- Line the inside of a 300-mL clear plastic cup with a paper towel folded in half. Then stuff several other paper towels into the cup.

- "Plant" the bean seeds between the paper towel and the cup, so that you can observe changes. Then moisten the paper towels. The towels should be kept wet until the seeds sprout.

- The bean seeds will sprout in about four to five days. Some seeds likely will not sprout. Provide each group with about four sprouted seeds per soil tested, and demonstrate how to plant the seedlings.

Keep Students on Track—Tasks 1–2

Review each student's suggestions from Worksheet 1 to make sure that each group member is participating in the planning of the project.

The number of growing materials that each group investigates can vary according to the number of students in the group. Each group member can choose one growing material. In this way, each student will be responsible for the plants in one pot.

Check that samples of local topsoil have been collected and all bean seeds have been planted.

By this point, all students should have recorded a prediction about which material will be best for the beans and made a data table. Each student should observe and record data daily.

Keep Students on Track—Tasks 5–7

Remind students to observe their plants' growth and record their data daily.

Encourage students to begin drawing conclusions about how the different soils affected plant growth.

Some students may have only limited success in growing the bean plants, even when another group's plants in the same material do well. Although this may be the result of poor care, it also may be the result of normal variation in seeds. This problem may be difficult to assess. Tell students that they won't be penalized for poor growth as long as they collect the data faithfully and present their results accurately to the class.

Chapter Project Wrap Up

Examine each group's plants, data tables, and other materials before presentation. Have students "talk you through" what they will say, and make suggestions about logical sequence or any missing information in their reports. As a group project, all group members should participate in a meaningful way in the presentation. Encourage all students to make a contribution.

Provide class time for the presentations. Allow each group to present its results, with an emphasis on the soils used, the data collected, and the conclusions drawn. Encourage other students to ask questions about the soils and how closely the group observed the growth of the plants. As an alternative, students can present their results in a poster session, during which they are available to discuss their projects and answer questions.

After all presentations have been made, discuss with students which investigations were best, both in planning and in results.

Encourage students to evaluate how well they planned and set up their investigations, how well they took care of their plants, and how their results and conclusions compared with those of other groups. Emphasize that they should identify in their journals ways in which they could have made their investigations better.

Extension

Encourage interested students to expand on the investigation by creating different soils, both by mixing various materials that they can purchase and by mixing materials with local topsoil. In this way, students can determine whether a sandy soil or a clay soil is better for beans. As an alternative, students can compare the growth of beans in several soils with the growth of other plants, such as radishes or mustard.

PROJECT OVERVIEW

Soils for Seeds

Think of all of the plants in your environment. Do you think it matters what kind of soil they grow in? If you have ever been around a farm, you know that farmers work hard in the spring to prepare their soil for planting. Farmers depend on good soil to grow and produce good crops.

In this Chapter Project, you will work with a group to determine which of several kinds of growing materials are best for the health and growth of bean plants. First, you will choose growing materials to investigate. Second, you will plant bean seeds in the growing materials and observe the plants' growth over a period of two weeks. During this period, you will collect and record data about these plants. At the end of the project, you will compare plants growing in different materials and draw some conclusions. Finally, you will present your results and conclusions to the class.

Project Rules

- Complete Project Worksheet 1 to help you get organized to carry out your investigation.

- Work with your group to choose one growing material per group member. The materials may include gravel, sand, vermiculite, potting soil, and local topsoil.

- Carefully examine the growing material you choose, and record a description of the material, including particle size and shape and composition.

- Plant bean seeds in the growing materials you have selected, and observe the plants' growth over two weeks. Control all other variables affecting plant growth, such as temperature and amount of light and water, so that you are testing only the effect the growing material has on the plants.

- Collect and record data about plant growth, including height, number of leaves, leaf width and length, color, and general health.

- With your group, prepare a class presentation of your results. As part of this presentation, you will analyze your data and draw conclusions about how well bean plants grow in different types of growing materials.

Project Hints

- Begin collecting the materials you will use to carry out the investigation as soon as possible. The sooner you choose your growing materials and plant your bean seeds, the sooner you can begin making observations and recording data.

- Don't plant your seeds too deep! Plant each seed 1–2 centimeters below the surface of the growing material.

- Your seedlings should be watered regularly. Keep the soil moist, but not soaked. You will probably need to water your plants about every two to three days.

- Collect as much data as you can as your plants grow. Project Worksheet 2 will help you make a data table.

- Observe your plants daily, and don't forget to record the measurements and other observations you make. If you have a camera, you can take pictures every two or three days.

- Near the end of the project, work with other group members to make comparisons and draw conclusions about the investigation. You can make a line graph to show how plants grew in different growing materials. You can also make a poster that includes photographs or sketches of the plants during the course of the project.

- As you prepare your presentation, think of what you want to say and the order in which you want to say it. You may want to make notes on index cards to help you remember what you want to say.

Project Timeline

Task	Due Date
1. Complete Worksheet 1.	_____
2. Gather materials needed for planting.	_____
3. Review plans with your teacher.	_____
4. Plant your bean seeds.	_____
5. Complete Worksheet 2.	_____
6. Complete data tables.	_____
7. Compare plant growth in different materials.	_____
8. Present your results and conclusions.	_____

PROJECT WORKSHEET 1
Planning Your Investigation

With the other members of your group, you will be planting bean seeds in different growing materials and observing how well the plants grow in each material. To help you begin thinking about how to proceed with this investigation, answer the following questions and share your answers with your group.

1. What variable will you be investigating in this project?

   _____

2. What other variables affect the growth of plants? How can you control each of these variables throughout the investigation?

   _____

   _____

   _____

   _____

   _____

3. The growing materials you may choose to investigate in this project include potting soil, vermiculite, sand, gravel, and local topsoil. Predict how you think plants will grow in each.

   Potting soil _____

   Vermiculite _____

   Sand _____

   Gravel _____

   Local topsoil _____

4. How will you measure the growth of your bean plants?

   _____

   _____

   _____

5. In what ways can you judge the health of a plant, other than by its height?

   _____

   _____

   _____

   _____

PROJECT WORKSHEET 2

Observing Plant Growth

You should observe the growth of your bean plants closely. To help in this task, use the chart below. This chart is for only one week, and it is for only one plant. Since you will have more than one plant in a pot, you should make a chart like this for each plant. In addition, make a chart like this for each plant for the second week of observation.

Weekly Growth Chart

Characteristic	Monday	Tuesday	Wednesday	Thursday	Friday
Height above ground					
Number of leaves					
Average leaf length					
Average leaf width					
Leaf color					
General health					
Other Observations					

SCORING RUBRIC

Soils for Seeds

In evaluating how well you complete the Chapter Project, your teacher will judge your work in four categories. In each, a score of 4 is the best rating.

	4	3	2	1
Preparing for Planting	Writes a thorough description of the growing material chosen with excellent details and sets up an investigation that carefully controls for all variables except type of soil.	Writes a good description of the growing material chosen and sets up an investigation that controls for all variables except type of soil.	Writes an adequate description of the growing material chosen and sets up an investigation that controls for most variables except type of soil.	Writes a poor description of the growing material chosen and sets up an investigation that fails to control for all variables except type of soil.
Observing and Recording Plant Growth	Collects complete data daily over the length of the project, making and completing growth charts for each plant in a pot.	Collects complete data almost every day over the length of the project, making and completing growth charts for each plant in a pot.	Collects some data almost every day over the length of the project, making and partially completing growth charts for each plant in a pot.	Collects little data on only a few days during the project, making and partially completing growth charts for some plants.
Presenting the Results	Makes a thorough and interesting presentation of the results, including a description of growing materials, comparison of data, and conclusions.	Makes an interesting presentation of the results, including a description of growing materials, comparison of data, and conclusions.	Makes an adequate presentation of the results, including a description of growing materials, comparison of data, and conclusions.	Makes a poor presentation of the results and does not include a description of growing materials, comparison of data, and/ or conclusions.
Working Cooperatively	Takes a lead in group planning, collection of data, and presenting results.	Participates in all aspects of group planning, collection of data, and presenting results.	Participates in most aspects of group planning, collection of data, and presenting results.	Participates minimally in group planning, collection of data, and/or presenting results.

Watching the Weather

The following steps will walk you through the Chapter Project. Use the hints and detailed directions as you guide your students through the gathering of information, presentation, and reflection.

Chapter Project Overview

Distribute and discuss with students the Project Rules in the Project Overview. If you wish, divide the class into small groups to carry out the project.

Hand out the Scoring Rubric, and review how you will assess students' work.

Set a deadline for the project presentation and interim dates for the different tasks. Suggest to students that they copy the dates in the Project Timeline.

Stress to students that their weather observations must not be based on instruments. In fact, they should try to avoid reading or listening to weather reports during the project, although this may be difficult. To help students think of ways to observe the weather, have them read the hints in the Project Overview.

Suggest to students that they try to categorize their weather observations by using a scale. This will make the observations less subjective and more consistent from day to day as well as help control other variables. Hand out copies of Project Worksheet 1, and have students work through it. It will show them ways they can categorize their observations of wind speed as an example.

Hand out copies of Project Worksheet 2 to give students practice and ideas for recording their weather observations.

Challenge students to use the hints and worksheets only as guides and to try to develop their own creative ways of observing and recording the weather.

Keep Students on Track—Tasks 1–2

Check that each student has selected at least two or three different weather variables to observe. You may wish to assign any variables that have not been selected so that all of the variables are covered by the class as a whole.

Make sure that the ways students have chosen to observe and categorize the weather variables are reasonable. Encourage students to use different kinds of observations to monitor the same variables.

Urge students to make their observations at the same time and in the same place each day. This will help them control other variables as well as make it easier for them to remember to make the observations. Encourage some students to make their observations in the morning and others to make their observations in the afternoon or evening.

Make sure that students are recording their observations in a weather log like the one in Worksheet 2. Stress the importance of making their logs as accurate and detailed as possible.

Keep Students on Track—Task 3

Have students look for trends in their weather data. They should note whether a variable rises or falls from day to day and by how much. Point out to the class that if there is a big change in one weather variable, then it is likely that other weather conditions are changing as well.

Stress to students that how a variable rises or falls may give an indication of what the weather will be like the next day. Wind direction, clouds, and especially air pressure can be useful for predicting upcoming weather.

Based on the hints in the Project Overview, have students predict what specific changes in these variables might mean for the next day's weather. After students have made their predictions, have them study their weather logs to see whether the predictions are confirmed by their own data.

Chapter Project Wrap Up

Review students' drawings, graphs, and tables summarizing their weather observations. If any students have difficulty summarizing their observations, urge them to "talk you through" their findings. Then guide students in organizing their observations in a coherent, logical display. Advise students to identify trends in their observations and include a discussion of the trends in their presentation.

Allow class time for student presentations. After each student presents his or her display, urge other students to ask questions or make comments.

Urge students to consider how successful they were at watching the weather. Challenge them to think of ways they might have done things differently for a more successful project.

Extension

- Some students may have noticed that weather conditions can vary from place to place at a given time. For example, students who come to school in town from a rural area may have noticed that it is usually cooler or windier where they live than at school. Use such observations as a starting point in discussing factors, such as lakes, hills, forests, and buildings, that may affect local weather conditions.

- Have students research weather folklore that may be helpful in assessing current weather conditions or making weather predictions. Point out that many of the hints given in the Project Overview are based on folklore that has a proven scientific explanation. Tell students that weather folklore pertaining to clouds or winds is most likely to be reliable. Caution students that some weather folklore, especially folklore about long-term weather predictions, has no basis in science and is unreliable. Whether a groundhog sees its shadow, for example, cannot be used to predict how much longer winter will last.

PROJECT OVERVIEW

Watching the Weather

In this project, you will be observing and recording weather conditions without using instruments. People, other animals, and plants often respond to changes in the weather. By observing their responses, among other changes, you can get an idea of current weather conditions and make some predictions about how the weather may change.

Project Rules

- Select at least two or three different variables you think you can observe, and decide how you will observe them.

- Make your observations of each variable at least once a day, preferably at the same time and place each day, for at least two weeks.

- Record all of your observations in a log, including when and how each observation was made. You will show your teacher your log when he or she requests it.

- As you continue to make and record your observations, periodically review the data in your log to see if you notice any patterns in the weather. Your teacher will ask you about patterns in your data.

- Create graphs, tables, and other means of displaying your observations for the class.

Project Hints

- Weather variables include temperature, wind direction and speed, cloud type and percentage of cloud cover, type and amount of precipitation, humidity, and air pressure.

- If possible, develop a scale for measuring each weather variable. This will make your observations more precise and consistent and your comparisons of weather data from day to day more meaningful. Project Worksheet 1 will help you develop a scale for measuring wind speed. Use it as a guide for developing scales for the other weather variables as well.

- Project Worksheet 2 will give you ideas for recording your observations in a weather log.

- You can get a good idea of the temperature by simply going outside. However, you should try to develop a more objective way of measuring temperature, such as the way most people are dressed.

- You can estimate wind speed using a scale like the one in Worksheet 1. Wind direction can be measured simply by noting the direction in which things blow in the wind. If a flag points toward the east, then the wind is blowing from the west. Wind direction can be an indicator of weather changes. In the Northern Hemisphere, a west wind often brings fair weather, an east wind stormy weather, a south wind rain, and a north wind cold temperatures.

- You can describe both cloud shape (thin and wispy or tall and puffy, for example) and color (white, gray, or black). You can also estimate about how much, or what percentage, of the sky is covered by clouds. Clouds are important indicators of changes in the weather. Dark clouds in the west, where most weather comes from in the Northern Hemisphere, may indicate an approaching storm. A ring or halo around the sun or moon is another indicator that stormy weather may be on its way.

- For precipitation, you can make several direct observations, including the type of precipitation, if any (rain, snow, sleet, hail); how much is falling (light, moderate, heavy); and how long it falls.

- Humidity is the amount of water vapor in the air. If the humidity is high, it may feel muggy outside, glasses containing cold drinks may "sweat," and doors and windows may stick shut. You may notice that your own body sweat does not evaporate easily. Some plants close up their flowers in very high humidity, including tulips, dandelions, and clover. Very high humidity is sometimes an indication that a thunderstorm is on the way.

- Although air pressure is difficult to measure without instruments, there are several clues that may indicate when the air pressure is low or falling. Compared to their usual behavior, swallows and other birds may fly lower, seagulls may stay closer to shore, cats may groom themselves more often, and mosquitoes may be more active. People may respond to low air pressure with joint pain, headaches, or irritability. Air pressure is one of the most important weather variables for predicting the weather. Rising air pressure means fair weather is coming, and falling air pressure means stormy weather is coming.

Project Timeline

Task	Due Date
1. Develop a plan for observing and recording weather data.	_____
2. Observe and record weather conditions for at least two weeks.	_____
3. Review the data in your log to look for patterns in the weather.	_____
4. Create graphs and other means to display your data.	_____
5. Present your data to the class.	_____

Name _____ Date_____ Class_____

PROJECT WORKSHEET 1
Measuring Wind Speed

In 1805, Sir Francis Beaufort, an admiral in the British Royal Navy, invented a scale to measure wind speed that does not depend on the use of instruments. The Beaufort Scale is shown in the table below. It is so useful that the United States Weather Service still uses it today. You can use it, too, but you will probably want to make some changes first because it is too detailed to be practical for this project. Weather forecasters usually use a simpler scale for categorizing and describing wind speed. This scale is also shown below.

In your weather log, create a scale of your own that combines the information in the two tables and reduces the scale to just four or five categories of wind speed. Your table should have the following columns: Effects of Wind, Wind Speed (miles per hour), Description of Wind.

Beaufort Scale

Beaufort Number	Wind Speed (miles per hour)	Effects of Wind
0	< 1	Smoke rises straight up. No perceptible motion of anything.
1	1–3	Smoke drift shows direction. Tree leaves barely move.
2	4–7	Leaves rustle slightly. Wind felt on face.
3	8–12	Leaves and twigs move. Loose paper and dust raised from ground.
4	13–18	Small branches move. Dust and paper raised and driven away.
5	19–24	Small trees sway. Large branches in motion. Dust clouds raised.
6	25–31	Large branches move continuously. Wind begins to whistle. Using umbrella difficult.
7	32–38	Whole trees in motion. Walking difficult.
8	39–46	Tree twigs break. Walking progress slow.
9	47–54	Slight structural damage.
10	55–63	Exposed trees uprooted. Heavy structural damage.
11	64–72	Widespread damage.
12	73+	Severe damage and destruction.

Forecasters' Scale

Wind Speed (miles per hour)	Description of Wind
1–7	light
8–12	gentle
13–18	moderate
19–24	fresh
25–38	strong
39–54	gale
55–72	whole gale
74+	hurricane

278
Atmosphere

Copyright © Pearson Education, Inc., or its affiliates. All rights reserved.

PROJECT WORKSHEET 2

Keeping a Weather Log

Use the sample weather log shown here as a guide in developing a log for recording your own weather observations. Your log may include fewer variables, but it should include all of the other information shown in the log below, including when and where each observation was made and any unusual weather conditions or additional observations about the weather variables. Allow plenty of room in your log for writing detailed observations. Also allow room in your log to record weather observations for a two-week period, not just two days as in the sample log.

The first line of the sample weather log has been filled in for you. For practice and to help you develop your own weather log, try filling in the rest of the log. Use the hints on the Project Overview, Worksheet 1, and your own experience with the weather. And don't forget your imagination!

Sample Weather Log

Weather Variable	Date	Time	Place	Observation of Variable	Value for Variable	Comments
Wind Direction	Oct. 1	10:00 A.M.	school yard	School flag is mostly blowing toward the north.	Wind is from the south.	Wind direction shifts a lot.
Wind Speed	Oct. 1					
Temperature	Oct. 1					
Percent Cloud Cover	Oct. 1					
Type of Precipitation	Oct. 1					
Wind Direction	Oct. 2					
Wind Speed	Oct. 2					
Temperature	Oct. 2					
Percent Cloud Cover	Oct. 2					
Type of Precipitation	Oct. 2					

Name _____ Date _____ Class _____

SCORING RUBRIC
Watching the Weather

In evaluating how well you complete the Chapter Project, your teacher will judge your work in four categories. In each, a score of 4 is the best rating.

	4	3	2	1
Collecting and Recording Observations	Measures at least three weather variables daily using appropriate and creative observations and maintains an accurate and detailed weather log.	Measures at least two weather variables daily using appropriate observations and maintains an adequate weather log.	Measures just one weather variable daily using acceptable observations and only partially maintains a weather log.	Does not measure weather variables on a regular basis and/or uses unacceptable observations and fails to maintain an adequate weather log.
Interpreting the Data	Correctly identifies and accurately explains all apparent trends in the weather observations and uses them to make appropriate predictions of weather conditions.	Identifies and adequately explains most trends in the weather observations and uses them to make mostly appropriate predictions of weather conditions.	Identifies some trends in the weather observations but may fail to explain them adequately or use them to make appropriate predictions of weather conditions.	Makes little effort to identify or explain trends in the weather observations or use them to make predictions of weather conditions.
Presenting the Results	Makes a thorough, interesting, and well-prepared presentation with well-constructed and creative visuals.	Makes an interesting and prepared presentation with only minor omissions and has satisfactory visuals.	Presentation is mostly complete, but not well-organized and with at least one visual.	Presentation is incomplete and unprepared with no or inappropriate visuals.
Working Cooperatively (optional)	Takes a lead in collecting and recording observations, interpreting data, and presenting results.	Participates in all aspects of collecting and recording observations, interpreting data, and presenting results.	Participates, but mostly at others' direction, in collecting and recording observations, interpreting data, and presenting results.	Participates minimally in collecting and recording observations, interpreting data, and presenting results.

Investigating Microclimates

The following steps will walk you through the Chapter Project. Use the hints and detailed instructions as you guide your students through the planning, assembly, testing, and presentation of their water treatment systems.

Chapter Project Overview

In this project, students will gather and compare weather data from three different microclimates. To introduce the project, take students on a walk around the school grounds or neighborhood, and encourage them to make observations about plants and animals living in different places. Focus students on the conditions each organism requires, such as direct sunlight, moist ground, or shade. Encourage students to offer comments and to ask questions about the organisms and the conditions that they observe.

Have students read the Chapter Project description in the Project Overview. After students have read the pages, answer any questions they have about the project. Hand out the Scoring Rubric and discuss with students what will be expected of them.

Divide the class into groups of three or four students. Emphasize that every group member is responsible for choosing at least three areas to study and for gathering and analyzing data.

Set a deadline for the project presentation and interim dates for the different tasks. Encourage students to fill in these dates on the Project Timeline.

Monitor groups as members brainstorm a list of places that could have different microclimates. Students do not have to choose places near the school, but the places should be convenient for students to visit at the same time every day during the two-week data-gathering period. Remind students not to enter private property without first gaining permission. Ideally, groups should choose to study three microclimates located close to one another.

Students should measure and analyze at least four weather factors for the microclimates they study. Be sure students understand that they must measure the same factors for each microclimate.

Materials and Preparation

Students will need instruments that measure weather conditions, such as thermometers, anemometers, rain gauges, wind vanes, wet- and dry-bulb thermometers, and light meters. If all groups choose to study microclimates near or on the school grounds, you do not need class sets of these instruments. You can schedule instrument use so that each group has a certain time each day to gather the data. Students will also need hand lenses to examine the organisms in the microclimate, a logbook, and graph paper. Field guides to identify plants and animals will also help students analyze their data.

Students can use three identical containers to collect rain from each of their microclimates. An empty tuna can makes a very nice rain gauge.

Keep Students on Track—Tasks 1–3

Review the locations chosen by each group. Make sure students can visit the locations at the same time each day for two weeks.

Distribute Project Worksheet 1. This activity, done individually, will help students organize their ideas about the kinds of data that they will collect in their logbooks.

Review group logbooks and the kinds of data students have chosen to collect. Give suggestions of what data to collect if students are having trouble defining the data they need.

Review the use of all weather instruments with students. When all students can use the instruments properly, they are ready to gather data from their microclimate study sites.

Keep Students on Track—Tasks 4–6

Review each group's logbook, making sure that the data are complete. Discuss with each group's members their ideas about graphing their data. Suggest that students construct tables or charts to help them analyze their observations of organisms and weather factors.

Distribute Project Worksheet 2. This worksheet provides practice for students in graphing and analyzing weather data.

Encourage students to draw conclusions about what weather factors cause the microclimates to be similar or different.

Chapter Project Wrap Up

Find out from groups how they plan to present their reports. Provide groups with bulletin board space or an overhead projector and transparency sheets, if needed. Remind students that all group members should participate in describing the conditions in each microclimate and their conclusions about each microclimate.

Provide class time for group presentations. Each group should compare the weather conditions and the organisms present in each of the study sites. Groups should also draw conclusions about the causes of different microclimates.

After all of the presentations have been made, discuss with students the factors that cause different microclimates. Prompt students to recall the climate factors that affect temperature and precipitation.

Encourage students to evaluate their investigation in their journals. Students should include in their journals suggestions for improving their investigation or additional information they would like to learn about microclimates.

Extension

- Challenge students to study a single organism and relate microclimate to the organism's behavior and where it lives.

- Gardeners learn which plants require more or less sunlight to grow. Encourage students to try growing a particular plant in a sunny location and in a shady location, with all other factors constant, to find out in which location the plant grows best.

Name _____ Date _____ Class _____

PROJECT OVERVIEW

Investigating Microclimates

Have you ever noticed that you find certain plants and animals in some areas, but not in others? How are the weather conditions in a small area related to the kinds of plants and animals living there? In this project you will compare and contrast weather data from three small areas that appear to be different microclimates.

First, you will form hypotheses about how the microclimates in three areas differ from one another. Second, you will collect weather data and record the living things in each area. Third, you will analyze the data you've gathered and develop relationships between the microclimate and the plants and animals living there. Finally, you will present your data and conclusions to the class.

Project Rules

- With your partners, choose three areas that you hypothesize to have different weather conditions, or microclimates. If any of these areas are located on private property, get permission from the property owner to collect data there. Remember that you will have to collect data from each area at the same time every day for two weeks. Tell your teacher which areas you will study.

- Complete Project Worksheet 1. With your partners, decide what equipment you will need to gather data from your study areas. Then develop a logbook in which you will collect data. Decide who will collect which data and when.

- Measure and record at least four different weather factors from each study area at the same time every day for two weeks. You should measure the same weather factors at each location. Also record your observations of living things and any other conditions.

- Complete Project Worksheet 2. This worksheet will give you practice graphing and analyzing weather data.

- Graph your data and look for any patterns. Work with your partners to compare and contrast the data from each area. Draw conclusions about why weather patterns differ in each area and how the weather conditions of each area are related to the kinds of living things found there.

- Prepare your class presentation. In making this presentation, you and your partners should report your hypotheses about each area, the data you collected, and your conclusions.

Project Hints

- Before you and your partners choose areas to investigate, preview the chapter to learn about climates. Then review weather factors such as temperature, precipitation, humidity, and wind speed. Decide as a group which weather factors you plan to study. It is a good idea to talk to other groups and compare your plans.

- Be sure to collect the same kind of data at the same time and place each day. You may need to mark the study areas or make a map.

- Carefully observe the living things in the study area. Think small. Many interesting living things are very small. Some might not even look like living things to you. Some insects and other small living things often hide from light. Don't be afraid to poke around and move things. Always be sure to return everything to the same position in which you found it. **CAUTION:** *Do not handle unfamiliar plants or animals. These could cause allergic reactions, bites, or stings.*

- Use field guides to help you identify the living things that you observe. If you still can't identify them, draw pictures of those organisms and ask your teacher for help.

- To compare the microclimates of your study areas, construct graphs for each weather factor you studied. For example, plot the temperature data for each study area on one graph, using a different color for each study area.

Project Timeline

Task	Due Date
1. Choose three microclimates to investigate	_____
2. Complete Project Worksheet 1	_____
3. Set up logbook	_____
4. Complete Project Worksheet 2	_____
5. Complete data collection	_____
6. Construct graphs and analyze data	_____
7. Make presentation to class	_____

Name _____ Date _____ Class _____

PROJECT WORKSHEET 1

Preparing to Investigate Microclimates

In what ways do you think the areas you have chosen to study will differ? This worksheet will help you design your logbook, which will help you compare the microclimates you choose to study.

1. Describe the environment of each study area. Be sure to include any living things that you have already observed.

   _____

   _____

   _____

2. Use the descriptions of each study area to determine what weather factors will help you compare the microclimates of each study area. List these weather factors below. You should choose at least four weather factors to measure.

   _____

   _____

3. What instruments or equipment will you need to measure weather factors and identify the living things in the study areas?

   _____

   _____

   _____

4. Where will you collect data from each study area? At what time each day will you collect data? If necessary, draw a map of the study area on a separate sheet of paper, and indicate on the map where you will collect the data.

   _____

   _____

5. Below is the beginning of a page for a logbook. Copy it onto another sheet of paper, and then add the other items for which you will collect data.

   Study area

   _____

   Date

   _____

   Time

   _____

PROJECT WORKSHEET 2

Analyzing Weather Data

Materials
- 4 sheets of graph paper
- ruler
- black, red, and blue pencils

Procedure

1. Use a black pencil to draw the axes of a graph on a sheet of graph paper. Plot temperature along the *y*-axis and the days along the *x*-axis.

2. Use the red pencil to plot the temperature data taken from Site 1. Connect the points to form a smooth, curved line.

3. On the same graph, use the blue pencil to plot the temperature data taken from Site 2 in the same manner as you plotted the data from Site 1.

4. Repeat steps 1 through 3 for relative humidity, precipitation, and wind speed.

Weather Data

Site 1—sunny, bottom of a south-facing hill

Day	1	2	3	4	5	6	7	8	9	10	11	12	13	14
Temperature (°C)	18	12	11	15	14	15	18	15	17	18	11	10	9	15
Precipitation (cm)	0	0	1.1	0	0	2.9	0	0.6	0	0	0	0.9	0	0
Relative Humidity	60	65	85	70	75	80	79	79	75	74	69	64	65	68
Wind Speed (km/hr)	6	10	8	6	15	2	10	6	5	4	5	6	4	6

Site 2—shaded, north side of building

Day	1	2	3	4	5	6	7	8	9	10	11	12	13	14
Temperature (°C)	7	11	11	14	14	15	16	14	11	9	10	11	9	10
Precipitation (cm)	0	0	0.8	0	0	2.5	0	0.5	0	0	0	0.5	0	0
Relative Humidity	60	67	85	72	76	81	79	79	76	76	69	66	66	69
Wind Speed (km/hr)	12	15	10	11	15	6	14	9	10	9	12	14	9	12

Analyze and Conclude

Answer the following items on a separate sheet of paper.

1. Describe the pattern in daily temperatures that you observe on the temperature graph. What could account for these temperature patterns?

2. Why might Site 2 have slightly less precipitation than Site 1?

3. What kind of pattern for relative humidity do you observe on the graph?

4. For most of the data-gathering period, the winds were from the north, northeast, and northwest. Which site appears to be sheltered from these winds? Why?

Name _____ Date _____ Class _____

SCORING RUBRIC

Investigating Microclimates

In evaluating how well you complete the Chapter Project, your teacher will judge your work in four categories. In each, a score of 4 is the best rating.

	4	3	2	1
Planning and Designing the Logbook	Logbook is neat and well organized. Includes detailed descriptions of where, when, and how data will be collected.	Logbook is complete and fairly well organized. Includes adequate descriptions of where, when, and how data will be collected.	Logbook is mostly complete, but somewhat unorganized. Includes vague descriptions of where, when, and how data will be collected.	Logbook is incomplete and unorganized. Includes few descriptions of where, when, and how data will be collected.
Collecting and Analyzing Data	All data are labeled correctly. Graphs clearly show the data of at least four weather factors measured daily for two weeks at each of the three study areas. Includes charts of living things and other environmental factors.	Most data are labeled correctly. Graphs show the data of at least three weather factors measured daily for two weeks at each of the three areas, but the graphs are somewhat unclear. Includes good observations of living things.	Only some data are labeled correctly. Graphs are confusing or fail to show the relationships among weather factors at each of the three areas. Includes some observations of living things.	Little if any data are labeled correctly. Graphs are incomplete or fail to show any relationships among the data and the study areas. Few observations of living things are noted.
Presenting the Results	Demonstrates a clear understanding of why the microclimates differ and how each is related to the organisms found there.	Demonstrates a good understanding of why the microclimates differ and how each is related to the living things found there.	Demonstrates some confusion about why the microclimates differ and how each is related to the living things found there.	Demonstrates a lack of understanding about why the microclimates differ and how each is related to the living things found there.
Working Cooperatively	Takes a lead in the group's collection and analysis of data and presentation of results.	Participates in all aspects of collecting and analyzing data and presenting the results.	Participates at others' direction in most aspects of collecting and analyzing data and presenting results.	Participates minimally in the collection and analysis of data and presentation of results.

287
Climate and Climate Change

Every Drop Counts

The following steps will walk you through the Chapter Project. Use the hints and detailed directions as you guide your students through the gathering of information, presentation, and reflection.

Chapter Project Overview

As you introduce the project, ask students to brainstorm a list of uses of water in and around the house. Write their suggestions on the board and ask them to copy the list. Tell students that they will be investigating how much water is used in their homes during the project.

In introducing the project, do the following demonstration.

1. Ask students to estimate how many liters each person uses each day in the United States.

2. After students have made their estimates, tell them that residential water use averages about 300 liters per person per day.

3. Have students illustrate that figure with 2-liter soda bottles. For example, 15 bottles represents one-tenth of the average daily use.

Distribute the Project Overview. Review the Project Rules. You may also wish to hand out the Scoring Rubric, which you will use for assessing students' work.

Set a deadline for the project presentation and some interim dates corresponding to the different tasks.

Divide students into small groups. Make sure they understand that each student will individually collect data for water use at home, both personal data and data for their households. Groups will collaborate in collecting data about another building in their community and in making a class presentation.

Point out that each student will make a table of the data they collect about water use in the home. At the end of the first week, each student must calculate a total water use. Students who get water from wells or do not have access to their water meters will have to rely on their estimates.

Demonstrate for students how to make their own estimates of how much water is typically used during a certain task, such as washing hands.

1. In discussion with students, come to some reasonable conclusion about how long it takes to wash hands, such as 1 minute.

2. Open a faucet for 30 seconds, collecting the water in a bucket.

3. Measure the amount of water in the bucket by pouring the liquid into a graduated cylinder repeatedly.

4. Multiply the measurement by 2 to find the amount of water that would be used in a 1-minute washing.

For students who plan to use water-meter readings to complete their projects, distribute the Project Worksheet 1. After students have read the worksheet and completed the examples, find out if they have any questions. If possible, provide other practice examples.

Some students will need to read a straight-line water meter rather than a round-dial meter. Straight-line meters are very similar to the odometer of a car. Advise students to read the number on the meter from left to right to get the correct daily figure. Remind them to note the unit the figure indicates, usually either cubic feet or gallons.

Distribute the Project Worksheet 2. Make sure students understand that they should record their daily meter readings on the worksheet.

Review with students how to make conversions to liters from other units, including cubic feet and gallons: 1 gallon = 3.8 liters; 1 cubic foot = 28.5 liters. Emphasize that they will have to convert all readings to liters. Provide some conversion examples for them to work.

Anticipate that some groups may have trouble finding the water use for the community building they choose to study. You might check on a few locations in advance to hold in reserve if student efforts fail. Try to find a wide range of buildings to compare, such as office buildings, hospitals, factories, and various retail buildings.

Keep Students on Track—Tasks 1–2

As you review students' data tables, make sure that each student has kept a daily record of water use and has several types of uses on the table.

Help students who have trouble making the calculations necessary to find daily water use. Guide them through the process of adding the figures for each use, adding all the figures together, and dividing by the number of days in the survey.

Help students with any problems in reading the water meters at home. In some cases, students may take the figures correctly but fail to make the subtractions necessary to determine daily use. Also provide support for students in calculating household water use based on estimates instead of meter readings.

Meet with each group to discuss a plan for contacting people at another building in their community. Encourage students who have not made a decision about this task to make a choice quickly. Guide some groups to buildings where you know they will gain cooperation. Advise group members to work together in contacting and visiting buildings.

Keep Students on Track—Tasks 3–4

Review with each group a plan for determining water use in a community building. For those students who have not been able to make a contact, provide information about a building you have already contacted.

If possible, make sure no building is being audited by more than one group. Try to have groups audit different types of buildings. Review with students the kind of data they need to gather, using the list on the Project Overview as a reference.

Advise students to organize their questions before making contact with someone at a building. In class, have some students role-play the situation. Then discuss how they should introduce themselves and what questions they should ask.

Work with students on how to graph the household-use data they have in their data tables. Demonstrate how to make circle and bar graphs on the board. Bar graphs can be set up to show days or types of use on the x-axis and total use on the y-axis.

Chapter Project Wrap Up

As you review students' data tables, graphs, and other materials, you may wish to have each group "talk you through" the presentation. Make suggestions for organizing the materials for a coherent and logical report.

Provide class time for group presentations. Allow each group to present the findings, and then encourage class members to ask questions.

After all the presentations have been made, discuss with students what conclusions they can draw from all the data they have gathered. Focus on household tasks that use the most water, businesses or industries that have particularly high water use, and methods of conservation.

Encourage students to evaluate how well they accomplished what they set out to do and to make suggestions that they think would have made the project better.

Extension

Students might want to compare the data they collect during this period with water use at another time of year. For example, residential water use may increase during summer months.

PROJECT OVERVIEW
Every Drop Counts

How important is water to your life? In this project, you have a chance to examine how much water you and others use in a week. You'll probably be surprised!

First, you will determine how much water you personally use at home during one week. Second, you will find out how much water your household uses during that same week. Then, you will work with other students to find out how much water a building in your community—such as a business, hospital, or government building—uses in one week. At the end of the project, your group will present your data to the class.

Data Table of Personal Water Use

Water uses	Day 1	Day 2	Day 3	Day 4	Day 5	Day 6	Day 7
Brushing teeth	3	3	3				
Washing hands	5	6	5				
Flushing toilet	3	5	4				
Washing dishes	1	2	1				

Project Rules

- Keep a daily record of your personal water use in the form of a data table. The table above is a brief example. You will have to show this data table to your teacher.

- Take readings of your water meter to determine how much water your household uses on a daily basis. You will have to show evidence of this work to your teacher. If taking meter readings is not possible, you can estimate your total household use instead. You will need to keep daily records of estimated water use for all family members.

- With your group, choose a building in the community to study, and find someone connected with that building to provide you with water-use data for the building.

- With your group, prepare a class presentation of the data you have collected. As part of this presentation, you will prepare a graph of your household water use with the data you collected from a water meter.

Hints for Determining Home Water Use

- For each water use, determine how much water is actually used.

- You may not have access to the water meter, especially if you live in an apartment. A building superintendent or manager might be able to help. You can also determine average daily use from a household water bill. Be sure to divide the total amount used by the correct number of days.

- You can follow these steps to determine how much water you and your family use.

   1. Make a list of your daily personal uses of water.

   2. Set up a data table on a separate sheet of paper.

   3. Determine how much water to assign to each type of use.

   4. Use your table to make daily records of your water use.

   5. Calculate the total amount of water you use in a week by multiplying the amount of water used for each kind of use by the number of times you used water for that purpose. Then add all the numbers together.

   6. If possible, take daily readings of the water meter in your home. Calculate the total amount used in a week based on your meter readings or on your estimates if you do not have access to a water meter.

   7. Make a graph that shows daily household water use.

Hints for Determining Water Use in Another Building in the Community

- Begin immediately to find a building in your community to study. Ask family members and friends for suggestions of buildings and people to contact.

- Your group should collect all of the following information.

   1. Name, location, and kind of building studied

   2. Name and job title of the person who helped you obtain the data

   3. All ways water is used in this building

   4. Amount of water used per month in the building

Project Timeline

Task	Due Date
1. Complete personal water-use inventory	_____
2. Calculate total household water use	_____
3. Obtain all information from building in community	_____
4. Complete graphs and presentation	_____

PROJECT WORKSHEET 1
Reading Round-Dial Water Meters

Round-dial water meters have several small, round dials, as shown in Figure 1 below. Notice that beside each small dial is a number that is a multiple of 10. In reading a round-dial meter, begin with the dial that has the highest number beside it. In most cases, that number is 100,000. On each dial, a pointer points to a number, which is the reading for that dial. If the pointer is between two numbers, the reading is the *smaller* number. Also note the units in which the water is measured. Now follow the steps below to learn how to read the meter in Figure 1.

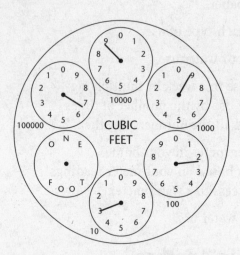
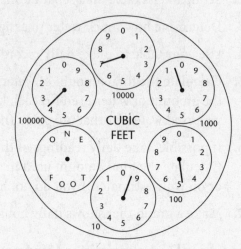

1. Read the 100,000 dial. Multiply that number by 10,000. Write the product on a sheet of paper. *For Figure 1, you would write 60,000.*

2. Read the 10,000 dial. Multiply that number by 1,000 and write the product below the first number. *For Figure 1, you would write 8,000.*

3. Read the 1,000 dial. Multiply that number by 100 and write the product below the second number. *For Figure 1, you would write 900.*

4. Read the 100 dial. Multiply that number by 10 and write the product below the third number. *For Figure 1, you would write 20.*

5. Read the 10 dial. Write that number down last. Then add all the numbers together to get the reading. *For Figure 1, you would write 3 and then add all the numbers together.* Write the final reading in the blank.

   _____ cubic feet

6. Now follow the steps again to read the meter in Figure 2. Write the final reading in the blank.

   _____ cubic feet

PROJECT WORKSHEET 2

Determining Household Water Use

To determine household water use, take a meter reading at the beginning of each day, as well as a final meter reading at the end of the week. Each morning, do your calculations on a separate sheet of paper, and then record the results here. Remember to convert your readings from the units on the meter to liters.

Household Water Use

Meter Reading	Water Used
Day 1 _____	
Day 2 _____	Difference = _____
Day 3 _____	Difference = _____
Day 4 _____	Difference = _____
Day 5 _____	Difference = _____
Day 6 _____	Difference = _____
Day 7 _____	Difference = _____
Day 8 _____	Difference = _____
	Total Use = _____

Making Conversions

The measurement unit that you will use in this project is liters. Yet you will likely discover that water meters and amounts supplied by building managers will be in cubic feet or gallons. This means you will have to convert those numbers to liters. The following conversion factors will help you do this.

    1 gallon = 3.8 liters
    1 cubic foot = 28.5 liters

    For practice, convert the readings you determined for the round-dial meters on Worksheet 1. Since those dials record water use in cubic feet, you need to divide the final figures by 28.5 to convert the readings into liters. Do your calculations on a separate sheet of paper and then write the answers in the blanks.

Figure 1: _____ liters

Figure 2: _____ liters

SCORING RUBRIC

Every Drop Counts

In evaluating how well you complete the Chapter Project, your teacher will judge your work in four categories. In each, a score of 4 is the best rating.

	4	3	2	1
Collecting Data in the Home	Collects data for at least 12 different types of household uses of water and accurately computes household use from daily water-meter readings.	Collects data for at least 9 household uses of water and computes household use from daily water-meter readings.	Collects data for at least 6 household uses of water and computes household use from at least 4 water-meter readings.	Collects data for 4 or fewer household uses of water and makes little or no attempt to compute household use from water-meter readings.
Collecting Data from Another Building in the Community	Collects all necessary data to compute the building's water use.	Collects most necessary data about the building's water use.	Collects only partial data about the building's water use.	Collects little or no data about the building's water use.
Presenting the Results	Makes a thorough and interesting presentation with a well-constructed graph of home water use and complete data about water use in a community building.	Makes an interesting presentation with a well-constructed graph and mostly complete data about water use in a community building.	Makes an adequate presentation with a completed graph and some data about water use in a community building.	Makes a poor presentation with an incomplete graph and little or no data about water use in a community building.
Working Cooperatively	Takes a lead in group planning and in the collection of data.	Participates in all aspects of group planning and in the collection of data.	Participates in most group planning and collection of data.	Participates minimally in group planning and collection of data.

Design and Build an Erosion-Proof Beach

The following steps will walk you through the Chapter Project. Use the hints and detailed directions as you guide your students through the gathering of information, presentation, and reflection.

Chapter Project Overview

Have students read the Project Overview. Review the Project Rules, and hand out the Scoring Rubric you will use for scoring students' work. Discuss with students what will be expected of them. If you wish, divide the class into small groups to carry out the project.

Set a deadline for the project presentation as well as interim deadlines. Encourage students to copy the dates in the Project Timeline.

Distribute copies of Project Worksheet 1 to help students plan their wave tank and Project Worksheet 2 to help them plan their models to scale. Also remind students to refer to the hints in the Project Overview as they plan and carry out the project.

This project may also be done in a single large class wave tank. Each group should take turns demonstrating their method and rebuilding the beach for the next group.

Keep Students on Track—Task 1

Check that each student has planned his or her wave tank to have a sloping bottom like the ocean floor in order for waves to break naturally on the beach.

Make sure students have a plan for generating waves that are consistent in size. Explain why it is crucial to control wave height in order to assess the effectiveness of different methods of erosion control.

Make sure students have selected beach materials that are fine enough to erode in the waves.

Remind students that their plans must include a way to measure erosion so they can test the effectiveness of erosion-control methods later in the project.

Keep Students on Track—Task 4

Encourage students to test at least one of the erosion-control methods listed in the Project Overview: groins, stabilized sand dunes, seawalls, and breakwaters. Share with students the sketch of a seawall and breakwater in the figure below if they do not think of these ideas on their own.

Make sure students are controlling all the relevant variables as they test methods of erosion control. They should be making the waves consistently and to scale and returning the beach to its original condition after each method is tested.

As an alternative to using toothpicks for keeping track of erosion, students may simply measure the distance from the water to the lighthouse after each wave or set of waves.

Encourage students to use different methods to record their erosion data, such as tables, line graphs, and to-scale drawings on graph paper.

You may wish to have students use a video camera to document the effectiveness of different methods of erosion control. However, they still should quantify erosion in order to make precise comparisons of the different methods.

Keep Students on Track—Task 5

If students build sand dunes for erosion control, urge them to stabilize the dunes with materials such as model plants, fences, or brush.

If students use groins for erosion control, make sure they have placed them perpendicular to the beach. Suggest that they experiment with different spacing and length of groins to find the best arrangement for protecting their beach. Point out how the groins increase erosion farther down the shore.

To clarify the difference between a seawall and breakwater, you might suggest that students construct and test first a seawall and then a breakwater made of the same materials. They should observe how the two different structures affect the movement of waves near shore and which works best to control erosion.

Challenge one or more students to try another method of erosion control called beach nourishment, which involves building up the beach with additional sand or soil.

Chapter Project Wrap Up

Students should demonstrate at least one method of erosion control. In their presentations, they should explain how the demonstrated method works and also its advantages over other methods.

Guide students in concluding that all of the methods of erosion control have drawbacks and that most are only temporary solutions to wave erosion.

Extension

- Students will learn more about waves and beach erosion if they vary some of the parameters of the project, such as the structure and composition of the beach and lighthouse and the way in which waves are generated. For example, students might build the lighthouse on a spit that extends out from the beach instead of building it on a featureless shoreline, or they might make waves with a fan or hair dryer instead of by moving an object up and down in the water.

- Students can use their wave tank and models to simulate longshore drift by generating waves at an angle to the beach. They should note where sandbars form and be able to explain which method of erosion control works best to prevent longshore drift.

- Students can make waves of different heights to simulate ocean waves on calm and stormy days. They should compare how much erosion occurs with each type of weather.

- Challenge students to generate a tsunami by simulating an earthquake across the water from the beach. They should compare the erosion caused by the tsunami with the amount caused by wind-generated waves.

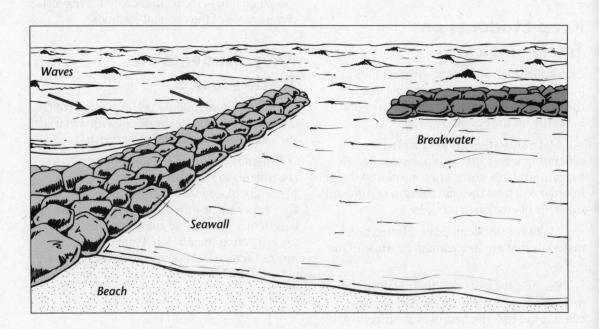

PROJECT OVERVIEW

Design and Build an Erosion-Proof Beach

As waves break on the shore, they wash away sand and deposit it elsewhere, constantly changing the shoreline. Lighthouses, homes, and many other structures are built on shorelines. Without protection, the shorelines and their structures may eventually be washed away by the action of the waves.

Project Rules

In this project, you will build a tank for making waves and then see how the waves erode a model beach and lighthouse. You will also apply at least one method of erosion control and measure how effective it is in preventing erosion on your beach. Follow these steps to complete the project successfully.

- Plan and sketch the wave tank and models, and make a list of materials.

- Build the wave tank, and practice making waves.

- Build the model beach and lighthouse.

- Apply and test methods of erosion control.

- Demonstrate and explain the best method of erosion control to the class.

Project Hints

The following hints will guide you through each of the major steps of the project.

- For a small wave tank, use a large aluminum baking pan or a paint roller pan. Unless you use a paint roller pan, which has a sloping bottom, build the sloping ocean floor out of sand and pebbles. For a larger wave tank, follow the instructions in Project Worksheet 1. Fill the wave tank to test for leaks and to practice making waves. Empty it before you build your model beach and lighthouse.

- You can make waves by moving the end of a wooden spoon or other object up and down in the water at one end of the tank. Each time, raise the object to the same height so that the waves are all the same size. Your waves should be the same scale as your beach and lighthouse. Project Worksheet 2 will show you how to make waves and other project components to scale.

- Your model beach should be able to hold its shape until the waves start to erode it. It should also be made to scale. Use fine sand and silt and very small pebbles. Try to use a variety of materials and shapes to make your beach realistic. Variation in materials and shape may also give you ideas for controlling erosion later in the project.

- Your model lighthouse should be built to scale and also should be similar to real lighthouses in ways that affect its ability to hold up to erosion. Look at pictures of lighthouses for ideas on size, shape, and construction materials. For example, use "mortar" of modeling clay to hold blocks together, and bury the base of the lighthouse deep in the sand. Also, place your lighthouse close to the shore, just like a real lighthouse.

- To control erosion, choose among groins, sand dunes that have been stabilized with plants or other materials, seawalls, and breakwaters. If any of these methods are unfamiliar to you, do some research to learn about them.

- To test which method of erosion control works best, measure how much erosion occurs with a given number of waves of the same height, both before and after you apply the method. One way to measure erosion is to stick toothpicks in the beach at regular intervals, starting with one row very close to the water and backed up by one or more additional rows a few centimeters apart. Put a small piece of masking tape on each toothpick so that you can number the toothpicks and keep track of them as they fall.

- Always return the beach to its original condition and make the waves in the same way for each test.

- Demonstrate the best method to the class. In addition to showing how your method prevents erosion, also explain how it works and why other methods were less effective.

Project Timeline

Task	Due Date
1. Complete design of model beach and list of materials	_____
2. Construct model shoreline and lighthouse	_____
3. Test effects of wave erosion on model	_____
4. Test method of erosion control	_____
5. Test improved method of erosion control	_____
6. Present model to class	_____

PROJECT WORKSHEET 1

Making a Large Wave Tank

Follow the instructions below to make a large wave tank.

Materials
- two large rectangular cardboard box tops, such as those from copier-paper boxes, or underbed storage boxes
- large sheet of clear plastic

- waterproof tape, such as adhesive or electrical tape
- scissors
- silt, sand, and small pebbles

Procedure ✂

1. Cut one of the short ends from each box or box top, and then tape the two boxes or tops together to form one long, shallow tank.

2. Cut a small observation window a few centimeters across in one of the short sides of the tank.

3. Completely line the tank, including the small window, with a single, large sheet of clear plastic.

4. Tape the plastic securely in place with waterproof tape.

5. Use silt, sand, and pebbles to build a sloping ocean floor on one long side of the tank.

6. Fill the tank with water to test it for leaks. Repair if necessary.

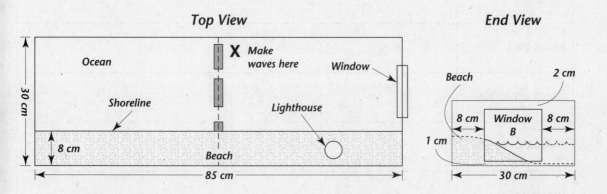

Measurements based on two copier-paper box tops

PROJECT WORKSHEET 2

Working to Scale

For a model to best represent the real world, it should be made to scale. This means that all of the parts of the model are the correct size relative to one another. Usually models are smaller than the real objects they represent. For example, a model might have a scale of 1 centimeter to 1 meter, meaning that 1 centimeter in the model represents 1 meter in the real world. A 40-meter stretch of beach would be represented by a 40-centimeter stretch of beach in this model.

Below is a list of items that might be found on a real beach. For each item, estimate its size in meters. Then calculate how large a scale model of that item would be in centimeters, using a scale of 1 centimeter to 1 meter.

Items	Estimated Size (in meters)	Size of Model (in centimeters)
lighthouse		
adult human		
child		
bush		
sea gull		
beach pail		
beach umbrella		
lifeguard stand		
beach towel		
fence		

Waves, like other project components, should be made to scale. In the ocean, most waves are about 2 to 5 meters high. Again using a scale of 1 centimeter to 1 meter, how high should the waves in your wave tank be? _____

300
Oceans

Name _____ Date _____ Class _____

SCORING RUBRIC

Design and Build an Erosion-Proof Beach

In evaluating how well you complete the Chapter Project, your teacher will judge your work in three categories. In each, a score of 4 is the best rating.

	4	3	2	1
Planning Models and Materials	Makes highly detailed plans of models and a complete list of appropriate materials.	Makes somewhat detailed plans of models and a nearly complete list of appropriate materials.	Makes partial plans of models and an incomplete list of appropriate materials.	Makes inadequate plans of models and lists few if any appropriate materials.
Building Models and Testing Erosion-Control Methods	Builds highly accurate models, tests three or more erosion-control methods, and collects and records complete erosion data.	Builds somewhat accurate models, tests two or more erosion-control methods, and collects and records nearly complete erosion data.	Builds inaccurate but workable models, tests one or more erosion-control methods, and collects and records some erosion data.	Builds unworkable models, fails to test adequately an erosion-control method, and collects and records little if any erosion data.
Presenting the Results	Demonstrates very effective control of erosion and explains accurately and convincingly why the selected method was chosen.	Demonstrates good control of erosion and explains clearly why the selected method was chosen.	Demonstrates some control of erosion and explains adequately why the selected method was chosen.	Demonstrates little if any control of erosion and does not explain adequately why the selected method was chosen.

301
Oceans

The Weather Tomorrow

The following steps will walk you through the Chapter Project. Use the hints and detailed directions as you guide your students through the gathering of information, presentation, and reflection.

Chapter Project Overview

Before students start the project, have them read the Project Overview. Tell them that the Project Rules spell out the tasks of the project for which they will be responsible. Advise them to refer to the Project Hints for help in carrying out these tasks.

Distribute the Scoring Rubric, and discuss how students' work will be assessed.

Hand out the Project Worksheets. Urge students to do the worksheets for additional information and practice interpreting weather maps.

Keep Students on Track—Task 1

Your local newspaper, if it is available before class time, may contain a useful weather map. Weather maps also are available on the Internet. Whatever weather maps students collect, make sure they show today's actual weather and not a prediction of tomorrow's weather. Check that each student's weather maps all have the same format.

If students do not know where to get weather maps, give them one or more ideas for sources, such as *USA Today* or their local newspaper. You might want to supply photocopies of weather maps so students are sure to have them.

Stress the importance of collecting a map for each day for comparative purposes. Point out to students that unless they can observe how the weather changes from day to day, they will not be able to detect patterns in the weather and learn how to make weather predictions.

Encourage students to select locations to follow from different parts of the country so the locations will be likely to vary in their weather conditions. Students should make sure that data are given on their maps for the locations they have chosen.

You may want students to select locations that have some special interest to them. Alternatively, you may want to assign specific locations to each student to ensure that a wide range of locations is covered.

Guide students toward focusing on air pressure, particularly high- and lowpressure centers, as they study their weather maps. Also steer them toward noting fronts, the weather that is associated with them, and how they are moving when students look for patterns in the maps from day to day.

Keep Students on Track—Task 2

When students make their predictions, make sure they have considered how the movement of air masses and fronts may affect the weather in their three locations.

Remind students that the symbols on a front line indicate not just the type of front but also the direction in which it is moving.

You may want to provide each student with a week's worth of outline maps for their weather predictions instead of having them trace their own. This will save them time and also ensure that all the maps are consistent so students can easily compare their prediction maps.

Make sure students include a key that identifies all of the symbols they use on their maps.

Keep Students on Track—Task 3

Students can compare their own forecasts with professional forecasts on the same day they draw their maps. They should look for forecasts in newspaper weather reports or on television. Suggest that they note which weather factors the professional meteorologists seem to rely on most when they make their forecasts and try to learn from the professionals.

Students can compare their own forecasts with the actual weather by comparing their prediction weather map with the next day's newspaper weather map. When students' predictions are incorrect, advise them to try to figure out why. Then, urge them to learn from their mistakes and apply what they learn to their next forecast. As the days go on, students should try to assess whether their ability to predict the weather is improving.

Chapter Project Wrap Up

Suggest to students that they display their weather maps in a way that makes it easy to compare their prediction weather maps with maps showing the actual weather and with professional forecast maps. For example, they might create a poster or bulletin board display in which they line up the three maps for each day's weather, side by side or one above the other. In their presentations, they should point out similarities and differences among the three maps.

To reduce the amount of class time devoted to student presentations, you might want to have each student focus on a comparison of maps for just one day, perhaps the day for which their own forecast was the most accurate.

Make sure students include in their presentations a description of the patterns they observed in the weather and an explanation of how they predicted the weather.

Extension

Challenge students to collect and assemble samples of national weather maps from a number of different sources for the same day's weather. Then have them compare how the maps communicate the same data. Students should consider the basic format of the maps, as well as how specific weather factors are represented. Invite students to share their collection of weather maps with the class and to explain which type of weather map they think is most informative.

PROJECT OVERVIEW

The Weather Tomorrow

In this Chapter Project, you will collect and compare newspaper weather maps to see how the weather changes from day to day. Then, after you have learned more about the weather and how it changes, you will try to predict the weather from one day to the next.

Project Rules

- Collect newspaper weather maps every day for at least two weeks.

- Select your own location and two other locations that are at least 1,000 kilometers away from where you live and from each other.

- Focusing on your three locations, compare weather maps from one day to the next and look for patterns in how the weather changes.

- Try to predict the weather for your three locations every day for a week, based on the current day's weather at each location.

- Compare your daily weather predictions with professional forecasts published in newspapers, as well as with the actual weather as it appears in the next day's newspaper weather map.

Overall Project Hints

- Use a weather map from the same source each day so that all of your maps will have the same basic format. This will make it much easier to compare how the weather symbols on the maps change from day to day.

- If possible, watch television weather reports while you are collecting and studying newspaper weather maps. They can help you understand why the weather changes and how to predict it. For example, television weather reports often show satellite images of the country or regions of the country that make it easy to see the movement of fronts, storms, and other weather patterns.

Hints for Interpreting Weather Maps

- Data usually are shown in much the same way on all newspaper weather maps. If just one temperature is given for a location, it usually is the average daily temperature. If two temperatures are given, they are the daily high and low temperatures. When you compare how the weather changes, make sure you compare high temperatures with high temperatures and low temperatures with low temperatures. On many weather maps, temperatures are indicated with colors. All of the areas that fall within a certain range of temperature are shown in the same color. For example, areas that fall between 70°F and 80°F are in one color, between 80°F and 90°F another color, and so on.

Hints for Interpreting Data on Air Pressure and Fronts

- To predict the weather, it is important to pay close attention to air pressure because high air pressure is associated with fair weather and low air pressure with clouds, precipitation, and storms. Air pressure may be indicated in numbers for each weather station, as it is in the example above. More commonly, however, air pressure is shown with lines called isobars. Project Worksheet 2 will introduce you to isobars and give you practice locating high- and lowpressure centers using isobars.

- Where warm and cold air masses meet, fronts form and bring changing weather conditions. Recognizing the different types of fronts and the direction in which they are moving is crucial for predicting changes in the weather. Complete Worksheet 2 to become more familiar with fronts as they are represented on weather maps. Read your text to learn how the different types of fronts change the weather.

Project Timeline

Task	Due Date
1. Collect and compare daily newspaper weather maps.	_____
2. Create your own weather maps to forecast the weather.	_____
3. Compare your forecasts with professional forecasts and actual weather conditions.	_____
4. Present your project to the class.	_____

PROJECT WORKSHEET 1
Predicting Tomorrow's Weather

Use this map of the lower 48 states to draw symbols to show what you think tomorrow's weather will be.

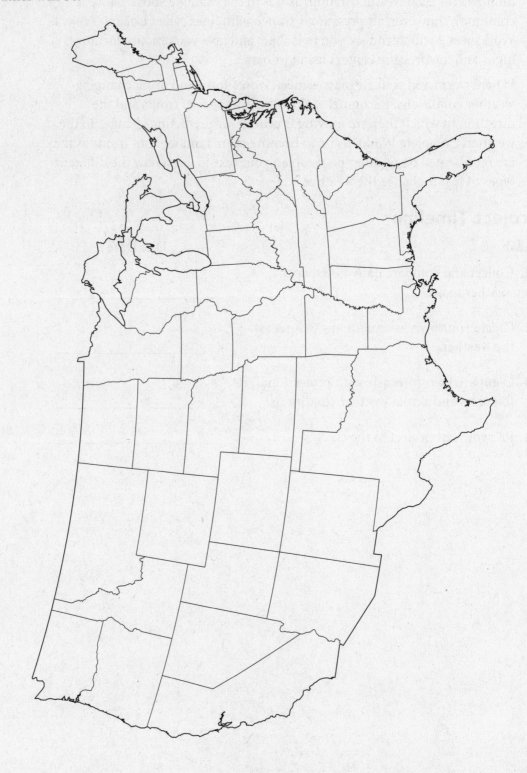

PROJECT WORKSHEET 2

Interpreting Weather Map Symbols: Fronts

When different air masses meet, a front forms. Fronts almost always cause changes in the weather. Most fronts bring clouds, they often bring precipitation, and sometimes they bring storms. After a front passes, the weather is likely to be warmer or colder and wetter or dryer than it was before the front came through.

There are four types of fronts: cold fronts, warm fronts, stationary fronts, and occluded fronts. The way each type of front is represented on weather maps is shown on the right. The symbols projecting from the front lines always point in the direction in which the front is moving.

The map below shows six different fronts. For each front, identify which type of front it is and the direction in which it is moving.

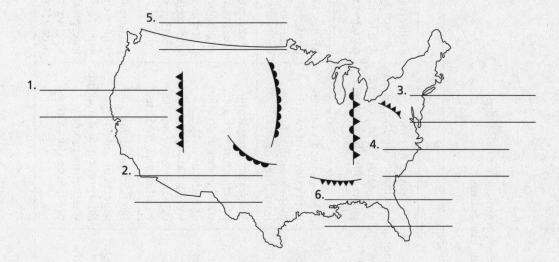

SCORING RUBRIC
The Weather Tomorrow

In evaluating how well you complete the Chapter Project, your teacher will judge your work in four categories. In each, a score of 4 is the best rating.

	4	3	2	1
Collecting and Interpreting Weather Maps	Collects 12 or more newspaper weather maps and identifies the most significant patterns in the weather.	Collects 9 or more newspaper weather maps and identifies important patterns in the weather.	Collects 6 or more newspaper weather maps and identifies some patterns in the weather.	Collects fewer than 6 newspaper weather maps and attempts but fails to identify patterns in the weather.
Predicting the Weather	Makes wellreasoned weather predictions for three locations for a week.	Makes sound weather predictions for two or more locations for at least three days.	Makes weather predictions for one or more locations for at least two days.	Tries to make at least one weather prediction.
Presenting the Results	Makes an excellent presentation with a clear demonstration of patterns in the weather and a convincing explanation of how the weather was predicted.	Makes an interesting presentation with a suitable demonstration of patterns in the weather and a reasonable explanation of how the weather was predicted.	Makes an adequate presentation and attempts to demonstrate patterns in the weather and explain how the weather was predicted.	Makes a weak presentation that fails to demonstrate patterns in the weather or explain how the weather was predicted.
Working Cooperatively (optional)	Takes a lead in collecting, interpreting, and making weather maps and predicting the weather.	Participates in all aspects of collecting, interpreting, and making weather maps and predicting the weather.	Participates, mostly at others' direction, in some aspects of collecting, interpreting, and making weather maps and predicting the weather.	Makes only a small contribution to collecting, interpreting, and making weather maps and predicting the weather.

Track the Moon

The following steps will walk you through the Chapter Project. Use the hints as you guide your students through planning, recording observations of the moon, and class presentations.

This project can be started during any phase of the moon. However, students may have more success with their first observations if you start between the new moon and the waning full moon. At this stage, students can easily see the moon during early evening hours. Students are more likely to have success and become comfortable with recording their observations. If the study starts during stages of the moon's cycle when the moon is not above the horizon during the early evening hours, remind students that noting that the moon is not visible on a clear night is an important observation and should be recorded.

Because students commonly associate the moon with night, they may notice the moon more easily if this project is done during the winter months, when night lasts longer.

Distribute copies of the Project Worksheets. Worksheet 1 will help students become familiar with the compass directions at their observation site. All students should record observations on an observation sheet similar to that in Worksheet 2. This will help students collect the appropriate data and allow class data to be combined. You may need to make additional copies of Worksheet 2.

Have students read the Project Overview. Review the Project Rules and hand out the Scoring Rubric you will use for scoring students' work. Discuss with students what will be expected of them.

Set deadlines for data analysis and presentations, and dates for interim stages of the project. Have students fill in the due dates on the Project Timeline.

Make your own observations during the assignment. This will help you know whether students might be having problems because of cloud cover. Keep a class record. This helps students increase their data pool and can help those who were unable to record their own observations.

Materials and Preparation

Introduce how to describe the moon's position in the sky by locating objects in your room. For example, suppose you have a map of the world hanging in the classroom. You can identify its position by saying that it is on the south wall, four feet up from the floor.

To introduce compass direction, draw a compass on the chalkboard. Explain how a compass works, and show how the compass rose is divided into eighths. Then take students outside, divide them into small groups, and have groups go to different parts of the schoolyard, with one compass per group. Have each group find landmarks at each of the eight compass directions.

To introduce measurement of altitude in degrees, take students outside. Choose a tree to estimate altitude. Have students make a fist and hold it at arm's length. How many fists above the horizon is the top of the tree? One fist above the horizon is about 10°, two fists is about 20°, and so on. Remind them that objects directly overhead are at 90°, and all others are less than 90°.

Best results may be obtained if students share their observations daily, and class members add to their data lists the information from their classmates. Moon sightings made at school could be pointed out for all students to record. Moonrise and moonset times might be recorded from a newspaper weather page.

Keep Students on Track—Task 1

Check students' direction maps of their observation sites, which they have made by completing Worksheet 1. Point out that if their landmarks are too near, the direction the landmarks are from the observer will change if the observer needs to move in order to get a better view of the moon.

Check that students know how to complete the data sheet (Worksheet 2). Do students understand how to measure altitude?

Keep Students on Track—Task 2

Check that students are making observations and recording that data properly. Are they filling in all the required information? They should be noticing that the moon does not rise at the same time every day.

Keep Students on Track—Task 5

By this stage, students will have recorded enough observations to find patterns in the changes of the moon's shape. Have students examine two sketches of the moon made a few hours apart. Do students' sketches show that the orientation of the moon changes in the sky? The moon's crescent shape appears to rotate clockwise a bit during the day.

Chapter Project Wrap Up

Have each student make a presentation based on their observations. The content and format of presentations may vary from student to student, depending on their data and interests. They may incorporate tables, maps, drawings, and graphs.

Have students graph data from their observations. Assign or have students choose data to graph. Options include these: calendar date versus time of moon rise (phases of moon should be noted along with the date), compass direction versus time of observation in the course of one day, and compass direction

versus frequency of sightings (this will show that the moon is seen only in certain parts of the sky, and never in others).

In a class discussion, emphasize the following patterns:

- In the course of a day, the moon's position changes from eastern sky, through southern, to western (because of Earth's rotation).
- Moonrise gets progressively later in the day throughout the cycle.
- The moon will be seen mostly in the southern half of the sky.
- The moon's location in the sky at sunset is more toward the east each day.
- The lit portion of the moon starts on the right side and waxes until full. As it wanes, the right side progressively becomes darker.

Extension

At any location on Earth, an eclipse of the moon (partial or total) occurs at least once a year. If an eclipse will occur when your students are doing this project, be sure students are aware that this is going to happen. If it happens early in the evening, the class might observe it together. Otherwise, students might get an adult to observe with them at home.

PROJECT OVERVIEW

Track the Moon

This project requires you to keep records of when and in what direction you see the moon in the sky. You will make and record your observations for a number of weeks. Then you will look for patterns in your observations and explain the patterns by using what you know about the moon's orbit around Earth and Earth's rotation. To help keep your observations organized, you need to record the following information:

1. **Date:** Record the calendar date (example: November 10, 2011).

2. **Time of observation:** For this project, you should try to make at least one observation each day. On at least one day, you should make at least two observations two or three hours apart.

3. **Moon visible:** Try to make your observations from a place where you can see the sky in all directions. If you can see the moon, determine its direction, altitude, and appearance. Write this information on the data sheet as explained below. If you do not see the moon, the reason might be that the moon is not above the horizon or that it is hidden behind clouds. If the sky is too cloudy to tell whether the moon is above the horizon, record that information on your data sheet.

4. **Position:** The moon travels a path through the sky as if it were an object moving on a dome over Earth. Any position on the dome can be described by its direction from the observation location and its altitude above the horizon.

    Directions follow the compass headings. A compass fixes one direction, north (N), and then all directions along the circle of the horizon can be described.

    The circle of the compass is divided into four directions, north (N), south (S), east (E), and west (W). Four other headings that fall exactly between the four main directions are usually marked on compasses—northwest (NW), northeast (NE), southwest (SW), and southeast (SE). For your observations, record in which of these eight directions you see the moon. Worksheet 1 guides you in making a map of your moon observatory and marking the compass directions on it.

    Altitude normally measures how high an object is above the ground. For very distant objects, a more useful way to record position in the sky is to measure the altitude in term of degrees above the horizon. When an object is on the horizon, its altitude is zero degrees (0°). When an object is directly overhead, its altitude is 90°. You can easily estimate altitude in degrees. Face in the direction of the moon, make a fist, and hold it straight out at arm's length, thumb side up. Count how many fists above the horizon the moon is. One fist above the horizon is about 10°, two fists are about 20°, and so on.

5. **Appearance:** Make a sketch of the moon by shading in the circle. As you shade in the circle to show the moon's phase, try to sketch any slant or tilt of the bright part of the moon. When you are finished, the white part of your circle should look like the bright portion of the moon that you observed.

Project Rules

- Record observations every day.

- Make observations more than once on at least one day. Try to schedule times that will be easy to remember. For example, you could look at the sky just before sunrise, just after sunset, and then right before you go to bed.

- Record all of the data listed in the table on Project Worksheet 2. Also use the worksheet to record any notes about your observations.

- After all observation data has been recorded, analyze the data. Make a class presentation about your observations. Your teacher will help you decide what should be included in your presentation. Your teacher will approve the idea for your presentation before you begin working on it.

Project Hints

- The best site for viewing the moon will have the night sky visible in all directions.

- Try to find an observation site that is away from bright lights so that you can see the stars on a clear night. This will allow you to determine whether the sky is cloudy (no stars visible).

- Complete Project Worksheet 1 to identify landmarks so that you can determine each of the eight compass directions.

Project Timeline

Task	Due Date
1. Direction Map (Worksheet 1) completed	_____
2. Moon observations begun	_____
3. Teacher check of data table	_____
4. Observations completed	_____
5. Data analyzed	_____
6. Presentation made	_____

PROJECT WORKSHEET 1
Make a Direction Map

1. Obtain or borrow a compass with a face that is at least 2 centimeters in diameter and that has marks for the eight directions (N, NE, E, SE, S, SW, W, NW).

2. During daylight hours, go to the site that you will use to record the moon observation data. On a blank sheet of paper, draw a large circle. Draw lines to divide the circle into halves, then quarters, and finally eighths. The center of the circle represents your position. Label your circle with the eight points of the compass.

3. Place the compass on a flat surface, such as a book. Make sure that the surface is level so that the compass needle is free to spin. Keep the compass away from metal objects because they will affect the compass readings.

4. Allow the compass needle to come to rest. One end of the needle (usually the end that is red or pointed) will be pointing north. Rotate the body of the compass until the needle lines up with the "N" on the face. Stand behind the needle and look in the "N" direction (the needle will be pointing in this direction). Identify a landmark, one far away if possible, and mark it on your drawn circle. Label it "north." If there is no landmark exactly north of your location, choose a landmark that is close to exactly north and put it in the approximate location on your direction map.

5. Now stand on the opposite side of the compass and look in the "S" direction. The back of the compass needle will be pointing south. Identify a distant landmark and mark it on your map. Do the same for all eight directions.

6. To check your direction map, stand at your observation location and throw an object, such as a ball, in any direction. Once it lands, use your map to determine in which compass direction the object lies relative to where you are standing. Next, use the compass to check the direction you obtained from your map (don't forget to align the needle and the "N"). If your map direction and compass direction do not agree, make the necessary corrections to your map.

Name _____ Date_____ Class_____

PROJECT WORKSHEET 2
Moon Observation Data Sheet

Date	Time	Moon Visible? (yes, no)	Direction (N, S, etc.)	Altitude (degrees)	Appearance (sketch)	Notes (for example, cloudy, or clear but not visible)
					◯	
					◯	
					◯	
					◯	
					◯	
					◯	
					◯	
					◯	
					◯	
					◯	
					◯	
					◯	
					◯	
					◯	
					◯	
					◯	
					◯	

SCORING RUBRIC

Track the Moon

In evaluating how well you complete the Chapter Project, your teacher will judge your work in four categories. In each, a score of 4 is the best rating.

	4	3	2	1
Making Moon Observations and Keeping Daily Record	Observations made daily. Data table complete and neat with accurate sketches and notation of cloudy skies.	Observations made almost daily. A few data are incomplete or inaccurate. No distinction between cloudy skies and clear skies when moon below horizon.	Most days have observations. Quite a few data are incomplete or inaccurate. No distinction between cloudy skies and clear skies when moon below horizon.	Many days have no observations. Many errors and omissions. Data table sloppy.
Making Graphs and Analyzing Data	Student makes complete and correct analysis of data. Graph is correct and clear.	Student makes mostly complete and correct analysis of data. Graph is correct.	Student's analysis of data is mostly correct but is partially incomplete. Graph may have minor errors.	Data analysis is minimal or significantly incorrect. Graph has at least one significant error.
Understanding Concepts and Presenting Results	Data analysis and presentation are thorough and indicate full understanding of how and why the position and appearance of the moon change over time.	Data analysis and presentation are adequate and indicate good understanding of how and why the position and appearance of the moon change over time.	Data analysis and presentation are acceptable and indicate some understanding of how and why the position and appearance of the moon change over time.	Data analysis and presentation are minimal and indicate important misunderstanding of how and why the position and appearance of the moon change over time.
Participating in Class	Communicates clearly and accurately. Participates fully in class discussion.	Communication is fairly clear and accurate. Class participation is adequate.	Communication mostly accurate but is limited. Participation is limited.	Communication is unclear or mostly inaccurate and class participation is minimal.

Space Exploration Vehicle

The following steps will walk you through the Chapter Project. Use the hints as you guide your students through the planning, designing, testing, and presenting of their space vehicles.

This project gives students an opportunity to learn about various landscapes that are found in our solar system. Designing and building a vehicle for these terrains gives students an understanding of some of the challenges faced by scientists and engineers when designing exploration vehicles. It also gives students hands-on experience in building a prototype of a design.

To introduce the project, talk about the lunar buggy from the *Apollo* moon landings. Ask students how something like a lunar buggy might be different from a car. Discuss the different design criteria for a lunar buggy, such as navigating in reduced gravity, rolling over loose gravel, and so on. After students understand that the design of the vehicle depends on the environment, ask them what they would need if they were to design a vehicle for exploring other planets or moons.

Distribute copies of the Project Worksheets. Worksheet 1, a homework assignment, will provide students with a chart to identify solar system landscapes. All students should answer the questions on Worksheet 2.

After students complete their homework, have them discuss in class what they found and list the various types of landscapes found in the solar system. All project activities should be done in small groups of about three students each.

Assign planets and moons to be researched by each group.

Materials and Preparation

Models can be built with simple materials such as cardboard, foam boards, wooden dowels or craft sticks, rubber bands, old CDs, and so on. The class may choose to brainstorm a list of acceptable materials to limit the types of materials used.

If students are testing their vehicles in the classroom, a test course can be constructed on the floor or on a large table. Use items such as books and boxes to simulate cliffs and steep hills, stones or paperweights to simulate boulders and rocks, or cardboard to make hills and inclines. This can also be assigned to students for extra credit. If a suitable outside area exists, such as a playground or a parking lot with curbs and grass, consider using it for a test site.

Keep Students on Track—Task 2

Review each group's worksheets. Then, as a class, narrow the list of landscapes by crossing out any items that are too difficult to address or test, such as the surfaces of the gas giant planets. This may be done by initially choosing a few landscapes and then narrowing the list by voting, or by focusing on one planet or moon and using the landscapes found on it. Choose at least two landscape features.

If groups have not yet decided which planet or moon to explore, have them do so now. Encourage them to brainstorm how a vehicle would move over the terrain of the selected planet or moon. Remind students that this landscape must be addressed in their design. The designs should be something that can be implemented in the classroom. At this point, it may be helpful to inform students about the different building materials available to them.

Keep Students on Track—Tasks 3–4

Check to make sure that vehicles are being designed to carry scientific equipment on board: These may be small items such as a film canister, a roll of tape, and so on. The class should decide on the item that will serve as the equipment. The equipment will be placed on the vehicle, and the vehicle must be able to navigate the course without damaging or dropping the equipment.

Also, make sure that each group generates a list of design requirements and completes the appropriate section of the worksheet. Design requirements should be specific, including statements such as "the vehicle must have good traction to navigate on ice." You may set additional design requirements if necessary, such as limiting the size of the vehicle. Explain to students that a string will be attached to the front of each vehicle so that it can be pulled through a test course. Have students draw a sketch of their design on the worksheet.

Keep Students on Track—Tasks 5–6

At this point, students have built their vehicles, using their design sketches as a reference. Have each group present its design to the class, testing it as part of the presentation, if possible. If vehicles are being tested, the presentation can be a brief description of the design and how each design requirement was addressed. If the vehicle is not being tested, the descriptions should be followed by predictions of how the students think the vehicles would perform.

Chapter Project Wrap Up

To complete the project, test the vehicles on a test course. Have students write in their journals about some of the challenges they faced while designing and building the vehicle. Journal entries should include a discussion of how the designs did or did not meet the design requirements and how the design might be improved. Students might also write about their classmates' designs.

Extension

Students may wish to refine their models or designs. The models may also be built of more sophisticated materials, such as programmable construction sets.

PROJECT OVERVIEW

Space Exploration Vehicle

How can you design a vehicle that will be used on the surface of a moon or planet that you have never visited? You already know the requirements of a vehicle that is used on Earth's surface. If you know about the landscape of the planet or moon and the purpose of the vehicle, you can design, build, and test a vehicle for the exploration of the planet or moon.

For this project, you will use the information you have learned about the different types of landscapes found on the planets and moons in our solar system. You will then use that knowledge to design and build a vehicle that can navigate the varied terrains.

Project Rules

- Identify the landscapes and geological features that are found on the planets and moons of the solar system.

- Brainstorm ways to build a vehicle that can overcome these terrains while carrying equipment.

- Design and sketch a model of the vehicle.

- Build a model vehicle.

- Present the vehicle to the class, and test it.

Suggested Materials

You will need design tools such as rulers, scissors, glue, and so on. Prototypes can be built from simple materials such as cardboard, foam board, and craft sticks. Wooden dowels may be helpful for wheel axles.

Attach a long string to each vehicle so that it can be pulled across the test course. If you are testing the vehicles in the classroom, a test course can be made by placing obstacles such as books, boxes, and rugs on the floor.

Project Hints

You will work on the project in small groups. First, focus on a small number of planets or moons to identify landscapes. After each group makes a list of potential landscapes, get together as a class to make a combined list. Then, with the class, eliminate those planets and moons with landscapes that cannot be navigated by a vehicle, such as the gas giants. Then, because it will be difficult to design for all possible landscape features, you may either choose a few of the identified landscape features as a design goal or choose a particular planet or moon on which to focus. As an alternative, if your teacher has designated a "test site" (for example, a playground), you can design for this site. Work with your group to brainstorm, design, and build a vehicle that will work well in your chosen landscape.

Project Timeline

Task	Due Date
1. Research planets and satellites.	_____
2. List possible landscapes to explore.	_____
3. Identify design requirements for the exploration vehicle.	_____
4. Sketch the design on paper.	_____
5. Make a prototype vehicle.	_____
6. Test and present the vehicle.	_____

PROJECT WORKSHEET 1

Solar System Landscapes

Planets and Major Moons	Description of Planet or Moon	Landscapes—Check all that exist on the planet or moon.							
		Dirt or Gravel	Rocks	Ice	Craters	Volcanoes/ Geysers	Cliffs/Cracks	Bodies of Water of Other Liquid	Other (Please exp
Mercury									
Venus									
Earth									
Moon									
Mars									
Phobos									
Deimos									
Jupiter									
Io									
Europa									
Ganymede									
Callisto									
Saturn									
Titan									
Uranus									
Miranda									
Neptune									
Triton									
Pluto									
Charon									

PROJECT WORKSHEET 2
Vehicle Design

1. List the types of landscapes that your vehicle may encounter on your chosen planet or moon.

   _____

   _____

   _____

   _____

   _____

2. List your design requirements. Be as specific as you can, and explain how the requirements relate to the landscapes that you may encounter.

   _____

   _____

   _____

   _____

   _____

3. Make a sketch of your vehicle. Be sure to include enough details and explanations of special features to allow others to understand your drawing.

SCORING RUBRIC
Space Exploration Vehicle

In evaluating how well you complete the Chapter Project, your teacher will judge your work in four categories. In each, a score of 4 is the best rating.

	4	3	2	1
Developing List of Design Requirements	List specifically describes the landscape that the vehicle will need to travel over and thoroughly explains how the requirements for the vehicle design relate to the landscape.	List includes a fairly detailed description of the landscape that the vehicle will need to travel over and provides a good explanation of how the requirements for the vehicle design relate to the landscape.	List includes a general description of the landscape that the vehicle will need to travel over and provides an explanation that shows some understanding of how the requirements for the vehicle design relate to the landscape.	List includes a limited description of the landscape that the vehicle will need to travel over and provides an explanation that shows a limited understanding of how the requirements for the vehicle design relate to the landscape.
Creating Sketches of Vehicle	Sketches show originality of design and a thorough understanding of the requirements of the terrain.	Sketches show some originality of design and a good understanding of the requirements of the terrain.	Sketches show an adequate design and some understanding of the requirements of the terrain.	Sketches show an incomplete or inappropriate design and little or no understanding of the requirements of the terrain.
Constructing Model of Vehicle	Model is well constructed and includes all design requirements.	Model is adequately constructed and includes all design requirements.	Model is adequately constructed and includes some but not all design requirements.	Model is inadequately constructed or does not include all design requirements.
Presenting the Model to the Class	Presentation is thorough and interesting and includes a clear, accurate explanation of how the vehicle meets its design requirements.	Presentation is fairly thorough and includes a satisfactory explanation of how the vehicle meets its design requirements.	Presentation is not thorough. Includes a partial explanation of how the vehicle meets its design requirements.	Presentation includes an incomplete or inaccurate explanation of how the vehicle meets its design requirements.
Participating	Takes a lead in planning,	Participates in all aspects of	Participates in most aspects	Plays a minor role in

Build a Model of the Solar System

The following steps will walk you through the Chapter Project. Use the hints as you guide your students through planning, model building, and presentations.

Before introducing the project, bring a model, such as a miniature Statue of Liberty, into the classroom to show to students. Talk about size and scaling. Measure features of the model, such as the statue's nose, and compare these measurements to those of the actual object.

Have students read the Project Overview. Review the Project Rules and hand out the Scoring Rubric, which you will use to score students' work. Discuss with students what is expected of them.

Set a deadline for the project presentation and interim dates for the different project tasks. Encourage students to copy the dates in the Project Timeline.

Distribute copies of Project Worksheet 1. This worksheet should help students think about scaling. Assess students' level of mathematical skill, and decide whether to let them work on this worksheet in groups. This will give you more of an opportunity to assist them. Project Worksheet 2 will help students get started with their projects as they begin to plan their models. Distribute this worksheet when you are sure that all students understand the concepts of size and scaling. Remind students to refer to the hints in the Project Overview as they plan and carry out the project.

Materials and Preparation

Consider building a large model of the solar system as a class activity, with more detail on each of the solar system's objects. Individual students or groups of students could be responsible for modeling particular planets, moons, asteroids, and comets. This could be done as a chalk drawing outside on the school sidewalk, as a larger papier mâché model, or with objects of various sizes in the school yard.

Meter sticks or metric rulers, tape measures, and calculators will help students with their model building. Objects such as beach balls, basketballs, baseballs, tennis balls, fruit (grapefruit, oranges), marbles, dried beans, ball bearings, and sand would make good models of planets, depending on their diameter and the scaling used. For the model in which students demonstrate the distance between planets, chalk drawings on the chalkboard or on a sidewalk outside will allow space for students to construct their models. City maps or a neighborhood map that you create will also be useful.

Additional materials that may assist students in thinking about size and scaling are available from such companies as the Astronomical Society of the Pacific, 390 Ashton Avenue, San Francisco, CA 94112, USA. The video *Powers of Ten* by Charles and Ray Eames may help students with their mathematical skills. It is available from the same location. A solar system chart that provides relative sizes, distances, orbits, and data about the planets and their place in the galaxy may help students understand the size of the solar system.

Keep Students on Track—Task 1

A major difficulty of this project will be the mathematics of manipulating large numbers. Monitor students carefully to make sure they are calculating correctly. Review with students how to convert kilometers to centimeters. For this part of the project, appropriately scaled distances can be found by dividing actual distances by 1,000,000,000,000 and expressing the final number in centimeters.

Make sure that students understand the concept of scaling. You could ask students to draw a model of the classroom where 1 centimeter = 1 foot. Explain that the ratio 1 cm : 1 ft represents that scale. Have students diagram their plans for demonstrating the distances between the planets.

Review students' plans before allowing them to begin this project. If they are planning to use a common school area, such as a hallway or sidewalk, make sure that they have obtained permission to do so.

Check students' completed data tables at the top of Worksheet 1. Make sure that they have selected an appropriate scale, such as those suggested previously. Check their mathematical calculations to ensure that students understand how to scale the distances between the planets proportionally.

Keep Students on Track—Task 3

Before having students complete the data tables at the bottom of Worksheet 1, you may want to review the SI and have students practice converting between meters, centimeters, and millimeters.

Check students' completed data tables at the bottom of Worksheet 1. Make sure that they have selected a scale for which they can choose objects of the correct size. One useful scale can be found by dividing actual diameters by 1,000,000,000—the results are in centimeters. Check mathematical calculations to ensure that students understand how to scale the diameters of the planets proportionally.

Check students' model plans. Be sure students have thought about objects that they can use as model planets.

Keep Students on Track—Task 5

Check students' completed data tables on Worksheet 2. Make sure that they have considered both the diameters of the planets and the distances between the planets.

Make sure that students have considered the difficulties in creating one model that illustrates both size and distance. Ask: Have you thought about how you will illustrate this? Have you considered whether it is possible to do so within the limits of the classroom?

Chapter Project Wrap Up

As students demonstrate their models, ask their classmates to take brief notes, writing down the major differences between models. Did everyone use the same scales? Did some scales work better than others?

After all the presentations have been made, have students discuss the different models. Have them decide which scales worked best for the project and what problems they encountered in building their models. Would they do anything differently the next time they build such models? Also discuss the vastness of space. Students should now have a better understanding of the size of the solar system and how much of it is empty space.

Extension

At the end of the project, take your students to a local planetarium where they can learn more about the planets in our solar system, as well as other astronomical topics.

PROJECT OVERVIEW

Build a Model of the Solar System

In this project, you will make models of our solar system in three different ways. In one model, you will represent the distance of each planet (and Pluto) from the sun. In a second model, you will illustrate the relative size of the sun, the planets, and Pluto. Finally, you will combine the concepts shown in the first two models. At the end of the project, you will present your models to the class.

Project Rules

- The first model will show the relative distance from each planet to the sun.

- The second model will show the relative sizes of the planets.

- The third model will show each planet's relative distance from the sun and its diameters.

- You must build your models to scale. The scale should be clearly posted as part of each model.

- Have your teacher approve your research and plans before you begin each model.

Suggested Materials

- Meter sticks or metric rulers, tape measures, and calculators will be needed for model building.

- For the model in which you demonstrate the distances between planets, drawings on the chalkboard, on cash register tape attached to a wall, or on a sidewalk will give you space to construct the models. You may also want to represent the positions of the planets by using a community map. Mark a central landmark or building as the sun.

- Objects such as beach balls, basketballs, baseballs, tennis balls, fruit (grapefruit, oranges), marbles, dried beans, ball bearings, and grains of sand would make good models of planets, depending on their diameter and the scale used.

Project Hints

- Use the Project Worksheets to help you start thinking about possible scales to use for your models.

- When you are working with the distances between the planets, it will be very difficult to fit all of the planets onto a sheet of paper. Think about other ways to model distances, such as on the chalkboard, on a sidewalk, in the schoolyard, or on a cash register tape.

- If your model uses distances that would put some planets out of the schoolyard, you can use a map to show that part of your model.

- Try several different scales. Do the mathematical calculations for the largest and smallest planets, and think about how you would model the sizes that you have calculated. Your scale must be able to demonstrate reasonably both the small and large sizes. Distances and planet diameters do not have to be expressed in kilometers. You may want to convert the units to meters or centimeters.

- To show a distance that may extend beyond the boundary of your model, you can label an arrow or a dotted line at the outer limit with the additional distance the planet extends from that boundary.

- If you decide to use a scale that creates a model that is too large to bring into the classroom, you might consider videotaping it. You could show the video as part of your class presentation.

Project Timeline

Task	Due Date
1. Scale for distances between planets selected and approved	_____
2. Model of distances between planets completed	_____
3. Scale for planet sizes selected and approved	_____
4. Model of planet sizes completed	_____
5. Scale for combination model selected and approved	_____
6. Combination model approved	_____
7. Class presentation completed	_____

Name _____ Date_____ Class_____

PROJECT WORKSHEET 1
Separate Distance and Diameter Models
Distance From Sun
Complete the following data table. When it has been completed, you are ready to get your teacher's approval and being modeling the distances between the planets.

Object	Radius of Orbit (km)	1:10,000,000,000 Scale	1:50,000,000,000 Scale	Your Scale (1: _____)
Sun	Center	Center	Center	Center
Mercury	58,000,000	5.8 m	1.2 m	
Venus	108,000,000	10.8 m	2.2 m	
Earth	150,000,000			
Mars	228,000,000			
Jupiter	779,000,000			
Saturn	1,434,000,000			
Uranus	2,873,000,000			
Neptune	4,495,000,000			
Pluto	5,870,000,000			

Planet Size
Complete the following data table. When it has been completed, you are ready to get your teacher's approval and begin modeling the sizes of planets.

Object	Diameter (km)	1:1,000,000,000 Scale	1:500,000,000 Scale	Your Scale (1: _____)	Model Object
Sun	1,392,000	1.39 m	2.78 m		
Mercury	4,879	5 mm	10 mm		
Venus	12,104				
Earth	12,756				
Mars	6,794				
Jupiter	143,000				
Saturn	120,500				
Uranus	51,100				
Neptune	49,500				
Pluto	2,400				

PROJECT WORKSHEET 2

Combination Model

Complete the following data table. Make a second data table like the one below in which you can use your own choice of scale. When your table has been completed, you are ready to get your teacher's approval and begin the combination model.

Object	Diameter (km)	1:10,000,000,000 Scale	Distance From Sun (km)	1:10,000,000,000 Scale	Model Object
Sun	1,392,000	13.9 cm	Center	Center	
Mercury	4,879	0.5 mm	58,000,000	5.8 m	
Venus	12,104		108,000,000		
Earth	12,756		150,000,000		
Mars	6,794		228,000,000		
Jupiter	143,000		779,000,000		
Saturn	120,500		1,434,000,000		
Uranus	51,100		2,873,000,000		
Neptune	49,500		4,495,000,000		
Pluto	2,400		5,870,000,000		

Analyzing and Presenting

Complete the following tasks on a separate sheet of paper. When they have been completed, you are ready to plan your presentation.

1. Write a paragraph summarizing your experience with model building. What scales did you choose? Why did you choose these scales? What problems did you encounter in your building model?

2. Write a paragraph discussing what you have learned about the size of the solar system. What did you notice about the spacing of the planets? Are some closer together than others?

3. Write a paragraph about scaling. What are the advantages of building models to scale? What are the disadvantages of building models to scale?

SCORING RUBRIC

Build a Model of the Solar System

In evaluating how well you complete the Chapter Project, your teacher will judge your work in four categories. In each category, a score of 4 is the best rating.

	4	3	2	1
Making Mathematical Calculations	Accurately computes all diameters and distances for all models.	Accurately computes most diameters and distances for the models.	Accurately computes some diameters and distances for the models.	Accurately computes only a few diameters and distances for the models.
Selecting Model Scales	All the scales chosen are useful for demonstrating planet diameters and distances. All objects chosen are the correct size for the scale.	Two of the scales chosen are useful for demonstrating planet diameters and distances. Most objects chosen are the correct size for the scale.	One of the scales chosen is useful for demonstrating planet diameters and distances. Some objects chosen are the correct size for the scale.	Scales for the models are impractical and not useful for illustrating planet diameters and distances. Objects chosen are not the correct size for the scale.
Understanding Size and Scaling	The student completely describes size and scale on the worksheets and in class discussions.	The student adequately describes size and scale on the worksheets and in class discussions.	The student somewhat describes size and scale on the worksheets and in class discussions.	The student minimally describes size and scale on the worksheets and in class discussions.
Making Class Presentation	The student makes a thorough, well-organized presentation. Student explains why particular scales for models were chosen.	The student makes an adequate presentation. Student partially explains why particular scales for the models were chosen.	Presentation is somewhat hard to follow. Very little explanation given for choice of particular scales.	Presentation is very brief and hard to follow. No explanation given for choice of particular scales.

Star Stories

The following steps will walk you through the Chapter Project. Use the hints as you guide students through choosing a constellation, researching it, developing a new myth, and presenting their new myth to the class.

This project asks students to bring together a number of different skills: using star charts to locate constellations, researching cultural history and background, thinking creatively, and communicating in writing. The goal is for students to research the stories that various cultures have told about a given constellation. Then each student will make up a name for the pattern observed in that constellation and write a story to support the name.

In this project, students get acquainted with classical mythology and also discover ways in which non-European cultures have interpreted the patterns of stars. They use their imaginations to write their own stories, following the steps of the writing process outlined in Project Worksheet 2.

Have students read the Project Overview. Review the Project Rules and hand out the Scoring Rubric, which you will use in scoring students' work. Discuss with students what will be expected of them.

Set a deadline for the paper submission, and project presentation and interim dates for the different project tasks. Encourage students to copy the dates in the Project Timeline.

Have students choose three constellations to try to observe in the night sky, using the star charts in the appendix of the textbook. Make sure that at least one of the constellations will be easy to see, as this will build students' confidence. Check the night sky a few days before beginning the project to determine which constellations are easiest to see.

Distribute copies of Project Worksheets 1 and 2. Worksheet 1 will help students get involved in the project and Worksheet 2 will help them write their story. Remind students to refer to the hints in the Project Overview as they plan and carry out the project.

Materials and Preparation

Gather research resources for the students. These might include:

Milton Heifetz and Wil Tirion. *A Walk Through the Heavens: A Guide to Stars and Constellations and Their Legends.* Cambridge University Press, 1996. (Note: Much of the violence in the mythology has been toned down.)

Chet Raymo. *365 Starry Nights: An Introduction to Astronomy for Every Night of the Year.* Prentice Hall Press, 1982.

John Gustafson. *Stars, Clusters and Galaxies. The Young Stargazer's Guide to the Galaxy.* Julian Messner, 1992.

Fred Schaaf. *Seeing the Sky. 100 Projects, Activities and Explorations in Astronomy.* John Wiley and Sons, 1990. (Note: The projects are generally for adults.)

Keep Students on Track—Tasks 1–3

Guide students' observations by pointing out constellations that are visible in the early evening (if cloudy weather makes observations impossible, students can study constellations from the star charts).

Make sure that students should understand that people in many different parts of the world have identified the same or similar patterns of stars in the sky.

Provide class time for students to tell some of the myths they find. From the resources suggested, you can give examples of how different cultures have interpreted the same constellation differently. You may want to have them discuss why, for example, farming peoples might associate certain stars with annual floods or seasonal changes. These stories and legends set the stage for the next step, when students will write their own stories to explain a star pattern.

Be sure to explain that one aspect of myths is their variability. They were passed down from person to person, and many versions of the same myths exist. The students aren't wrong if their stories differ from those of other students.

Keep Students on Track—Task 4

The writing exercises at the top of Worksheet 2 are the first step in the writing process, called prewriting. Along with researching, prewriting techniques can include brainstorming ideas, listing possible subjects, narrowing the focus, identifying the audience, and making an outline.

If students are having trouble thinking of ideas for re-imagining and renaming their constellations, have them brainstorm with several classmates. Students may also need help focusing on one pattern and name.

Keep Students on Track—Tasks 5–6

The middle steps of Worksheet 2 are perhaps the most important in the writing process. Be sure that students actually go through the two distinct steps of writing a first draft and then revising/editing it. A story need not be longer than an anecdote of one or two paragraphs, although some students will write more elaborate explanations. Remind students that their final goal is to re-imagine the pattern of stars in a constellation, name it, and then write a story that explains the name they have chosen.

Chapter Project Wrap Up

Students' final presentation generally will show whether they have done the appropriate research and completed the writing assignment. As you discuss with students the form of their final presentations, you will be able to assess the quality of their research. Students should show familiarity with at least the myths associated with their constellations. One likely choice of presentation is a poster illustrating the constellation and the story that the student has invented, but be receptive to other ideas. Encourage students who have studied the same constellation to discuss their different approaches to it.

Extension

Although it is important for students to locate and recognize constellations in the night sky, you can get more variety in research projects by letting students choose constellations that are not visible at this season. To ensure variety and avoid having too many students choose the same constellation, you may want to assign students the constellations that they will research.

PROJECT OVERVIEW

Star Stories

For this project, you will first use a star chart from the appendix of your textbook to identify three constellations that are visible in the night sky during the current season. Using your star chart, you will go outside on a clear night and identify these constellations in the sky. You will then research the name of one constellation, finding stories about the constellation from different cultures. After the research, you will rename the constellation based on what the star pattern looks like to you. You will then come up with a story to explain the new name of the constellation. Finally, you will write your story and present it to the rest of the class.

Project Rules

- After you choose your three constellations, check with your teacher to make sure they will be visible during the current season.

- Have your teacher approve the constellation that you choose to research.

- Find as many stories about your constellation as you can.

- After writing a rough draft, show it to your teacher to make sure that you are on the right track.

Suggested Materials

You will need research sources, such as encyclopedias and books on mythology. Project Worksheet 1 summarizes the myths of several cultures that apply to some major constellations.

You may need art materials if you choose to make posters for your final presentation. These might include poster board, glue, drawing paper, pens, and pencils.

Project Hints

- Carefully study the star maps in the appendix of the textbook before looking for constellations in the night sky. Try to find an area away from outside lights to view constellations.

- Libraries and the Internet are good places to find information about the constellation that you choose to research. Worksheet 1 may also help you get started.

- When trying to decide upon a new name for the constellation that you have chosen, sketch the positions of the stars in the constellation, and then spend some time looking at your sketch from many different angles. Write down all the things that you see in your constellation.

- When you are trying to come up with a story for your constellation, do not be afraid to use your imagination. There is no "wrong" story.

- Before you begin writing your story, go over Project Worksheet 2, which gives an outline of the stages of writing that you should follow.

Project Timeline

Task	Due Date
1. Three constellations selected and observed	_____
2. One of these three constellations chosen for research	_____
3. Research of story behind chosen constellation completed	_____
4. New story formulated for constellation	_____
5. First written draft of story shown to teacher	_____
6. Final written draft turned in and story presented to class	_____

PROJECT WORKSHEET 1
Star Stories

Orion: Orion the Hunter is one of the easiest constellations to see in the winter sky, especially the three bright stars that make up his belt. In Greek myth, Orion was a mighty hunter, and he boasted that he could wipe out all the animals on Earth. As punishment for Orion's bragging, the Earth goddess Gaia sent a poisonous scorpion to bite him. (The scorpion is also a constellation, called Scorpius, is at the opposite end of the sky. Therefore, the two will never meet again.) Arabic cultures and Indians in Brazil also viewed the Orion constellation as a hunter.

Two hunting dogs follow Orion—the Great Dog, Canis Major, near his foot, and the Little Dog, Canis Minor, at his shoulder. Sirius, the "Dog Star," is at the head of the Great Dog. It is the brightest star in the night sky.

The Egyptians saw the constellation Orion as the major god Osiris, who dies and is reborn each year as the constellation disappears for 70 days and then reappears in the sky.

Orion's belt has many names, too. European sailors called it the "Yardarm," which is the name for the crosspiece of the mast on a sailing ship. In parts of Latin America, the three stars are the "Three Kings."

Stars, Constellations, and Their Myths

Constellation/Star	Classical Story (Greek/Roman)	Other Stories
Pleiades	Seven sisters or flock of doves	Native American: Lost children
Lyra	Orpheus' lyre or harp; Romans saw a vase.	Persia: Tortoise or clay tablet; Also, eagle, falcon, or vulture
Northern Crown(Corona Borealis)	Crown of jewels put in sky by Bacchus as a wedding present for Ariadne	Native American: Council of chiefs in a circle, or den of the Great Bear Arabia: "Beggar's Bowl" Siberia: "Polar Bear's Paw" China: Coins on a string
Virgo	Identified with goddess of harvest (Persephone), holding sheaf of wheat, or as goddess of justice	Ancient Britons: Harvest goddess Eostre Ancient Egypt: Identified with goddess Isis
Sirius (Dog Star)	Name means "scorching." Romans blamed it for hot weather.	Ancient Egypt: Sothis or Anubis, the jackal god; Believed to cause the yearly Nile floods

PROJECT WORKSHEET 2
Star Stories

When writing a paper, you may find it useful to go through the following sequence:

1. **Prewriting:** During the prewriting stage, you will perform any activities that must be done before the actual writing of your story. These include:

   - researching your constellation to become familiar with the stories told about it by various cultures

   - brainstorming ideas for a possible story of your own concerning the constellation

   - narrowing the focus so that you decide upon a particular story to write about

   - identifying the audience that you will be writing the story for (your teacher and classmates)

   - making an outline of the story

2. **Writing a first draft:** You need to write a first draft so that you have something that you can edit and revise as needed. Writing a first draft and then revising and editing this draft are perhaps the most crucial steps in the writing process.

3. **Revising the first draft:** Once you have the first draft, you will need to revise and edit it. You might want to add particular details to the story that you overlooked in the first draft. You might wish to change the introduction or the ending, revise sentences to clarify them, change words or sentences to make your writing more interesting, and choose more exact words. The content of the first draft, how it is presented, and the language used should be carefully revised.

4. **Writing a final draft:** Rewrite your story, incorporating changes you made during the revising stage. Then proofread the final version. Carefully check your spelling, vocabulary, grammar, capitalization, and punctuation.

5. **Publishing:** You then have to decide how you will present the final draft of your story, whether in manuscript form, in an audiovisual presentation, or in some other form.

Name _____ Date _____ Class _____

SCORING RUBRIC
Star Stories

In evaluating how well you complete the Chapter Project, your teacher will judge your work in four categories. In each, a score of 4 is the best rating.

	4	3	2	1
Researching Constellation	Thoroughly researches the myths involving the chosen constellation. Able to tell the original myth and answer questions about the myth.	Adequately researches the myths behind the chosen constellation. Able to tell the original myth in outline and answer some questions about the myth.	Has done some research on the myths. Unable to recount many of the details of the myth.	Has done very little research on the myths. Has little familiarity with the myths.
Creating First Draft of Paper	First draft finished and well-prepared by due date.	First draft finished and adequately prepared on due date.	First draft finished but poorly prepared by due date.	First draft barely unfinished by due date.
Finishing Final Draft of Paper	Paper contains a complete, easy-to-follow story of the new constellation name. Paper is well-written, with no spelling or grammatical errors.	Paper contains a complete story of the new constellation name. Paper has a few spelling or grammatical errors.	Paper contains a somewhat complete story of the new constellation name. Paper is poorly written, with spelling or grammatical errors.	Paper contains an incomplete story of the new constellation name. Paper is poorly written, with many spelling and grammatical errors.
Making Presentation	Identifies constellation and clearly and creatively presents new name and story behind the name.	Identifies constellation. New name and story behind the name are adequately presented.	Identifies constellation. New name and story behind the name are presented, but not clearly.	Does not adequately identify constellation, and does not adequately present story behind new name.

Stars, Galaxies, and the Universe

Make Your Own Indicator

The following steps will walk you through the Chapter Project. Use the hints as you guide your students through planning, indicator extraction, and pH testing.

Chapter Project Overview

In this project, students will make their own acid-base indicators from foods, plants, or other materials. They will use these indicators to test the pH of common household substances and compare their results with the results obtained with pH test papers.

Before introducing the project, do a class presentation in which you use tea as an acid-base indicator. Students should observe color change as you add a couple of drops of the tea to test tubes of vinegar and ammonia. Explain to students that they will be using colored materials, like the tea, to test the pH of various substances.

Decide on the number of indicators that students will extract and the number of substances students will test. Have students read the Project Overview. Review the Project Rules and hand out the Scoring Rubric you will use for scoring students' work. Discuss with students what will be expected of them.

Set a deadline for the project presentation and interim dates for the different project tasks. Encourage students to copy the dates in the Project Timeline.

Group students. Have them brainstorm a list of naturally occurring substances they can use to obtain indicators. Go over their suggestions and discuss the advantages and drawbacks.

Review students' choice of materials and the procedures they intend to use for indicator extraction. Once students have your approval, they may begin extracting their indicators.

Distribute copies of Project Worksheet 1. Have them use this worksheet to organize their data. Project Worksheet 2, will help students analyze their data and prepare for the presentation. Distribute this worksheet once students have completed their data collection.

Remind students to refer to the hints in the Project Overview as they plan and carry out the project.

Materials and Preparation

Substances that would make good indicators include rose petals, day lilies, tea (flavored or unflavored), red cabbage, beets, radishes, rhubarb, red grapes, red onions, blueberries, blackberries, tomato skins, tomato leaves, grass, and greens (collards, spinach, mustard, and carrot). Or students may try other colored substances as indicators. In particular, they should look for bright, definite colors. (Some white flower petals, such as roses, also work.)

Some substances you might have students test include vinegar, milk, lemon juice, apple juice, carbonated drinks, soapy water, salt water (35 g NaCl to 1,000 mL H_2O), household ammonia, household bleach, household cleaners, and shampoo. Warn students not to mix ammonia and bleach together. Avoid testing water as it is sensitive to the pH of the indicator and will cause students to get inaccurate readings.

Students will need equipment such as electric blenders, mortars and pestles, cheesecloth, and strainers for extracting indicators. They will also need empty bottles with screw-top lids for storing their indicator juices once they have been made.

Consider organizing the class in groups for this project. If space and time are limited, you may want to have students use different indicators to test the same substances. Alternatively, you may have students use the same indicator to test different substances. This will provide a wider range of data.

Assign one particular indicator source to each student. Have the student determine the indicator's pH range by testing various substances. Alternatively, you can have each student test acidity and basicity of one substance using a variety of indicators. One way to do this would be to have pairs of students make one indicator, then distribute all indicators to the class.

Consider grouping students according to the indicators used and/or substances tested. Have them combine their data and summarize their results. Direct groups to discuss their results. Instruct each group to present its findings to the rest of the class.

Keep Students on Track—Tasks 2–4

Check students' procedures for isolating indicator juices. Make sure they plan to use similar amounts of starting materials. Also, be sure they rinse all equipment after each round of indicator extraction.

If students want to use an electric blender to isolate their indicators, plan to run the blender for them for safety purposes. If students are using a mortar and pestle, have them add a little fine sand to the mortar. This will help them grind the sample.

Make sure students store their indicators in the refrigerator to prevent spoilage.

Keep Students on Track—Tasks 5–6

Set a minimum number (six, for example) of substances for students to test with their indicators. If students have used different materials to make their indicators, you may choose to have all students test the same substances so they can compare results.

Check students' data tables. Be sure students have separate columns for the indicator source, the substance tested, the color of the indicator before it was used, and the color of the solution after it is tested. They will need another column for the pH of the tested substance.

Keep Students on Track—Task 7

Check students' data tables for completeness. They should indicate actual pH values for tested substances.

Make sure students have listed all tested substances from low to high pH. They should begin to think about how the color changes relate to the actual pH values.

Chapter Project Wrap Up

Tell students analyzing their data means looking at their observations, summarizing them, finding patterns, and deciding what these patterns tell about the indicators.

As students give their reports, ask their classmates to take notes, writing down observed color changes and actual pH values.

Extension

Students could make indicator paper by soaking strips of filter paper in the indicator solutions and letting the strips dry. The strips could then be stored in an airtight container and used to test pH in other activities. Students should label the container with the source material used to make the indicator and its pH range.

PROJECT OVERVIEW

Make Your Own Indicator

Acidic and basic solutions can be detected using substances called acid-base indicators. Perhaps you are familiar with litmus paper, a common indicator. The active chemical in litmus is made from a natural substance found in lichens, which are living organisms. The litmus is applied to paper to make it more convenient to use.

There are many other naturally occurring substances that can also act as acid-base indicators. In this project, you will first select a few substances that you think might be good sources of indicators. Using these indicators, you will test a variety of acidic and basic substances such as vinegar and ammonia. You will then use standard pH test paper to assign pH values to the different colors of the indicators you have selected. Finally, you will rank the substances you have tested according to their pH value.

Project Rules

- You must write a procedure that you will use to obtain your indicators. Have your teacher approve your materials and procedures before you begin extraction.

- All indicators must come from naturally occurring substances. Do not use indicators produced in the lab.

- Your teacher will tell you how many substances to test with your indicators. All materials to be tested must be readily available substances commonly found in the home. You may not use acids and bases that are standard laboratory supplies.

- Do not taste the acids or bases from food sources.

- Once you have used your indicators to test your substances, use pH test paper to determine their actual pH values.

Suggested Materials

- Substances that might make good indicators include rose petals, day lilies, tea (flavored or unflavored), red cabbage, beets, radishes, rhubarb, red grapes, red onions, blueberries, blackberries, tomato skins, tomato leaves, grass, and greens (collards, kale, spinach, mustard, and carrot).

- Some substances you might test include vinegar, milk, lemon juice, apple juice, carbonated drinks, soapy water, salt water, household ammonia, household bleach, household cleaners, and shampoo.

- You will need equipment such as electric blenders, mortars and pestles, cheesecloth, and strainers for extracting indicators. You will also need empty bottles with screw-top lids for storing your indicator juices once they have been made.

Copyright © Pearson Education, Inc., or its affiliates. All rights reserved.

Project Hints

- Be creative when selecting your indicator sources. They may be recognized by bright, definite colors. Look for reds, blues, purples, or yellows.

- When designing your procedure for indicator extraction, plan to use similar amounts of starting materials. This will make the concentrations of your indicators similar.

- If using a mortar and pestle for indicator extraction, add a small amount of fine sand to your mortar. This will help you grind up your material.

- Your indicators should be liquids. Make sure that you get rid of all remaining solid materials before using each of your indicators.

- Store all extracted indicators in the refrigerator to prevent spoilage.

- Use small, equal volumes (1–2 mL) of both indicator and test substance for each test. This will reduce the amount of each indicator you will need to make and give definite color changes.

- Be sure to rinse test tubes and droppers between each test in order to avoid contamination between one test and the next.

Project Timeline

Task	Due Date
1. Materials selected.	_____
2. Extraction procedure written.	_____
3. Materials and procedure approved.	_____
4. Extraction completed.	_____
5. Substances tested with indicators.	_____
6. pH of substances determined with pH test paper.	_____
7. Data analysis and list of substances completed.	_____
8. Class presentation made.	_____

PROJECT WORKSHEET 1

Project Planning and Data Collection

Making Plans

Complete the following tasks using a separate sheet of paper. When the tasks have been completed, you are ready to get your teacher's approval and begin the Chapter Project.

1. List the naturally occurring substances that you plan to use for making your indicators.

2. Write the procedure that you plan to use for extraction. Make sure you include the amount of starting materials, how you intend to grind up these materials, and how you plan to separate the liquid indicator from the remaining solid materials. As you prepare your indicators, you may need to modify your extraction process in order to meet unexpected circumstances. For example, you may need to dilute a too-dark indicator, or not dilute a pale indicator at all.

3. List the household substances that you plan to test with your indicators.

4. Some indicators may stain skin and clothing. Wear a lab apron when preparing and using your indicators. Wash your hands throughly when finished.

Recording Observations

Record your observations in a data table organized like the one below. Include indicator source, the substance tested, the color of the indicator before it was used, and the color of the indicator after it was used. You will be completing the last column later in the project.

Indicator Source	Substance Tested	Indicator Color Before Use	Solution Color After Testing	pH of Substance

PROJECT WORKSHEET 2

Analyzing and Presenting Your Data

Use a table similar to the one below to organize your tested substances by pH. Include the colors that you observed for each of your indicators.

Tested Substance	pH of Substance	Color of Indicator #1	Color of Indicator #2	Color of Indicator #3

Complete the following tasks on a separate sheet of paper. When they have been completed, you are ready to put together your presentation.

1. What qualities are required of a good indicator? Which of your indicators exhibited these qualities?

2. Did any of your indicators work poorly? Explain why you think they were not good indicators.

3. Write several sentences summarizing your research.

4. Write several sentences summarizing your observations from the data table. Did you notice patterns in the response of your indicators? For instance, did the indicators turn the same color in an acid? Did the indicators work equally well for all acids and for all bases?

5. Decide how you want to communicate what you have learned to your classmates. Make a list of the things you will need to make this presentation.

SCORING RUBRIC

Make Your Own Indicator

In evaluating how well you complete the Chapter Project, your teacher will judge your work in three categories. In each, a score of 4 is the best rating.

	4	3	2	1
Planning and Preparing Indicator	Written description of indicator preparation is thorough and complete, including details describing quantities and equipment used.	Written description of indicator preparation is good, including most details describing quantities and equipment used.	Written description of indicator preparation is adequate, including some details describing quantities and equipment used.	Written description of indicator preparation is minimal, including few details describing quantities and equipment used.
Following Rules and Organizing Data	Makes the required number of indicators and tests the required number of substances. Carefully follows safe lab practices. Makes complete and accurate written observations on color changes and actual pH values.	Makes the required number of indicators and tests the required number of substances. Follows safe lab practices. Makes fairly complete written observations on color changes and actual pH values.	Makes the required number of indicators and tests more than half of the required number of substances. Lab practices are fairly safe. Written observations on color changes and actual pH values are somewhat disorganized or incomplete.	Makes fewer than the required number of indicators and tests half or less than half of the required number of substances. Lab practices are unsafe. Written observations on color changes and actual pH values are disorganized and incomplete.
Analyzing and Presenting the Data	Makes a thorough, well-organized presentation. Clearly explains which indicators are useful for testing which ranges of pH. Prepares well-designed visual aids.	Makes an acceptable presentation. Explains which indicators are useful for testing which ranges of pH. Prepares useful visual aids.	Presentation is somewhat hard to follow. Explanation of which indicators are useful for testing which ranges of pH is unclear. Prepares one visual aid.	Presentation is brief and hard to follow. Explanation of which indicators are useful for testing which ranges of pH is unclear. Prepares no visual aids.

Acids, Bases, and Solutions

Models of Compounds

The following steps will walk you through the Chapter Project. Use the hints and detailed directions as you guide your students through planning, model construction, and presentation.

Chapter Project Overview

To introduce the project, bring a ball-and-stick modeling kit into the classroom to show to students. Talk about how different colors of balls represent different elements. Also, discuss how bonds between atoms are represented in this kit.

Have students read the Project Overview. Review the Project Rules, and hand out the Scoring Rubric that you will use for scoring students' work. Discuss with students what will be expected of them.

Set a deadline for the project presentation and interim dates for the different project tasks. Encourage students to copy the dates in the Project Timeline.

Group students. Have them brainstorm a list of possible materials they can use for modeling. Go over their suggestions and discuss the advantages and drawbacks of using these materials.

Distribute copies of Project Worksheet 1. Have students read over the questions that they will need to answer in the planning stage of this project. Students may then complete the worksheet.

Check over students' answers to Worksheet 1, and make sure that they have planned out how they will construct their models. Once students have your approval, they are ready to begin building their atoms.

Project Worksheet 2 will help students think about constructing their compounds. Distribute this worksheet after students have finished building their atoms.

Remind students to refer to the hints in the Project Overview as they plan and carry out the project.

Tell students they will be making a class presentation of their models in which they will explain how each aspect of atoms and bonding is represented.

Consider organizing the class in groups to do the project. If space and time are limited, you may want to select the compounds that students will model.

Materials and Preparation

You will need a ball-and-stick model kit for the project launch.

When students are building their atoms, they will need a variety of materials such as raisins, gumdrops, jellied fruit candies, marshmallows, jellybeans, and clay. Allow students to be creative when selecting these materials. They will also need permanent markers to illustrate valence electrons on their atoms.

Additionally, students will require items such as tape, toothpicks, pipe cleaners, and paper clips when they begin joining their atoms into compounds.

Consider allowing students to work in pairs for this project. Make sure each partner contributes equally to the model planning and building.

Instead of allowing students to select the compounds that they will model, assign different compounds to different students. This will increase the diversity of compounds that will be modeled.

Keep Students on Track—Tasks 1–3

Check each student's selection of materials for appropriateness before allowing students to begin making their atoms. If they select edible materials, make sure they know not to eat them. If the materials are perishable, have students plan ahead so they can make their models close to the date of the class presentations.

Make sure students have considered how they will attach atoms with chemical bonds. Using soft materials will make this easier.

Make sure students have thought about how they will illustrate the valence electrons. They should distribute these electrons evenly around their atoms. You may want to make some sample models of several different unbonded atoms to show that each model atom must include information on the number of valence electrons.

Check that students are making multiple models of each atom for later use in compound modeling.

Keep Students on Track—Task 4

Check that students are modeling several different ionic compounds. Check their models for accuracy. Make sure they are modeling compounds, not mixtures. They should understand the difference.

Point out that compounds containing ionic bonds do not occur as molecules. They are better modeled as crystals with indefinite boundaries.

Keep Students on Track—Task 5

Check students' models for accuracy. Make sure they have made several different molecules, including diatomic gases and compounds.

Students should understand the differences between single, double, and triple bonds. All three types should be demonstrated in their models.

Make sure students understand that each atom in molecules containing covalent bonds should have eight valence electrons (except for hydrogen, which should have two).

Keep Students on Track—Task 6

Tell students to be prepared to explain how they made their models and why they chose the materials they did.

Chapter Project Wrap Up

In their class presentations, be sure that students fully explain how they represented different nuclei, valence electrons, ionic bonds, and covalent bonds in their models. Ask: Why did you make those particular choices? (*Samples: materials were soft and easily penetrated, came in several different colors, readily available*)

You may suggest that students make a chart giving an overview of all their atoms and compounds. This may help to make their presentations go more smoothly.

Have students turn in any written work you require. Students may then dispose of any perishable models. Make sure they do not eat any edible materials.

Extension

For some of the simpler molecular compounds modeled, have students speculate which may be polar or nonpolar. Ask: What further information would you need to know to be certain of your answers? (*An atom's pull on electrons; the arrangement in space of the atoms in the molecule*).

PROJECT OVERVIEW
Models of Compounds

In this chapter, you will be learning about atoms and the bonds that form between them. To illustrate bonding, chemists use ball-and-stick modeling kits. These kits usually contain balls that represent the atoms and sticks that represent the chemical bonds between the atoms. The balls are usually color-coded, with different colors representing different elements. Different stick types are usually included so that different types of chemical bonds (single, double, or triple) can be modeled.

In this project, you will create your own modeling kits. Your kits will contain several different atoms with their valence electrons clearly illustrated. They will also contain chemical bonds that you will use to join the atoms together. You will use these kits to create compounds that contain either ionic or covalent bonds. You can use your models to build simple molecules having single covalent bonds, as well as models of molecules containing double or triple bonds. At the end of the project, you will give a brief class presentation in which you explain your models and discuss why you used particular materials when constructing your models.

Project Rules

- Have your teacher approve your materials before you begin building your models.

- You must show valence electrons on your atom models.

- You should create at least six models—three with ionic bonds, and three with covalent bonds. You must model all three types of covalent bonds—single, double, and triple.

- You will be giving a brief class presentation in which you explain each of your models. You must be able to explain your choice of materials.

Suggested Materials

- Be creative when selecting the materials for building your models. Some suggestions include raisins, gumdrops, jellied fruit candies, marshmallows, jellybeans, and clay.

- Chemical bonds can be modeled by using items such as tape, toothpicks, pipe cleaners, and paper clips.

- Permanent markers can be used to illustrate valence electrons on your atoms.

Project Hints

- When selecting your materials for making atoms, think about how you will join your atoms together. Softer materials (marshmallows) may work better than harder items (hard candies) because you can join them with toothpicks or paper clips.

- If you plan on using materials that are perishable, make sure you construct your models close to the date of the class presentations so that the models do not spoil before you present them. You might also consider storing your models in a refrigerator to slow the decay process. **CAUTION:** *Do not eat any food materials you use in this project.*

- When making your atom models, make sure that you make multiples of each kind of atom because you will need several when creating your models of compounds.

- Compounds containing ionic bonds form crystals of indefinite size. Each ion is held in place by the attractive force between it and neighboring ions with opposite electric charges. Such compounds can be modeled as patterns of alternating ions with no two ions of the same element next to each other.

- Some of your models may include elements that exist as molecules made of one kind of atom.

- When preparing for your class presentation, it might be helpful to create a chart that gives an overview of all your models. This chart could act as a key, explaining how you have illustrated different elements and types of bonds.

Project Timeline

Task	Due Date
1. Materials selected.	_____
2. Materials approved.	_____
3. Atom models completed.	_____
4. Models of compounds with ionic bonds completed.	_____
5. Models of molecules with covalent bonds completed.	_____
6. Class presentation made.	_____

PROJECT WORKSHEET 1
Models of Compounds

Complete the following tasks using a separate sheet of paper. When the tasks
have been completed, you are ready to get your teacher's approval and begin the
Chapter Project.

Constructing Atoms

1. What materials will you use to model your atoms?

2. How will you differentiate between atoms of different elements?

3. How will you illustrate valence electrons on your atoms?

4. Here is a table of some elements that you will be modeling. Complete the table by
recording the number of valence electrons for each element. Also, indicate what
material you will use to model each element. For example, if you are using differently
colored gumdrops, indicate the color that you will use for each element. Add to the
table other elements you wish to model.

Element (Symbol)	Number of Valence Electrons	Model Key
Carbon (C)		
Chlorine (Cl)		
Fluorine (F)		
Hydrogen (H)		
Iodine (I)		
Magnesium (Mg)		
Nitrogen (N)		
Oxygen (O)		
Sodium (Na)		
Sulfur (S)		

PROJECT WORKSHEET 2
Models of Compounds
Compounds Containing Ionic Bonds

Complete this table with the compounds that you plan to model. List the ions that come together to form each compound and the charges of the ions. Also, describe how you plan to construct your model.

Compound	Ions	Ionic Charge	Plan for Model
Sodium Chloride (NaCl)	Na^+	1+	
	Cl^-		
Potassium Oxide (K_2O)			

Molecules Containing Covalent Bonds

Complete this table with the molecules that you plan to model. Name the type of covalent bond found in the molecule, and give a brief description of how you plan to construct your model.

Molecule	Type of Bond (Single, Double, Triple)	Plan for Model
Water (H_2O)		
Carbon Dioxide (CO_2)		
Chlorine (Cl_2)		
Hydrogen (H_2)		

Name _____ Date_____ Class_____

SCORING RUBRIC

Models of Compounds

In evaluating how well you complete the Chapter Project, your teacher will judge your work in four categories. In each, a score of 4 is the best rating.

	4	3	2	1
Planning for Model Construction	Student's plans include all information about joining atoms, illustrating valence electrons, and differentiating between elements.	Student's plans include most information about joining atoms, illustrating valence electrons, and differentiating between elements. Makes minor omissions or errors.	Student fails to plan for one of the following: joining atoms, illustrating valence electrons, or differentiating between elements. Makes several omissions or errors.	Student makes significant omissions or errors in planning the joining of atoms, illustrating valence electrons, or differentiating between elements.
Constructing Atom Models	Student correctly builds multiple models of all required elements and includes the appropriate number of valence electrons on atoms.	Student correctly builds multiple models of most required elements and includes the appropriate number of valence electrons on atoms.	Student correctly builds models of most required elements, but fails to make multiples or include the appropriate number of valence electrons.	Student builds some models, but fails to make multiples or include the appropriate number of valence electrons.
Constructing Compound Models	Student correctly makes more than six model compounds and correctly distinguishes between ionic and covalent bonds. All three types of covalent bonds are represented.	Student correctly makes at least six models and correctly distinguishes between ionic and covalent bonds. Only two types of covalent bonds are represented.	Student makes four or five models, but fails to represent one or two types of covalent bonds. Distinction between ionic and covalent bonds is fairly clear.	Student makes fewer than four models and represents at most one type of covalent bond. Incorrectly distinguishes between ionic and covalent bonds.
Presenting the Models	Student makes a thorough, well-organized presentation with a clear explanation of reasons for material choices.	Student makes a good presentation with a mostly clear explanation of reasons for material choices.	Student makes a presentation, but it is hard to follow. Some reasons for material choices given.	Student gives a brief or confused presentation. Reasons for material choices are very sketchy.

Design and Build a Closed Reaction Chamber

The following steps will walk you through the Chapter Project. Use the hints and detailed directions as you guide your students through design, construction, and presentation.

Chapter Project Overview

In this chapter, students will design and build a closed reaction chamber. They will use the reaction chamber to confirm that matter is not created or destroyed in a chemical reaction.

Introduce the project by asking students to identify reactants and products in an open chemical reaction with which they are familiar. A good example is logs burning in a camp fire or fireplace. Lead a discussion of how the masses of some of the reactants and products (logs, ashes) could easily be measured, whereas others (oxygen, carbon dioxide, water vapor) could not be measured in the open system. Conclude the discussion by telling students they will design and build a chamber that can contain all the reactants and products of a reaction so they can be measure.

Explain to students that they will use their closed chambers to burn sugar. On the board, write the equation for the combustion of sugar:

$$C_{12}H_{22}O_{11} + heat \rightarrow 12\ C + 11\ H_2O$$

Point out that using their closed reaction chambers will allow them to determine the masses of the reactants and products of the reaction. Explain the law of conservation of mass. Then, challenge students to predict how the mass of the products should compare to the mass of the reactants if their chambers function well. Ask them how they could determine whether matter is created or destroyed in the reaction.

Distribute the Project Overview. Review the Project Rules. You may also want to hand out the Scoring Rubric so students will understand what is expected of them.

Organize the class into groups. Instruct the groups to brainstorm how they could build a closed reaction chamber in which they could burn sugar. Give them a list of suggested materials, and challenge them to think of how they could be combined to produce the chamber. After the groups have had their brainstorming session, encourage the class as a whole to share ideas about constructing the chamber. You may want to have students work in their groups to complete the project.

Set a deadline for the project presentation and some interim dates for the different project tasks. Have students copy the dates in their Project Timeline.

Distribute Project Worksheet 1. Tell students that Worksheet 1 will help them design their reaction chambers. Then, hand out Project Worksheet 2 and tell students that Worksheet 2 will help them record and analyze their data when they use their chambers to burn sugar.

Materials and Preparation

Review the use of the triple beam balance before students need to use it. Remind students that the triple beam balance measures mass in grams.

Reaction chambers can be constructed from empty metal food cans, plastic bottles, and balloons. You may want to have each student bring in one can and one bottle with similar diameters.

To construct the chamber, students may need rulers, scissors, hot glue guns, and duct tape. To use the chamber for the combustion of sucrose, students will need a heat source (candle or gas burner) and a way of holding the reaction chamber steady over the heat (ring stand or metal tongs).

Review safety guidelines with students before they begin their work.

Keep Students on Track—Tasks 1–2

The diameter of the bottle should be just large enough that the bottle slips over the can. If students have difficulty measuring the diameters, they can compare the sizes of bottles and cans by wrapping a string around the circumference and measuring the length of the string with a ruler.

The most likely setup of the materials is shown in Worksheet 1. Make sure that students have completed Worksheet 1 before they construct their chambers. Remind students to check their completed chamber for leaks before topping the bottle with the balloon.

Keep Students on Track—Task 3

Once students have constructed and tested their reaction chambers, they can add a small, measured mass of table sugar to the container, seal the container with the balloon, and find the mass of the sealed container. Then, they can light the heat source and heat the reaction chamber. During the reaction, students should record all observations and draw a picture of the experimental setup. Once the sugar has blackened, students should remove the chamber from the heat source and measure the mass of the vessel again. Remind students to record their observations and measurements in the Student Data Table in Worksheet 2.

Keep Students on Track—Task 4

Check that students have conducted the sucrose combustion reaction correctly and recorded the measurements of initial and final mass on Worksheet 2. List the measurements from all the students or groups of students on the board, and tell the class to copy them into the Class Data Table on Worksheet 2. Have students use the class values to find the average change in mass for the class. Then, ask students the following questions to guide them in interpreting the data. How does the final mass of the reaction vessel compare with the initial mass? From this, what can you conclude about the masses of the reactants and products in the chemical reaction? What happens to the reactants in the sucrose combustion reaction? How do they change? Why is it important for the reaction vessel to remain closed during the reaction? How would the experiment differ if the reaction chamber were not closed?

Keep Students on Track—Task 5

Remind students to prepare posters or other visual displays of their work. Tell them to include in their presentations a description of the design and construction of their closed reaction chambers. They also should include the results of the chemical reactions and their conclusions about the results.

Chapter Project Wrap Up

Have students take turns presenting their work to the class while other students ask questions. You might want to make it a requirement that each student ask at least one question during the presentations. Challenge students to try to explain any differences in the results. Ask them what might have caused the discrepancies. If students have strong math skills, have them calculate the percent change in mass in their individual tests, and then have them compare their values with the class data as another way to analyze their results.

Extension

Let students use their closed reaction chambers to carry out other simple chemical reactions. For each reaction, students can identify the reactants and products and observe the reactants change into other substances. They also can gather additional mass data and relate it to conservation of mass.

PROJECT OVERVIEW

Design and Build a Closed Reaction Chamber

The principle of conservation of mass states that matter is neither created nor destroyed in a chemical reaction. The mass of reactant atoms is always equal to the mass of product atoms. This project focuses on a simple chemical reaction, the combustion, or burning, of sucrose (table sugar). When heat is added to sucrose, hydrogen and oxygen atoms are converted to water vapor, leaving solid carbon behind.

How can you measure the mass of these products? For this and many other chemical reactions, it is difficult to gather evidence to support the law of conservation of mass. In this chapter project, you will try to solve the problem of containing the reactants and products of a chemical reaction. By measuring the masses of reactants and products, you will also determine if mass is changed or remains the same after the chemical reaction.

Project Rules

- Design a solution for the problem of containing reactants and products in the combustion of sucrose. You must use the materials your teacher provides or approves. Your design must be approved as well.

- Using your design, build a closed reaction chamber.

- Evaluate your chamber, test it for leaks, and modify it as needed.

- Follow the safety guidelines that your teacher has spelled out.

- Carry out the combustion of sucrose in your completed reaction chamber. Observe, measure, and record the results of the experiment.

- Interpret your data and the pooled class data to determine whether mass is conserved in the reaction.

- Present your findings in a visual display and oral presentation. In your presentation, you should include a description of the chamber you designed and the design process, as well as your experimental results and conclusions.

Project Hints

- As you begin to design your reaction chamber, complete Project Worksheet 1. It will guide you in designing and building an effective closed reaction chamber that is suitable for the sucrose combustion experiment.

- At the beginning of the sucrose experiment, add a small amount of sucrose of known mass to the can through the open bottle top. Record the mass of the sugar in the space provided in the Student Data Table on Project Worksheet 2.

- After adding the sucrose, cover the bottle top with a balloon, and then find the mass of the chamber plus sucrose. Record this value in the space provided in the Student Data Table.

- When you burn the sucrose in the chamber, make sure the flame is centered beneath the can. Otherwise, the adhesive between the can and the bottle may melt. Make sure the flame is not too high for the same reason.

- **CAUTION:** *Always use proper safety precautions when using a flame. Safety goggles and lab aprons should be worn at all times.*

- Heat the sucrose until it turns black. Use tongs to handle the heated can or let the can cool before handling. Measure the mass of the reaction chamber. Record the final mass in the Student Data Table on Worksheet 2.

- Use the Class Data Table on Worksheet 2 to pool data from the entire class. Use a calculator to find the class average. Also calculate the amount by which your change in mass differs from the class average. Record the results of your calculations in the spaces provided in the Student Data Table.

- Use the data tables, or graphs made from the data tables, in your class presentation. Prepare for your presentation by writing note cards that summarize how you designed your closed reaction chamber and any problems you had to resolve; how you carried out the experiment and what the results were; and the conclusions you drew about conservation of mass based on your data and the pooled class data.

Project Timeline

Task	Due Date
1. Complete Worksheet 1 and design chamber.	_____
2. Build, test, and modify chamber.	_____
3. Complete sucrose combustion experiment.	_____
4. Complete Worksheet 2 and draw conclusions.	_____
5. Make presentation to the class.	_____

PROJECT WORKSHEET 1
Closed Reaction Chamber

This worksheet will walk you through the steps involved in making one type of closed reaction chamber suitable for burning sucrose. The reaction chamber is shown below. Use the figure below as a guide.

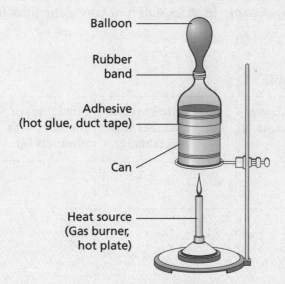

Balloon

Rubber band

Adhesive (hot glue, duct tape)

Can

Heat source (Gas burner, hot plate)

1. Obtain an empty metal food can. Also obtain an empty plastic water or soda bottle with about the same diameter as the can. Wash the can and bottle, and remove all the labels.

2. Cut off the top third of the bottle with scissors. Slide this part of the bottle over the open end of the can as in the figure. Fasten the bottle to the can in this position using glue or tape.

3. Test the seal between the can and bottle by blowing into the top of the bottle and listening for escaping air. Find and seal any leaks.

4. Before adding the balloon to the bottle, add the sugar for the sucrose combustion experiment. Make sure you use the triple beam balance to measure the mass of the sugar first. Don't forget to record the mass in the Student Data Table on Worksheet 2.

5. After adding the sugar, put the balloon over the mouth of the bottle. An inadequate seal between the balloon and mouth of the bottle may result in a leaky chamber and loss of mass. This can be avoided by placing a tight rubber band over the balloon around the neck of the bottle.

6. Measure and record the mass of the chamber plus sugar.

7. Set up the heat source as shown in the figure, and obtain your teacher's permission to carry out the experiment. **CAUTION:** *Wear safety goggles and a lab apron. Tie back loose hair and clothing. Use an oven mitt or other hand protection when handling hot materials.*

PROJECT WORKSHEET 2
Data Tables for Sucrose Combustion Experiment

This worksheet consists of data tables to record your data and the data from the rest of the class. The tables also have spaces for you to record individual changes in mass, the class average change in mass, and how your data differ from the class average.

Student Data Table

Data source	Mass of sugar (g)	Initial mass of chamber with reactants (g)	Final mass of chamber with products (g)	Change in mass (g)
Your data				
Class average				
Deviation from class average				

Class Data Table

Data source	Mass of sugar (g)	Initial mass of chamber with reactants (g)	Final mass of chamber with products (g)	Change in mass (g)
Student 1				
Student 2				
Student 3				
Student 4				
Student 5				
Student 6				
Etc.				

SCORING RUBRIC

Design and Build a Closed Reaction Chamber

In evaluating how well you complete the Chapter Project, your teacher will judge your work in four categories. In each, a score of 4 is the best rating.

	4	3	2	1
Constructing Reaction Chamber	The student correctly constructed a closed reaction chamber according to the instructions in Worksheet 1. The reaction chamber remained tightly closed throughout the experiment.	The student constructed an adequate reaction chamber, but the reaction chamber may have leaked slightly during the experiment.	The student constructed a reaction chamber, but the reaction chamber leaked significantly during the experiment.	The student attempted but failed to construct a usable reaction chamber.
Conducting Experiment	The student precisely conducted a valid experiment and accurately recorded all relevant observations and measurements in the data tables.	The student correctly conducted the experiment and recorded most relevant observations and measurements.	The student conducted the experiment but made some errors; the student recorded some relevant observations and measurements.	The student may have tried to conduct an experiment but did it incorrectly or failed to complete it; the student recorded few if any relevant observations or measurements.
Interpreting Data	The student accurately interpreted the data on change in mass and correctly related it to the principle of conservation of mass.	The student interpreted the data on change in mass and related it to the principle of conservation of mass, but the student made one or two minor omissions or errors.	The student attempted to interpret the data on change in mass and relate it to the principle of conservation of mass, but the student made several omissions and/or errors.	The student attempted to interpret the data on change in mass and relate it to the principle of conservation of mass, but the student made several omissions and/or errors.
Presenting Findings	The student made a thorough, well-organized presentation using an interesting and highly appropriate visual display.	The student made a satisfactory presentation using a suitable visual display.	The student made a presentation using a visual display, but the presentation was disorganized or too brief, and/or the visual display was flawed or inappropriate.	The student may not have made a presentation and/or visual display; if a presentation or visual display was made, it was seriously flawed.

Survey Properties of Metals

The following steps will walk you through the Chapter Project. Use the hints as you guide your students through discussions, observations, and conclusions.

Chapter Project Overview

This project deals with the properties of metals. Students will observe visible properties of metals. They will also design and conduct tests for other properties such as electrical and heat conductivity. When introducing the project, show the class a sample of metal and have them describe its visible properties. Also demonstrate a brief test of thermal or electrical conductivity.

Have students read the Project Overview. Review the Project Rules and hand out the Scoring Rubric. Discuss with students what will be expected of them.

Set a deadline for the class presentations and interim dates for the different project tasks. Have students fill in the due dates on the Project Timeline.

Since many of the known properties of metals cannot be easily or safely tested in the lab, students have a limited set of properties to test. Some of these properties are simply observed, such as metallic luster, malleability, and ductility. Other properties students can test are thermal and electrical conductivity, corrosion, and magnetism. Point out that corrosion and magnetism are not common to all metals.

Malleability and ductility can be inferred from observation of different shapes and forms available for the same element, or they can be tested by hammering or by bending with pliers and observing closely with a hand lens. Small-diameter rods and wires are easy to manipulate. Electrical conductivity can be tested using a small circuit composed of a battery and a light bulb. Observing temperature changes with time as the metallic object is put in contact with warm or hot water can test thermal conductivity. Magnetism is easily tested with a magnet.

Corrosion, caused by the reaction with oxygen in the presence of water, can be tested for all metals, but only a few of them will actually corrode. A simple test for corrosion is to leave a wet sample of the metal exposed to air and observe changes over time. To speed the process, place the test in sunlight. The addition of table salt and acid (vinegar) can also accelerate corrosion. Students can compare the effects of water versus vinegar on the corrosion process. Some reactive metals, such as aluminum and magnesium, normally have a thin surface layer of oxide which prevents further corrosion. Advise students to polish the surface of the metal with steel wool to remove this outer oxide layer when checking for corrosion.

Distribute copies of Project Worksheet 1. This worksheet will help students begin thinking about the properties of metals.

Once students have used the periodic table to obtain as much information as possible about their metallic elements, distribute Project Worksheet 2. This worksheet will help them record their observations about their metals and design their tests.

Materials and Preparation

Pure metals can be obtained from hardware stores, chemical supply companies, or jewelry supply companies. Examples include copper rods or wires, aluminum rods or sheets, iron nails, silver wire, platinum wire, gold wire, and magnesium ribbon.

Students will need additional materials for conducting the tests, including magnets, hot plates, conductivity testers, thermometers, batteries, light bulbs, steel wool, table salt, and vinegar (a weak acid).

Simplify the project by giving each student only one representative element from each of the main classes of metals. Use magnesium, aluminum, and iron if you choose this approach.

Keep Students on Track—Tasks 1–2

Encourage students to use the periodic table to make predictions about the properties their samples may have. Remind them that elements in a family are generally most similar and that metals are generally less reactive from left to right in the periodic table.

Check students' data tables for completeness and accuracy.

Keep Students on Track—Task 3

Students should have prepared a data table of visible and inferred properties of their metals.

Check students' test designs to make sure they are practical, feasible, and safe for students to conduct. Doing this step in small groups may speed the process and help students improve the design of their testing procedures.

Keep Students on Track—Tasks 4–5

Make sure students are exercising all necessary safety precautions when conducting their tests.

Encourage students to test the nonmetals sulfur and carbon for comparison, especially when conducting heat and electrical conductivity tests. Remind them to use a rating system to compare properties between samples.

Chapter Project Wrap Up

Make sure students have made charts for their class presentations. They should group their metals in such a way that they are easily compared.

Students should make brief presentations to the class in which they discuss the expected and observed outcomes of their tests. They should hypothesize reasons for any differences.

Extension

Give students three mystery elements and ask them to design and conduct several tests that will allow them to determine if the mystery elements are metals or nonmetals. Two of these mystery elements can be metals, but the third should be a nonmetal such as a piece of charcoal, representing carbon.

PROJECT OVERVIEW

Survey Properties of Metals

In this project you will use the periodic table to predict the properties of several different elements. Your teacher will provide you with several different metals to survey. Some of the properties of these metals are easily observed. Other properties will require testing. You will design and conduct tests of these properties.

   For this project, you will make a data table in which you record all of your observations. At the conclusion of this project, you will make another chart that organizes your data in such a way that you can compare and contrast the properties of the metals that you observed. You will present this chart and discuss it with your class.

Project Rules

- Use the periodic table to begin identifying properties of each metal.

- Your experimental plan must include tests for at least three properties of each metal.

- You must obtain your teacher's approval of your experimental plan before you begin testing your samples.

- Make sure the design of your tests includes necessary safety precautions.

- You must predict the expected outcome of each of your tests before beginning.

- During your class presentation, you must discuss which properties are shown by only some metals and which are shown by all.

Suggested Materials

- Samples of metals will be provided by your teacher.

- For testing your elements, you will need materials such as magnets, hot plates, conductivity testers, thermometers, batteries, light bulbs, steel wool, table salt, and vinegar (a weak acid).

Project Hints

- Plan ahead. Make a list of all possible properties, and decide which ones can be safely tested using everyday materials.

- Consult your textbook or another resource to learn about properties of metals.

- Keep track of the properties that you will be testing, making sure to include both properties that are shared by most metals as well as properties that only certain metals possess.

- You will want to compare properties between samples. A convenient way to do this, for example, might be to rate a sample's conductivity as very high, high, average, and so on.

Project Timeline

Task	Due Date
1. Research of assigned metals completed.	_____
2. Observations of assigned metals completed.	_____
3. Experimental plan approved by teacher.	_____
4. Tests completed.	_____
5. Class presentation of expected and actual results with comparisons made.	_____

PROJECT WORKSHEET 1

Properties of Metals

The following tasks will help you begin thinking about the chapter project.

1. List five properties of most metals.

   _____

   _____

   _____

   _____

   _____

2. List two more properties only some metals have.

   _____

   _____

3. Once you have your metal samples, use the periodic table to complete the following data table.

Element	Symbol	Atomic Number	Atomic Mass	Group Number	Family Name	Period

PROJECT WORKSHEET 2

Initial Observations and Test Design

Initial Observations

The following chart will help you organize your observations of the visible properties of your metallic elements. For some of these properties, you may want to make comparisons based on a rating system you devise.

Element	Shininess	Malleability	Ductility	Physical State at Room Conditions (solid, liquid, gas)

Test Design

Complete the following on a separate sheet of paper. Once you have answered all of these questions, obtain your teacher's permission and begin testing.

1. What properties will you be testing?

2. Write up a procedure for each test that you plan to conduct. Include details about the materials you will need and any safety precautions you will need to take. How will you compare properties between the elements you will test?

3. For each element that you will be testing, predict the expected outcomes for each of your tests. Give reasons for your answers.

4. Design a data table in which you can record the results of your tests.

SCORING RUBRIC
Survey Properties of Metals

In evaluating how well you complete the Chapter Project, your teacher will judge your work in four categories. In each, a score of 4 is the best rating.

	4	3	2	1
Interpreting the Periodic Table	Thoroughly researches the assigned elements using the periodic table.	Adequately researches the assigned elements using the periodic table.	Researches the assigned elements but omits some important information.	Does little research for the assigned elements.
Observing the Visible Properties of the Elements	Thoroughly describes properties for each element.	Adequately describes most of the properties for each element.	Describes properties for some of the elements.	Describes properties for a few of the elements.
Designing and Conducting Tests	Written plan of each test is thorough, logical, safe, and clear and includes all expected results. All tests are performed, and written results are complete and unambiguous.	Written plan of each test is fairly thorough, logical, safe, and clear and includes most expected results. All tests are performed, and written results are fairly complete and unambiguous.	Written plan of some tests is fairly complete and includes some expected results. Some tests are performed, and written results are adequate.	Written plan is incomplete and unclear. Some tests are performed, but written results are incomplete and unclear.
Presenting the Results	Presentation is thorough and well organized, and compares and contrasts properties in detail. Logical explanations are made for all differences between expected and observed results.	Presentation is fairly thorough and organized, and compares and contrasts some properties. Adequate explanations are made for most differences between expected and observed results.	Presentation is somewhat incomplete or disorganized, and compares and contrasts a few properties. Explanations are made for some differences between expected and observed results.	Presentation is incomplete or disorganized, and compares and contrasts one property. Explanations are missing or illogical for most differences between expected and observed results.

Design and Build a Density-Calculating System

The following steps will walk you through the Chapter Project. Use the hints and detailed directions as you guide your students through design, construction, data collection, and reflection.

Chapter Project Overview

In this project, students will work in small groups to design and build a system for measuring the mass and the volume of liquids and powdered solids. Students will use the data they collect to calculate the density of the materials. Students will gain a better understanding of density through the design, construction, and use of their density-calculating systems.

Introduce the project by inviting students to infer whether a pound of sand or a pound of feathers takes up more space. Explain that a pound of feathers takes up much more room because feathers are less dense than sand.

Write the formula for density on the board. Explain that density is the relationship between the mass and the volume of an object. Review the units used for density. Give the formula for calculating the volume of a rectangular solid. Make sure students can differentiate between mass and weight.

Display a graduated cylinder and a balance. Find out if students know their functions, and then demonstrate their use. Explain that data collected from these devices are used to calculate density.

Distribute the Project Overview. Review the Project Rules. You may also want to hand out the Scoring Rubric so students will understand what is expected of them.

Organize the class into small groups. Make sure students understand that each member will make sketches and develop a design for a density-calculating system before meeting with other members. Members will then collaborate in creating and testing the final design.

Set a deadline for the project presentation and some interim dates for the different project tasks. Have students copy these dates in their Project Timeline.

Distribute Project Worksheet 1. After students have read the worksheet, ask if they have any questions.

Discuss key features of making an accurate balance, such as creating a balance point that attaches to the base structure and devising a way to attach pans or containers to the balance arm. Explain that students will use a set of metric weights to determine the mass of their samples.

Invite students to consider whether they should measure mass or volume first. Suggest that they design a method for finding volume based on their answer.

Materials and Preparation

Materials students might use for balances include wooden dowels, coat hangers, sections of plastic pipe, and paper or plastic plates. Materials should be durable enough for repeated use. Each group will also need a set of metric weights.

To measure volume, students should select containers that are uniform and easily attached to their balances, such as small disposable cups, yogurt containers, milk cartons, plastic food storage containers, empty medicine bottles, or empty film canisters. They will need more than one container of the same type and size as some substances may be difficult to remove. They will need a beaker or graduated cylinder to calibrate their containers.

You might provide construction materials and tools such as glue, staples, tape, string, paper clips, straws, index cards, rubber bands, and a hole punch for students to use for construction.

Provide at least five different liquids and powdered solids for students to measure. Materials you might consider include honey, molasses, syrup, water, yogurt, sugar, flour, talc, cornmeal, and sand. Choose materials that have significantly different densities to help students observe how density varies.

Keep Students on Track—Tasks 2–3

As you review students' designs, make sure the chosen materials are durable enough for repeated measurements. Closely examine the methods students have chosen to attach the balance arm to the base of the balance. Look for methods of attachment that allow for some flexibility, or that only attach at one point so the arm can easily pivot.

Talk with each group at their first meeting. Make sure members take each other's sketches and ideas seriously. Tell students to think about the materials they will need and to begin collecting them so that they can begin constructing the balance.

Keep Students on Track—Tasks 4–6

Give students objects with known masses to calibrate their balances. Then, students should see how accurately they can measure the mass of the object multiple times. Based on the results of their tests, students should redesign their balances to improve accuracy and repeatability.

Check students' methods for measuring volume. Students should choose a container and calibrate it with a beaker or graduated cylinder.

Keep Students on Track—Task 7

Distribute Project Worksheet 2. Also distribute the five test materials for students to measure. Students can record all their measurements on the worksheet, as well as their density calculations. Emphasize that students should show all of their calculations for density.

Chapter Project Wrap Up

Provide class time for group presentations. Allow each group to present its density-calculating system and describe its accuracy. Encourage other students to ask questions about the design, the construction, and the accuracy and reliability of the system.

After all the presentations have been made, discuss which systems seemed to work best. Invite students to explain how they might improve their systems.

Extension

Invite interested students to determine how a balance differs from a scale. Challenge these students to modify their balances or develop a completely new design for a scale.

PROJECT OVERVIEW
Design and Build a Density-Calculating System

How do you find the density of something if you don't have a balance to measure its mass? In this project, you will design and build a device for collecting data that can be used to calculate the density of liquids and powdered solids.

First, you will learn about density and how it is related to mass and volume. You will also research balances to learn how they work. Then you will be ready to design your own balance. Once your teacher approves your design, you will be ready to test the accuracy and reliability of your balance with objects of known masses. You may have to redesign and retest your balance to improve its accuracy and reliability.

Volume is the other measurement required to calculate density. As you are designing your balance, you will also develop a method to measure volume without using beakers or graduated cylinders.

Once your density-calculating system is ready, your teacher will give you five liquids and powdered solids. You will measure the mass and volume of these materials, then calculate their density.

Project Rules

- Research how balances work and how they are constructed. You might use internet resources or look for books in the library.

- Design a balance based on the results of your research. Use Project Worksheet 1 to help you focus your research into a design. Make a sketch of the balance and list the construction materials you plan to use. Your teacher must approve your design before you begin building.

- Develop a method to measure volume. Think about how you will actually use your density-calculating system to measure mass and volume. Which will you measure first—volume or mass? This will help you choose a container for measuring volume. It might also affect the design of your balance.

- Test your balance using materials of known masses. Your balance should be accurate to within 0.5 gram. Your balance should also be reliable; it should measure the same item as the same mass every time. If your balance does not pass these tests for accuracy and reliability, redesign the balance and retest it.

- Measure the mass and volume of the materials given to you by your teacher. Record your data in Project Worksheet 2. Also write your density calculations on the worksheet. Your teacher will want to see all of your calculations.

- Prepare a class presentation that summarizes your experience. Describe the most difficult part in the design and construction of your system. Also tell what you thought was the easiest part. Be prepared to defend the accuracy and reliability of your system.

Suggested Materials

Your teacher will provide some materials for you to use. You might also have to collect some from home.

- Suitable materials to build the balance include coat hangers, wooden dowels or sticks, old wooden rulers, paper clips, tacks, string, and small paper plates.

- Suitable materials for measuring volume include clean yogurt containers, film canisters, small paper cups, and small milk cartons.

Project Hints

- Collect enough identical containers for each material you will test. Some materials may be difficult to remove from the containers.

- If you choose to measure the mass of a substance in the container used to measure volume, remember to take the mass of the container into account. Either subtract the mass of the container from the total mass, or offset the mass of the container on the other side of the balance.

- Don't be afraid to change the design of your balance if it is not accurate or reliable. Ask your teacher for suggestions, or observe other classmates' designs for new ideas.

Project Timeline

Task	Due Date
1. Research balances.	_____
2. Design balance.	_____
3. Construct balance.	_____
4. Select containers and develop method to measure volume.	_____
5. Test balance.	_____
6. Redesign and retest balance.	_____
7. Make density measurements of unknown materials.	_____
8. Present project summary to the class.	_____

Name _____ Date _____ Class _____

Design a Density-Calculating System

This worksheet will help you focus your research on balance construction and apply it to your design. It will also help you design a method to measure volume.

Measuring Mass

1. How does an equal-arm balance work?

   _____

   _____

2. What features must an equal-arm balance have?

   _____

   _____

Measuring Volume

3. Which will you measure first, mass or volume? Explain how your answer will affect your design.

   _____

   _____

   _____

4. Consider the materials you might be asked to measure. What if you are given honey? Will you be able to completely remove the honey from your measuring container? How will you address this problem in your design?

   _____

   _____

5. Explain how you will measure the volume of a material. How will you know that your measurement is accurate?

   _____

   _____

   _____

Designing the System

On a separate sheet of paper, make a detailed sketch of the design of your density-calculating system. Bring your sketch to a group meeting, and work together to make a final sketch of the group's design. Be sure to make a complete list of materials required to build the system.

PROJECT WORKSHEET 2
Finding the Density of Materials

Use this worksheet to record the data you collect with your density-calculating system. You also have space to calculate the density of the materials your teacher gives you.

Collecting Data for Mass and Volume

1. Record your volume and mass measurements in the table below.

Material	Volume (mL)	Mass (g)

Calculating Density

2. Write the formula for density.

_____

3. Are the units of mass and volume in the formula the same as the units you measured? If not, how will you change them?

_____

_____

4. In the space below, calculate the density of each material. Be sure to show all of your calculations.

Name _____   Date _____ Class _____

SCORING RUBRIC

Design and Build a Density-Calculating System

In evaluating how well you complete the Chapter Project, your teacher will judge your work in four categories. In each, a score of 4 is the best rating.

	4	3	2	1
Designing and Constructing Density-Calculating System	Design shows originality and a thorough understanding of how balances work and how to measure volume. System is well-constructed, durable, and shows imagination and common sense in the choice of materials.	Design shows some originality and an adequate understanding of how balances work and how to measure volume. System is adequately constructed with good material choices.	Design shows an incomplete understanding of how balances work and how to measure volume. System is hastily constructed or is missing some parts.	Design shows a lack of understanding of how balances work and how to measure volume. System is poorly constructed and is missing some parts.
Making Balance Accurate and Readable	Balance is accurate to the nearest 0.5 gram and consistently measures the same object as the same mass.	Balance is accurate to the nearest 0.5 gram, but inconsistently measures the same object as the same mass.	Balance is accurate to the nearest gram and consistently measures the same object as the same mass.	Balance is accurate to the nearest gram and inconsistently measures the same object as the same mass.
Calculating Density	Density values are correct and all calculations are shown.	Density values are correct, but calculations are not shown.	Some density calculations are incorrect.	Most density calculations are incorrect.
Making Class Presentation	Makes a thorough and interesting presentation that includes a clear and engaging description of the design and construction process.	Makes a thorough presentation that includes an adequate description of the design and construction process.	Makes a presentation that includes a partial description of the design and construction process.	Makes a presentation that includes an incomplete or misleading description of the design and construction process.

A Story of Changes in Matter

The following steps will walk you through the Chapter Project. Use the hints and detailed directions as you guide your students through skit and cartoon planning, storyboard creation, and presentations.

Chapter Project Overview

In this project, students will work in groups to create a cartoon or skit that demonstrates how particles of matter behave as they change state. Students will outline their skits and cartoons in storyboards before producing the skits or illustrating the cartoons.

Before introducing the project, bring a cartoon into the classroom to show to students. Talk about how cartoons use exaggeration, slapstick humor, and puns to make ideas easier to remember. Discuss how a skit is similar to a cartoon in that they both are visually oriented and involve humor.

Give students the Project Overview. Review the Project Rules. Hand out the Scoring Rubric. Discuss with students what will be expected of them.

Set a deadline for the project presentation and interim dates for the different project tasks. Encourage students to copy the dates in the Project Timeline.

Group students. Have them brainstorm a list of the properties of solids, liquids, and gases. Have students think about ways they could use cartoons and skits to model the properties of solids, liquids, and gases. Go over their suggestions and discuss the advantages and drawbacks.

Distribute copies of the Project Worksheet 1. Discuss storyboards. Make sure students understand how their storyboards should help them plan for the final product of their project. Have students begin working on their storyboards.

Distribute Project Worksheet 2. This worksheet will help students think about how physical changes affect the particles of matter. They should complete this worksheet and then work on revising their storyboards. Remind students to refer to the hints in the Project Overview as they plan and carry out the project.

Materials and Preparation

Consider organizing the class in groups to do the project. Groups working on cartoons should be limited to two students. Groups working on skits can have up to four students.

Encourage students to be creative when selecting props for their skits. An example of a prop that they might use would be winter jackets to represent a decrease in temperature.

Students who choose to do cartoons will need paper that is at least 8.5" × 11". They should use one sheet of paper for each frame of their cartoon. This will allow them to make their cartoons large enough to be seen by the entire class during the presentations.

Keep Students On Track—Tasks 1–2

Check students' descriptions of how particles behave in each of the three states of matter. Make sure they understand this basic concept.

Discuss storyboards with students. They should understand that a storyboard is a kind of outline of their final product. Review their storyboards, making sure they have included both visual and narrative parts.

Have students exchange their storyboards. The peer reviewers should check the storyboards for completeness and accuracy. Have them make a list of any confusing parts of the other student's work.

Keep Students On Track—Tasks 3–6

Check students' storyboards again, making sure they have made all necessary revisions.

Give students guidelines for their cartoons and skits. Discuss unacceptable words, actions, drawings, and behaviors. Set limits for the cartoons and skits. A good minimum for cartoons might be four 8.5" × 11" frames. Skits should take 2–5 minutes to perform.

To ensure that students are prepared for their class presentations and that their skits will not run too long, have students write brief summaries of their presentations. These descriptions should include approximate time lengths.

Remind students of the project due date, and make sure they know to collect all props and bring them to class before that day.

Chapter Project Wrap Up

As students make their presentations, watch the time. Do not allow students to take up too much time; otherwise, students who make later presentations might feel rushed.

Encourage students to take brief notes about the positive points of each presentation.

After all presentations have been made, have students evaluate their projects. Invite them to discuss similarities and differences between different depictions of physical changes.

Extension

You might consider allowing students to use other forms of presentation media to produce their projects. As long as the final product is a visual display, you may encourage students to use their varied artistic talents through music, art, video production, etc., if they wish.

PROJECT OVERVIEW
A Story of Changes in Matter

For this project, you will expand your understanding of the particle nature of matter. You will learn that not only is matter made of very small particles, but also that these particles are moving. Imagine yourself shrinking down to their size. You would see the particles behaving much like billiard balls moving around a pool table. How the particles move determines whether the matter is a solid, liquid, or gas.

Your project is to demonstrate your understanding of the particle nature of matter through a visual display. You will create a skit or cartoon that demonstrates how the particles of matter behave as matter changes from a solid to a liquid, from a liquid to a gas, and then from a gas to a liquid to a solid.

Project Rules

- You will begin this project by describing in words the particles of matter in each of the three states of matter.

- You will begin working on a storyboard. This storyboard will act as the plan for your project. It must contain both visual and narrative parts.

- You will revise your storyboard to include any new information you have learned.

- At the end of this project, you will do a class presentation in which you either present your cartoon or perform your skit.

Suggested Materials

- Storyboards can be done with notebook-sized paper and pen or pencil.

- **Skits:** An example of props you might use would be winter jackets to represent a decrease in temperature. If the props needed are too complicated, the skit might include narration or signs suggesting what the setting should look like.

- **Cartoons:** Do each frame on a sheet of paper at least 8.5 inches × 11 inches. This will enable the class to see the drawings easily. The final product should be done in paint, marker, or dark inks so that your classmates can see the images from a distance.

Project Hints

- Writing a verbal description will help you understand what you will be presenting visually.

- Before you begin working on your project, practice making a storyboard using a common event from your life that involves change. Use the storyboard to tell its story. Possible examples include making breakfast, cleaning your room, or the view from a camera in your bookbag as you go through school.

- Make a table comparing the changes in particle speed, particle attraction, distance between particles, and temperature during state changes.

- Consider the suggestions from classmates. Add the good ideas to your storyboard before producing the final version.

- If you are doing a skit, recruit your performers in advance, and be sure to practice your presentation before the final due date.

Project Timeline

Task	Due Date
1. Complete written descriptions of particles during changes of state.	_____
2. First draft of storyboard completed and checked by teacher.	_____
3. Storyboard revised.	_____
4. Cartoon completed or skit rehearsed.	_____
5. Presentation of skit or cartoon completed.	_____

PROJECT WORKSHEET 1
Making Storyboards

Writers of visual projects, like skits or cartoons, use a storyboard to plan the sequence of the project. The left column illustrates or describes what is being seen—what the performers are doing, what they look like (their costumes and the props they will use), and the appearance of the background. It may be done in pictures or words. The right column lists what is being heard. In a skit, this will be the words spoken by performers and any background sounds. In a cartoon, all words that will appear in the "balloons" should be written here. Below is an example of a storyboard made for a skit.

Sample Storyboard

Title or Subject: *Making Breakfast*

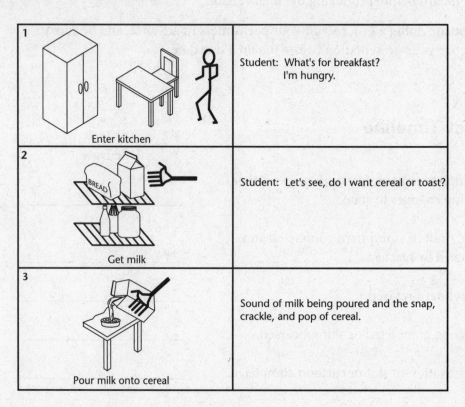

Complete the following tasks on drawing paper.

1. Pick any event in your life, such as taking care of your pet, buying a soft drink, or filling your bicycle tire with air. Make a storyboard similar to the one above in which you describe this event. Specify whether your storyboard is for a cartoon or a skit.

2. Using what you know about the three states of matter, make a practice storyboard that shows how the particles of matter behave in a solid, in a liquid, and in a gas.

PROJECT WORKSHEET 2

Understanding Physical Changes

Many properties vary as matter changes from a solid to a liquid and then from a liquid to a gas. Use what you have learned about the properties of matter to complete the following table, describing the change as increasing or decreasing. After you have completed the table, use the information to revise your storyboard.

Property	Change From Solid to Liquid	Change From Liquid to Gas
Particle speed		
Attraction between particles		
Distance between particles		
Temperature of sample		

Analyzing and Presenting

Complete the following tasks on a separate sheet of paper. When they have been completed, you are ready to revise your storyboard and put together your presentation.

1. Describe the shape and volume of solids, liquids, and gases. How do pressure and temperature affect the volume of a gas?

2. Answer these questions if your chapter project is a skit. Write several sentences describing your class presentation. How long will it take to perform your skit? How many times have you rehearsed? What props will you require? Have you brought all of the props into the classroom?

3. Answer these questions if your chapter project is a cartoon. Write several sentences describing your class presentation. Are your cartoons large enough to be seen by all of your classmates during the class presentation? Are they drawn clearly and with dark lines so everyone can see them well? Are they on stiff paper or poster board so you can display them easily?

SCORING RUBRIC

A Story of Changes in Matter

In evaluating how well you complete the Chapter Project, your teacher will judge your work in four categories. In each, a score of 4 is the best rating.

	4	3	2	1
Planning for the Project	Written descriptions and storyboard accurately describe physical change. Visual and narrative parts of storyboard are complete.	Written descriptions and storyboard adequately describe physical change. Visual or narrative parts of storyboard have a minor omission.	Written descriptions and storyboard do not fully describe physical change. Visual or narrative parts of storyboard have some omissions.	Written descriptions and storyboard are inaccurate in their descriptions of physical change. Visual and/or narrative parts of storyboard have major omissions.
Working Cooperatively	Takes a lead in group discussions. Works well in skit/cartoon development.	Participates in all aspects of group discussions and is helpful in skit/cartoon development.	Participates in most group discussions and is somewhat helpful in skit/cartoon development.	Participates minimally in group discussions and in skit/cartoon development.
Applying Chapter Concepts	Correctly applies concepts of particle speed, attraction and distance between particles, temperature, volume, and pressure in the presentation.	Adequately applies concepts of particle speed, attraction and distance between particles, temperature, volume, and pressure in the presentation.	Correctly applies some concepts of particle speed, attraction and distance between particles, temperature, volume, and pressure in the presentation.	Presentation shows major errors in applying concepts of particle speed, attraction and distance between particles, temperature, volume, and pressure.
Presenting the Skit or Cartoon	Makes a thorough, well-organized presentation. Skit/cartoon creatively and accurately presents chapter concepts.	Makes a good presentation. Skit/cartoon presents chapter concepts somewhat creatively and accurately.	Makes presentation, but it is somewhat hard to follow. Skit/cartoon is somewhat lacking in creativity or accuracy.	Presentation is haphazard. Skit/cartoon lacks creativity and accuracy.

Cause for Alarm

The following steps will walk you through the Chapter Project. Use the hints and detailed directions as you guide your students through design, test phase, and presentation.

Chapter Project Overview

In this project, students will work individually or in small groups to construct an alarm circuit that will light a bulb in response to an event of their choosing.

To introduce the project, construct a "Penny Detector" to show students how contact between the ends of two wires can turn on a light. Tape an uninsulated end of a piece of wire to a penny. Connect the other end of the wire to a light bulb. Connect the light bulb to a dry cell. Tape the other pole of the dry cell to an empty metal can. Dropping the penny into the can will turn the light on.

Have students read the Project Overview. Review the Project Rules and hand out the Scoring Rubric you will use for scoring students' work. Discuss with students what will be expected of them.

Set a deadline for the project presentation and interim dates for the different project tasks. Encourage students to copy the dates in the Project Timeline.

Group students. Have them brainstorm a list of detectors, triggers, and alarms they see in their everyday lives. Indicator lights in cars, thermostats, fire and smoke alarms, car and home burglar alarms, and lights that turn on automatically at sunset are a few examples of what are actually switches in an electric circuit.

Distribute copies of Project Worksheet 1. Have students work with a partner to answer the questions. These should help them think about different types of circuits. Project Worksheet 2 will help students through planning, building, testing, and presenting their circuits. Remind students to refer to the hints in the Project Overview as they plan and carry out the project.

If students are having a hard time designing their detector switches, help them along by providing hints as to how they might get the two ends of the wires to come in electrical contact with each other. For example, they might connect a wire to a ping pong ball wrapped with aluminum foil, floating in a container of water that is lined with aluminum foil. As water drains out of a hole in the bottom of the container, the ball will come in contact with the liner, completing the circuit.

Materials and Preparation

Consider organizing the class in groups to do the project. If space and time are limited, you may want to use a few generic setups consisting of a light bulb, one or two dry cells, and about 3 meters of wire. Have individual students connect their detector switch to the wire during the presentation part of the project.

Each student will need one or two 1.5-volt batteries, about 3 meters of insulated wire, and a light bulb. Make sure to select bulbs that require only 1.5 volts from a single battery or 3 volts from two batteries connected in series. Additionally, students may need aluminum foil, paper clips, screws, washers, nails, metal cans, electrical tape, basins or bowls, water, or salt.

If holders and sockets for the dry cells and bulbs are not provided, alligator clips will make it easier for connections to be made. You may need screwdrivers for securing connections to the various components.

Keep Students on Track—Tasks 1–2

Help students understand that a switch does not have to be a ready-made device like those we find on the walls for homes or the front panels of our stereos. A switch is simply a device that allows you to close and open a circuit.

Have students meet in groups to brainstorm events that cause a light, buzzer, or machine to automatically turn on. Their lists might include indicator lights in cars, the light in a refrigerator, alarms in stores, and libraries that prevent theft, etc.

Encourage students to begin working on their circuit design. They should also make a list of materials they will need for constructing their circuit.

Keep Students on Track—Task 3

Check students circuit designs and lists of required materials. If their plans are reasonable, they will be able to construct these circuits with the resources available to them. Make sure students conduct several tests of their circuit. If their circuit fails to function properly, they should modify their design.

If students are having difficulties getting started with their design, you may want to make some suggestions of possible ideas. You may also want to give some hints as to how students might get the two ends of the wires to come in electrical contact with each other.

Keep Students on Track—Task 4

Students should have completed initial tests of their circuits and begun redesigning to find solutions to any problems. Help students analyze their circuits, and make suggestions that will improve the completion of the circuit when the event occurs. Encourage students whose designs function fairly well to look for ways to improve both the design for more efficient function.

Keep Students on Track—Task 5

Check that all students have completed testing their alarm circuits and finished their redesigns. Help those students having difficulty by suggesting ways in which they can improve their designs to make the alarm circuit function as planned.

Encourage students to begin planning their presentations. Suggest that they make an outline of how they will present their alarm circuit and then practice their presentation.

Chapter Project Wrap Up

Many students will need to make final connections and adjustments when they set up their projects. You can speed up the presentations by creating four stations around the room so that four students can set up their projects simultaneously.

As students make their presentations, ask their classmates to think about the circuitry of the alarm. The presenter could ask the other students to explain how the alarm works. Then the presenter could fill in the missing pieces of the explanation with his or her own remarks and diagrams.

Have students turn in any written work you require, such as the one-page description, circuit diagram, and, if appropriate, the drawing of hidden parts.

Extension

Have all students design burglar alarms. As you test these alarms, pose as a burglar, doing your best to disarm the alarm before stealing the "precious" object. Tell students at the beginning of the project that you will be attempting to snip exposed wires and do anything else you can so that you don't set off the alarm. Students will enjoy the extra challenge of trying to make their alarms foolproof.

PROJECT OVERVIEW

Cause for Alarm

Most drivers rely on lights, buzzers, and bells to tell them when the fuel or oil is low, the temperature is too high, or the seat belts are not fastened. These lights, buzzers, and bells are examples of alarm circuits. Building an alarm circuit is just a matter of causing a switch to close so that there is electric current through a light or buzzer. The figure below shows a cross-sectional view of a circuit that will turn on a warning buzzer when somebody attempts to take the cookie from the counter. Lifting the cookie will cause the metal washer to connect the two pieces of aluminum foil. In this project, you will build a similar alarm circuit that turns on a light when it detects some event that you choose.

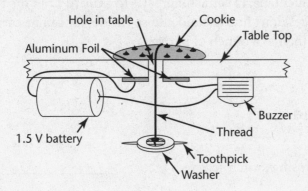

Project Rules

- Have your teacher approve your circuit design plan before you build your alarm.

- You may use only one or two 1.5-volt batteries as the power supply of your circuit.

- For your class presentation, you must make a display that includes a description of your circuit, as well as a circuit diagram. If your alarm includes any parts that are hidden from view, you must also include a diagram of these hidden parts in your display.

- You will need one or two 1.5-volt dry cells, about 3 meters of insulated wire, and a light bulb. Make sure to select bulbs that require only 1.5 volts from a single battery or 3 volts from two batteries connected in series.

- You will also find it helpful to gather various metal materials to use as part of your switch. These might include aluminum foil, paper clips, screws, washers, nails, metal cans, electrical tape, basin or bowl, water, or salt.

- You may want to use tape to hold connections together. If holders and sockets for the dry cells and bulbs are not provided, alligator clips will make it easier for connections to be made. You may need screwdrivers for securing connections to the various components.

Project Hints

- Brainstorm a list of events that you could use to trigger your alarm. You might want to discuss possible circuit designs with a partner.

- Test! Test! Test! Make sure your device works reliably so that you can feel confident that it will work when you demonstrate it to the class.

- Once you have successfully produced your circuit, improve both the durability and appearance of your design. Some suggestions include: (1) twisting wires together before taping them; (2) where bare wire must make contact with screws, cans, pennies, or other pieces of metal, you can improve the connection by scraping the insulation from 2.5 cm of wire, wrapping it around the object, if possible, and using a strong tape such as electrical tape or duct tape; (3) attaching parts to a board or to the inside of a container so pieces don't flop around and so the device can be carried as a single unit rather than as a bunch of parts.

Project Timeline

Task	Due Date
1. Event to trigger closing switch selected.	_____
2. Circuit diagram completed.	_____
3. Circuit design plans approved.	_____
4. Initial alarm completed.	_____
5. Tests and revisions made.	_____
6. Class presentation made.	_____

Name _____ Date _____ Class _____

Building Circuits for Detection

Work with a partner to think about ways in which you could detect each of the events described below. Write a paragraph explaining how the circuit works and draw a circuit diagram for each question. Use another sheet of paper if you need more room.

1. Water reaches the maximum level in a container.

2. A single drop of water is placed on a specific spot of your device.

3. A fine mist from three squirts of water from a spray bottle lands on a surface. (*Hint:* A circuit could be designed to detect the weight of the water.)

4. A door or lid opens.

5. A door or lid closes.

6. A window fan set on its lowest setting and placed three meters away blows on your device.

7. The attempted theft of a "precious" object. Make sure that you make your alarm tamper-proof, because you wouldn't want the thief to be able to cut any of your wires and disarm it!

PROJECT WORKSHEET 2
Building a Circuits
Getting Started

On a separate sheet of paper, answer the following questions about the circuit that you intend to build. Once you have obtained your teacher's permission, you are ready to build your circuit.

1. What event have you chosen that will close your circuit?

2. Make a detailed sketch of your alarm. Label the parts.

3. List the materials that you will need for building your circuit.

Testing and Revising

Create a table like the one below that you can use when you test your circuit.

Test #	Problems Encountered	Revisions Made to Circuit
1		
2		

Analyzing and Presenting

Complete the following tasks on a separate sheet of paper. When they have been completed, you are ready to put together your presentation.

4. Write a paragraph to summarize what your circuit does.

5. What difficulties did you have in building your circuit? How did you overcome the difficulties? Describe any revisions you made to your circuit.

6. Are any parts of your circuit hidden from view? If so, make a sketch of these hidden parts.

7. Name at least one practical application of your circuit.

Name _____ Date _____ Class _____

SCORING RUBRIC
Cause for Alarm

In evaluating how well you complete the Chapter Project, your teacher will judge your work in three categories. In each, a score of 4 is the best rating.

	4	3	2	1
Planning and Building the Circuit	Planning is thorough, with detailed and useful notes, sketches, and materials list. Student follows all Project Rules. Circuit design is very creative and works perfectly.	Planning is good, with useful notes, sketches, and materials list. Student follows most Project Rules. Circuit design is fairly creative and works most of the time.	Planning is adequate, with somewhat useful notes, sketches, and materials list. Student follows some Project Rules. Circuit design is somewhat creative and works sometimes.	Planning is minimal, with brief notes, sketches, and materials list. Student fails to follow many of the Project Rules. Circuit design lacks creativity and seldom works.
Testing and Modifying the Circuit	Extensive testing is performed that leads to significant modifications to the circuit.	A fair amount of testing is performed that leads to some modifications to the circuit.	Some testing is performed. Some modifications to the circuit are made. Some are related to testing.	Very little testing is performed. Few modifications to the circuit are made. They are unrelated to testing.
Making Class Presentation	Makes a thorough and well-organized presentation. Explains the process of design, construction, testing, and modification of the circuit in detail.	Makes a good presentation. Explains most of the process of design, construction, testing, and modification of the circuit.	Presentation is adequate. Explains some of the process of design, construction, testing, and modification of the circuit.	Presentation is brief and hard to follow. Student fails to explain major parts of the project.

Copyright © Pearson Education, Inc., or its affiliates. All rights reserved.

Design and Build a Roller Coaster

The following steps will walk you through the Chapter Project. Use the hints as you guide your students through discussions, observations, and conclusions.

Chapter Project Overview

This project uses roller coasters to demonstrate potential and kinetic energy. To get students excited about this project, begin with a class discussion about roller coasters. Allow students to describe their past experiences with roller coasters, including any features of the roller coaster that made the ride particularly enjoyable (*steep downhills, fast turns, vertical loops, etc.*). Have students think about how the speed of the roller coaster vehicle changed as it moved downhill or uphill. Ask: How can you apply the terms *kinetic energy* and *potential energy* to their vehicle at different points on these hills?

During this project, students will be making modifications to their tracks, such as adjusting hill heights and adding turns and loops. Review experimental design with students, pointing out the importance of keeping good records of all experiments. Students should keep a log in which they record variables that were changed, variables that were kept constant, and the outcome of trial runs.

After introducing the project, divide the class into groups of three or four students each. Emphasize that *every* group member shares the responsibility for planning and building the model. Then, have students brainstorm materials they can use in designing their roller coaster tracks. They should keep in mind that they will have to make several modifications to these tracks, so they need to select a material that is easily changed.

Have students read the Project Overview. Review the Project Rules, and hand out the Scoring Rubric that you will use for scoring students' work. Discuss with students what will be expected of them.

Set a deadline for the class presentations and interim dates to keep students on track. Encourage students to copy the dates in the Project Timeline.

Distribute copies of Project Worksheet 1. This worksheet will help students work on their initial roller coaster designs. They will be asked to draw their initial designs to scale. You may have to help them to understand scaling.

Once students have successfully built their initial roller coasters with three hills, distribute Project Worksheet 2. This worksheet will help them set up their logs for making modifications to their roller coasters. They should first experiment with hill height in an attempt to determine the greatest heights for their second and third hills. Next they should try to add turns and vertical loops to their roller coaster. They may need to change their hill heights to add these modifications.

Materials and Preparation

For the roller coaster tracks, students might use cardboard, posterboard, garden hoses, rubber or vinyl tubing, foam pipe insulation, and drinking straws.

Suggestions for vehicles include marbles, ball bearings, rubber balls, or toy cars.

Additional materials that the students may need include string, tape, glue, paper clips, bricks, shoe boxes, blocks of wood, stopwatches, cups, or buckets.

Encourage students to suggest and use other materials as well, but make sure that they consider the cost and availability of these materials.

Keep Students on Track—Task 1

Make sure that students have selected all of the materials they will use in designing their roller coaster tracks and vehicles, and that they are experimenting with different hill heights to find the maximum heights that they can use for the second and third hills.

Check that students are keeping complete records of their modifications and trial runs.

Keep Students on Track—Tasks 3–5

Make sure that students have a basic roller coaster with three hills built and that their vehicle can successfully complete the entire track without stopping or leaving the track.

Check that students are able to apply key concepts such as energy transformation, the law of conservation of energy, and friction to the description of their roller coaster. They should be able to indicate where potential and kinetic energies are highest and lowest.

Make sure that students are experimenting with adding turns and vertical loops to their roller coasters and conducting several different trials to determine the best location for these modifications.

Check students' logs to make sure that they are complete, including all variables that they changed and the success of each trial.

Chapter Project Wrap Up

Students should make brief presentations to the class. In their presentations, they should demonstrate their roller coasters and summarize their experiences in creating these roller coasters. They should be able to relate chapter concepts such as energy transformation, friction, and the law of conservation of energy to their projects.

After the presentations, have students discuss the project. They should talk about their experiences in creating their roller coasters, including any difficulties they encountered. Also, have students discuss energy as it applies to the projects. Students should understand how friction interfered with the movement of their vehicle along the track. Have them consider ways in which they could have reduced friction.

Extension

- Consider making additional requirements for the roller coasters. You could specify that the height of all three hills must total two meters. Another requirement could be that the vehicle must roll an additional three meters after leaving the track. You could also require that it take no longer than five seconds for the vehicle to complete the track.

- Have students research an existing roller coaster. They should make a report on the height of the hills and any loops or turns it has. Does this roller coaster require the input of additional energy during its route?

PROJECT OVERVIEW

Design and Build a Roller Coaster

In this chapter, you will be studying energy transformation, friction, and the law of conservation of energy. This project will help you to understand these concepts by allowing you to apply them to something that may be familiar to you—roller coasters. Have you ever ridden a roller coaster? Did you find the ride exciting or scary? Why? What happens to the speed of a roller coaster as it goes uphill, downhill, or through a turn? What features of roller coasters make them fun—giant hills, fast turns, vertical loops? If you were to design your own roller coaster, what features would you include?

In this project you will have the opportunity to create your very own roller coaster. Your vehicle will begin its journey on top of a hill that is no more than one meter in height. (Think about the potential energy in that vehicle!) It must then travel the full length of your track, climbing over two additional hills, without stopping or falling off the track. Once you have successfully created this basic roller coaster, you will modify your track to include the more complex features, like turns and/or vertical loops.

Project Rules

- Your first hill may not be higher than one meter in height.

- Your vehicle must complete the entire track without stopping or falling off. Once you have placed your vehicle on top of the first hill, you cannot add any energy to the system to help your vehicle complete its route.

- Before you begin building your roller coaster, you must write out design plans that include the materials you plan to use, and a sketch (drawn to scale) of your basic roller coaster track. Your teacher must approve these plans.

- You must make several modifications to your track. The first set of modifications will be to determine the maximum height possible for your second and third hills. The second set of modifications will be to add turns and/or vertical loops to your track.

- You must keep detailed records of any modifications that you make to your track, including the success of your vehicle's trial runs.

- You must be able to apply key terms such as *kinetic energy, potential energy,* and *energy transformation* to the description of your roller coaster.

- You must present your roller coaster to the class. During this presentation, you will have to describe all modifications that you made to your roller coaster. You will also have to show your understanding of energy transformation, friction, and the law of transformation of energy.

Suggested Materials

Be creative when selecting materials to use for your tracks. Some possibilities are cardboard, posterboard, garden hoses, rubber or vinyl tubing, foam pipe insulation, and drinking straws. Possible vehicles include marbles, ball bearings, rubber balls, and toy cars. You may also find that you need string, tape, glue, paper clips, bricks, shoe boxes, blocks of wood, stopwatches, cups, or buckets.

Project Hints

- Think about things that may adversely affect the performance of your roller coaster, such as friction. Can you think of ways to decrease the friction on your vehicle?

- When modifying your track, the results will be clearer if you only alter one variable at a time, such as hill height or distance between hills.

Project Timeline

Task	Due Date
1. Roller coaster building materials chosen.	_____
2. Project design with sketch of roller coaster completed.	_____
3. Basic roller coaster with three hills completed.	_____
4. Maximum heights for second and third hills determined.	_____
5. Turns and/or vertical loops added to roller coaster.	_____
6. Make class presentation of Chapter Project.	_____

PROJECT WORKSHEET 1
Design and Build a Roller Coaster

Complete the following tasks using a separate sheet of paper. When the tasks have been completed, you are ready to get your teacher's approval and begin constructing your roller coaster.

Thinking About Energy

1. A student plans to build a roller coaster in which his second hill is taller than his first hill. Would it be possible for his vehicle to complete the track? Why or why not? Use what you have learned in the text to justify your answer.

2. A student plans to build a roller coaster in which his first and second hills are of equal height. Would it be possible for his vehicle to complete the track? Why or why not? Use what you have learned in the text to justify your answer.

3. A student plans to build a roller coaster in which his third hill is taller than his second hill. Would it be possible for his vehicle to complete the track? Why or why not? Use what you have learned in the text to justify your answer.

Planning Your Roller Coaster

4. What materials will you be using to build your track? How will you secure your track in place? Do these materials allow you to make modifications easily?

5. What do you plan to use as your vehicle? Will your vehicle fit onto the track?

6. What is the mass of your vehicle?

7. Sketch out your basic roller coaster design, including three hills. Make this sketch to scale (for example, 1 cm in this sketch is equal to 10 cm on your actual roller coaster). Remember that your first hill may not exceed one meter!

8. On the sketch of your roller coaster, indicate the following:
   - Height of each hill
   - Distance between hills
   - Point of maximum potential energy
   - Point of maximum kinetic energy

PROJECT WORKSHEET 2
Design and Build a Roller Coaster
Part I: Finding the Maximum Hill Heights

Create a chart similar to the one below to record all modifications that you make to your track.

Modification number	Variable that you changed	Variables that remained constant	Heights of second and third hills	Distances between hills of trial run	Outcome and observations
1					
2					
3					

Answer the following questions on a separate sheet of paper.

1. How did changing the height of the second hill affect the distance that your vehicle traveled up the third hill?

2. How did changing the distance between hills affect your vehicle's performance?

3. What was the maximum hill height that you found for your second and third hills?

Part II: Adding Twists

Create a chart similar to the one below to record all modifications that you make to your track.

Modification number	Variable that you changed	Variables that remained constant	Outcome and observations of trial run
1			
2			
3			

Answer the following questions on a separate sheet of paper.

4. How did the placement of your turn or vertical loop affect the success of your vehicle in completing the track?

5. How did adding turns and loops to your track affect your vehicle's performance on the hills?

6. What problems did you encounter in making these modifications? For example, did you have to create a barrier to keep your vehicle from leaving the track on a sharp turn?

SCORING RUBRIC

Design and Build a Roller Coaster

In evaluating how well you complete the Chapter Project, your teacher will judge your work in four categories. In each, a score of 4 is the best rating.

	4	3	2	1
Planning and Building the Roller Coaster	The student is able to plan and build a roller coaster according to the specifications in which the vehicle successfully completes the track.	The student has only minor difficulties in either planning or building a roller coaster in which the vehicle successfully completes the track.	The student has significant problems either in planning or building a roller coaster in which the vehicle successfully completes the track.	The student attempts, but is unable to plan and build a roller coaster in which the vehicle successfully completes the track.
Conducting Experiments and Modifying the Design	The student is able to make all modifications to the roller coaster. Detailed descriptions of these modifications are well-organized and recorded in a data table.	The student makes most of the modifications to the roller coaster, and data tables are fairly complete and organized.	The student makes some modifications to the roller coaster but data tables are somewhat incomplete and disorganized.	The student makes minimal attempts to modify the roller coaster or does not keep track of modifications.
Applying Concepts and Using Terminology	The student uses chapter terms correctly in descriptions of the roller coaster.	The student uses most chapter terms correctly in descriptions of the roller coaster.	The student uses some chapter terms correctly in descriptions of the roller coaster.	The student has problems using most chapter terms correctly in descriptions of the roller coaster.
Presenting the Roller Coaster	The student makes a thorough, well-organized presentation. He or she displays well-designed visual aids.	The student makes a good presentation. He or she displays helpful visual aides.	The student makes a presentation, but it is hard to follow. He or she uses few visuals.	The student gives only a brief, poorly organized presentation. He or she uses no visuals.

Newton Scooters

The following steps will walk you through the Chapter Project. Use the hints as you guide your students through planning, construction, testing, improvements, and presentations.

Chapter Project Overview

To introduce the project, perform the following demonstration. Release an inflated balloon into the air, and ask students to consider what makes the balloon move forward. Explain that the balloon moves forward by expelling air backward.

Group students so they can brainstorm vehicle designs other than four-wheeled cars and think about how they might propel a vehicle without using any form of electrical energy or the force of gravity. Also, have students think about ways they can keep the vehicle going in a straight line.

Distribute the Project Overview and Scoring Rubric. Discuss the purpose of the project and your expectations of what the final product should include. Explain that students will be demonstrating their vehicles to the class and that they should test and modify their vehicles before their demonstrations. Review the Project Rules and Scoring Rubric with the entire class so that students will be clear about your expectations.

Set a deadline for the project presentation and interim dates for the different project tasks. Encourage students to copy the dates in the Project Timeline.

Distribute copies of Project Worksheet 1. Have students complete the worksheet, then discuss the answers as a class.

Preview Newton's third law of motion with students before they begin their designs.

After students have designed their vehicles, distribute Project Worksheet 2. Have students complete the worksheet and keep it for use in the testing and modification phase of this Chapter Project.

Materials and Preparation

Students will need a variety of materials to build their Newton Scooter. Some ideas are recycled materials from home, balloons, springs, toys or building-block sets, fishing lines, paper towel rolls, and straws.

If time, space, and resources are limited, have students work with a partner on this project. You will have to ensure, however, that both students participate equally in vehicle design and construction.

You could require that all of the students build balloon-propelled vehicles. In this case, give each student three identical balloons: two for vehicle-testing at home, and one for the class demonstration. This will make your class discussions easier because you will be able to focus on a single type of vehicle. Keep in mind that this option does, however, restrict the creativity of the students.

Keep Students on Track—Tasks 1–2

Review students' vehicle diagrams and make sure that they have added labeled arrows to the diagrams to show all the forces acting upon the vehicle.

Have students work in groups to discuss ways they can reduce friction in their vehicles, such as sanding rough areas or using a lubricant.

Keep Students on Track—Task 3

Lead a class discussion in which students think of ways they can apply Newton's third law of motion to their project. Use the chalkboard to list students' ideas for increasing the force on their vehicle and decreasing the mass of their vehicle.

Review students' vehicle design sketches. Make sure that they are thinking of practical ways in which they can build these vehicles. Make suggestions for materials they can use.

Set aside time in class for students to discuss their designs with other students. Peer input can help them to improve their designs and to select the one that they think will work best.

Keep Students on Track—Tasks 4–5

Check students' diagrams to make sure that they have added new arrows to show the force exerted by the vehicle and the force exerted on the vehicle. Also, check that Newton's third law of motion powers the vehicle they plan to build.

Set aside time in class for students to meet with a partner to discuss their designs. Do not allow students to begin construction of their vehicles unless they are able to explain how all the forces in their diagram operate.

Check once again that students have reasonable plans for building their vehicles and that they are sure that all of the materials they need are available to them.

After students have built their vehicles, have them use Worksheet 2, which they completed earlier, to test and modify their vehicles.

Chapter Project Wrap Up

Allow each student to present his or her vehicle, and encourage class members to ask questions about features on the vehicle.

Be sensitive to students whose vehicles fail to operate properly. Encourage these students to think about what might have gone wrong with their demonstration.

After all the presentations have been made, discuss with the class different ways in which students could have improved their vehicles. Allow them to think freely and to include ideas that might be possible if unlimited materials were available.

Extensions

- The vehicles could be tested on different surfaces to demonstrate how friction affects the performance of vehicles.

- Variations of the 1.5-meter horizontal distance could be used. You might consider a 1.5-meter vertical distance, a requirement that the vehicle make a 90° turn, or an obstacle (such as a stack of books) that the vehicle must maneuver around or over. Also, consider allowing students to choose higher levels of difficulty, such as having their vehicles travel 2.5 meters or travel 1.5 meters, cross the finish line, and then return to the starting line.

- As an alternative to having vehicles move along the floor, place a chair at either end of the course and tie a string or fishing line between them. Students could use this "track" to guide their vehicles through the air. Vehicles could be suspended from a paper towel roll or a straw with the "track" running through it. Vehicles that float on water are another possibility.

- To encourage students to build vehicles that are not car-like, give extra credit for designs that don't have wheels.

PROJECT OVERVIEW

Newton Scooters

Imagine what would happen if you and a friend were standing on roller skates and you gave your friend a forward push. What would happen to you? Would you stand still or would you travel backward? The backward motion that you would experience can be explained by Newton's third law of motion, which describes an equal and opposite reaction to every action.

In this project, you will use Newton's third law of motion to design a vehicle. This vehicle must travel forward 1.5 meters by pushing backward on the floor, the air, or some other object. At the close of this project, you will demonstrate your vehicle and explain its features to the class.

Project Rules

- Have your teacher approve your vehicle design plans before you begin construction of your vehicle.

- Your vehicle must use Newton's third law of motion to move forward; it must move forward by pushing backward on the floor, the air, or some other object.

- You must build your vehicle from scrap materials. Don't use a ready-made vehicle.

- Your vehicle must travel forward 1.5 meters and completely cross the finish line. The path of your vehicle should stay within a width of 1 meter.

- You are not allowed to interfere with the movement of your vehicle. You cannot give your vehicle a push as you launch it, and you cannot help it in any way as it travels from the starting line to the finish line.

- You cannot use any form of electricity or the pull of gravity to move your vehicle. This means that you cannot use a downhill ramp to get your vehicle started.

- You may use a "track" such as a toy car track or a string running from the starting line to the finish line to guide your vehicle. Not only will this help reduce friction, but it may also help you to keep your vehicle within the boundaries.

- Your vehicle does not have to move along the ground. If your vehicle moves through the air, you could use a string stretched between two chairs as a "track" to guide your vehicle.

- For the class presentation, you must have diagrams of your vehicle that illustrate the forces that act upon it. You should also be able to explain any modifications that you made to improve the performance of your vehicle.

Suggested Materials

Here are some ideas for materials to build your vehicle: recycled materials from home, toys or building-block sets, balloons, springs, straws, fishing lines, paper towel rolls

Project Hints

- Be creative! Don't limit yourself to vehicles that have wheels. Think about other ways that you could get your vehicle to move a distance of 1.5 meters. The rules state that the vehicle has to stay within a width of 1 meter, but it is allowed to leave the ground!

- What happens if you inflate a balloon and release it into the air? Can you use Newton's third law of motion to explain this movement? How could you use the balloon's movement to push your vehicle? Can you think of any other objects like this that you could use to push your vehicle?

Project Timeline

Task	Due Date
1. Sketches of possible vehicles completed.	_____
2. Forces of friction and gravity applied to sketches.	_____
3. Newton's third law applied to sketches.	_____
4. One sketch chosen as design for vehicle.	_____
5. Vehicle construction completed.	_____
6. All improvements completed.	_____
7. Class presentation completed.	_____

PROJECT WORKSHEET 1

Thinking About Newton's Third Law of Motion

Everyday Examples

Newton's third law of motion can be seen in action in many places. In the space provided, describe how this concept explains the following events.

1. An untied inflated balloon zooms around the classroom when released.

   _____

   _____

   _____

   _____

2. A squid squirts through the water without using its fins or tentacles.

   _____

   _____

   _____

   _____

3. A salmon swims upstream.

   _____

   _____

   _____

   _____

4. A hummingbird stays motionless in the air while flapping its wings.

   _____

   _____

   _____

   _____

Energy Sources

In designing your vehicle, you will need to apply Newton's third law of motion. List three different ways to propel your vehicle. The first one is done for you.

1. An inflated balloon

2. _____

3. _____

PROJECT WORKSHEET 2

Improving Your Vehicle

New cars aren't released to the public until after they have been tested and modified. Often, this stage of development can take months as the engineers and designers change features on the car to improve performance and safety. After you complete your vehicle, you too will need to spend time modifying your vehicle to ensure that it will travel straight down the course and cross the finish line.

The Spring-Loaded Design

Jeremy decided to use a spring-loaded launcher to propel his vehicle. His vehicle will soar off an uphill ramp so there would be less time for friction to act between the vehicle's wheels and the floor of the classroom.

    Jeremy thought about different variables that would affect the movement of his vehicle and made a table of these. Can you think of any variables Jeremy left out?

_____

_____

_____

_____

Variable	Ways to Test or Improve Vehicle
Angle of ramp	Test different ramp angles.
Mass of vehicle	Consider different materials for vehicle. Make the vehicle smaller. Don't use wheels.
Type of spring	Experiment with different springs.
Smoothness of ramp	Sand ramp to reduce friction.

Your Own Vehicle

By now you should have sketched a design of your vehicle. Use a table similar to the one above to think of all of the variables that might affect the performance of your vehicle. Indicate experiments that you will want to conduct in order to improve your vehicle's performance.

SCORING RUBRIC
Newton Scooters

In evaluating how well you complete the Chapter Project, your teacher will judge your work in four categories. In each, a 4 is the best rating.

	4	3	2	1
Planning	Student thoroughly considers the forces that would affect the vehicle. Sketch of the vehicle is useful and includes measurements.	Student adequately considers the forces that would affect the vehicle. Sketch of the vehicle is useful.	Student considers some of the forces that would affect the vehicle. Sketch of the vehicle is rough.	Student minimally considers the forces that would affect the vehicle. Sketch of the vehicle not made.
Building Vehicle	Student follows all Project Rules, and work shows evidence of having thoroughly tested and modified the vehicle.	Student follows most of the Project Rules, and work shows evidence of having adequately tested and modified the vehicle.	Student follows some of the Project Rules, and work shows evidence of having tested or modified the vehicle.	Student did not follow many of the Project Rules, and work shows little evidence of having tested or modified the vehicle.
Making Project Presentation	Presentation is thorough and well organized. Student communicates all appropriate features of the vehicle.	Presentation is adequate. Student communicates most of the appropriate features of the vehicle.	Presentation is appropriate but is hard to follow. Student communicates some of the features of the vehicle.	Presentation is inappropriate and hard to follow. Student communicates a few features of the vehicle.
Participating with Group	Student takes a lead in group discussions.	Student participates in all aspects of group discussions.	Student participates in some aspects of group discussions.	Student minimally participates in group discussions.

Magnetic Art

The following steps will walk you through the Chapter Project. Use the hints and detailed directions as you guide your students through research, testing of materials, construction, and presentation.

Chapter Project Overview

In this project, students will work in groups to design and create a magnetic sculpture. The sculpture should be held together only by magnets and objects with magnetic properties, be at least 20 cm tall, and keep its shape for at least two hours.

In introducing the project, have students name at least ten ways in which magnetism is used in their daily lives. Responses will vary but might include magnetic catches on appliance doors, speakers, magnets that hold notes in place, some children's toys, TV screens, doorbells, CD and DVD players, sensors, airport metal detectors, computer hard drives, credit card strips, some hand and power tools such as screwdrivers and drills, magnets used to separate metals, directional compasses, and electric guitars, among many others. At the end of the discussion, demonstrate for students how to make a temporary magnet by rubbing a ferromagnetic material with a permanent magnet.

Distribute the Project Overview. Review the Project Rules. You may also want to hand out the Scoring Rubric so that students will understand what is expected of them.

Organize the class into small groups. Make sure students understand that each member will participate in researching magnets, creating the magnetic sculpture, making a diagram of the sculpture, and presenting the sculpture to the class.

Set a deadline for the project presentation and some interim dates for the different project tasks. Have students copy assigned dates in their Project Timeline.

Distribute Project Worksheet 1 and Worksheet 2. After students have read the worksheets, ask if they have any questions.

Discuss how to make a diagram of their finished sculptures. Tell students that their diagrams should serve as an aid in presenting the magnetic sculpture to the class. It should show the materials used and the forces that hold the sculpture together.

Before students begin this Chapter Project, go over the safety guidelines that are pertinent.

Materials and Preparation

Ask students to start bringing in old magnets about two weeks before you plan to assign this project. Magnets can also be obtained from a variety of online distributors, most of which give discounts for bulk orders. Allow at least 15-20 small magnets per group. Limit the number of larger magnets to just a few per group.

Also ask students to bring in nuts, bolts, screws, nails, paper clips, metal buttons and other metallic objects that are attracted to a magnet and/or that can be magnetized. Allow at least 25-50 of such items per group.

Provide each group of students with a strong magnet to test and magnetize materials.

Appropriate bases for the sculptures include small pieces of flexible magnetic sheets, ceramic ring magnets, and large bar magnets. You might want to have students glue their magnetic bases to small pieces of foam to aid in moving the sculptures.

Keep Students on Track—Tasks 1–3

Check to see that students have done the research and have taken accurate notes on the information. Groups should begin collecting different kinds of magnets and testing a variety of materials to determine which are magnetic and which can be made into temporary magnets.

Repeat, if necessary, a demonstration of how to create a temporary magnet.

Keep Students on Track—Task 5

At this point, all students should have begun constructing their sculptures. Encourage students to use both permanent and temporary magnets in their works of art.

Tell students that once they have a completed sculpture, they might consider documenting the work of art by taking several pictures of it. This will ensure that even if the sculpture is disturbed or if some of the magnetic forces holding it together weaken, students will have a record that a sculpture was produced.

Keep Students on Track—Tasks 6–7

All students should now be finished with their sculptures and should be ready to present their works of art as well as their diagrams of what they have built.

You might want to provide a sign-up sheet for students to schedule their own presentations.

Chapter Project Wrap Up

As you review each group's magnetic sculpture, you may wish to have the members "talk you through" the presentation. Make suggestions for organizing the presentation. When appropriate, encourage some students to take a greater role in presenting the sculpture.

Provide class time for group presentations. Allow each group to present its sculpture, explain how it was built, and describe the process that resulted in the sculpture. Encourage other students to ask questions about the design of the sculpture and what magnets or other materials were used.

After all presentations have been made, discuss with students which magnetic sculptures seemed to be the best constructed—which were the most attractive and met the requirements.

Encourage students to evaluate how well they accomplished what they set out to do. Invite students to make suggestions about what they think would have made the project better.

Extension

Challenge interested students to apply what they've learned about magnetism to construct new sculptures that are identical to their original sculptures but that are much larger. Have students experiment to see if they can double or triple the size of their sculptures.

PROJECT OVERVIEW

Magnetic Art

For this project, you will build a sculpture—a three-dimensional work of art. Many well-known sculptures are made of stone, plaster, or welded metal. Unlike these works of art, your sculpture must be held together using magnetism.

   Before you begin your masterpiece, you will need to review the information on magnetism in your textbook. Working with a group, you will then research temporary magnets and how they can be made. You will use your findings to collect the materials that might be used to make your sculpture. These materials will include magnets, of course, but also objects that you think can be magnetized, as well as any other materials approved by your teacher. With your group, you will test your objects to see if they are attracted to a magnet. Then you will determine which objects can be temporarily magnetized. After analyzing the results, you and your group will choose materials to build a magnetic sculpture that meets the requirements of the project.

   Once your sculpture is complete, you will make a diagram of your sculpture that shows what materials are included and how they are held together. At the end of the project, your group will present your magnetic sculpture to the class.

Project Rules

- Work with your group to plan how to carry out this project. Your plan might include drawings of possible sculptures and a list of possible materials.

- Do research about magnetism, magnets, and temporary magnets. Work with your group in magnetizing various materials.

- Test a variety of materials to find out which are magnetic and how different materials can be held together by magnets and objects with magnetic properties.

- Have the design of your group's magnetic sculpture approved by your teacher.

- Use the Project Timeline to pace yourself. Work on your project every day so that you meet the project deadlines given to you by your teacher.

- Use the Project Worksheets 1 and 2 to guide you with this project.

- Follow the safety guidelines that your teacher has reviewed as you test your materials and construct your sculpture.

- When your sculpture is complete, work with your group in making a diagram that shows the materials used in the sculpture and how those materials are held together.

Project Hints

- Review the information in the chapter. Concentrate on the material that discusses magnetic poles and interactions between like and unlike poles. Also review the concept of magnetic domains. Record notes on this information in the space provided on the Project Worksheet 1 for this chapter project.

- Find out about temporary magnets and how certain objects can be temporarily magnetized. Record your findings on Worksheet 1.

- The materials you and your group use to make your sculpture should include different kinds and sizes of magnets and a variety of small metal objects such as washers, nuts and bolts, screws, paper clips without plastic coverings, nails, and thin, flexible wire. Depending on your proposed sculpture, you might also use small pieces of paper or fabric. Remember, though, that the only "glue" that can hold the sculpture together is magnetism.

- A piece of foam board can serve as a base for your sculpture, if your group decides that works best.

- As you and your group construct your sculpture, think about what you will say when you present your work of art to your classmates. Practice your presentation aloud as you help construct the sculpture.

Project Timeline

Task	Due Date
1. Complete the research for Worksheet 1.	_____
2. Collect magnets and other materials.	_____
3. Test the materials for magnetic properties.	_____
4. Choose the materials you will use.	_____
5. Build the magnetic sculpture.	_____
6. Make a diagram of the sculpture.	_____
7. Prepare class presentation.	_____
8. Present the piece of art to the class.	_____

Name _____ Date_____ Class_____

PROJECT WORKSHEET 1
Planning the Sculpture
Use this worksheet to help you plan this chapter project.

1. Record your notes on magnetic poles, magnetic domains, and temporary magnets in the appropriate spaces below. Use another sheet of paper, if necessary.

Notes on Magnetic Poles and Magnetic Domains:

_____

_____

_____

_____

_____

_____

Notes on Temporary Magnets and How to Make Temporary Magnets:

_____

_____

_____

_____

_____

_____

_____

2. Determine which of the materials you have chosen are attracted to a magnet. Record your findings in the data table on the Worksheet 2.

3. Use your test results and your research on temporary magnets to determine which materials can be temporarily magnetized. Record your results in the data table.

4. Replace any materials that you cannot use with magnetic materials or objects that are can be made into temporary magnets.

Name _____ Date _____ Class _____

Recording Observations

Use the table below to organize your observations.

Possible Objects to Use to Construct Magnetic Sculpture

Object	Attracted to Magnet? (yes or no)	Can be Magnetized? (yes or no)

SCORING RUBRIC

Magnetic Art

In evaluating how well you complete the Chapter Project, your teacher will judge your work in four categories. In each, a score of 4 is the best rating.

	4	3	2	1
Creating Magnetic Sculpture	Sculpture is original, attractive, and well constructed, held together only by magnets and objects with magnetic properties, is 20 cm tall or higher, and keeps its shape for two hours.	Sculpture is mostly attractive and well constructed, held together only by magnets and objects with magnetic properties, is 20 cm tall, and keeps its shape for two hours.	Sculpture is adequately constructed, held together only by magnets and objects with magnetic properties, is less than 20 cm tall, and keeps its shape for less than two hours.	Sculpture is not well constructed, held together with materials other than magnets and objects with magnetic properties, is less than 20 cm tall, and keeps its shape for less than two hours.
Making Diagram	Diagram is attractive and accurate, with labels and arrows showing how the sculpture is held together.	Diagram is mostly accurate, with labels and arrows showing how the sculpture is held together.	Diagram is only somewhat accurate, with only a few labels and arrows showing how the sculpture is held together.	Diagram is inaccurate, with few labels and arrows showing how the sculpture is held together.
Presenting the Sculpture to the Class	Makes a thorough and interesting presentation that includes a clear, accurate description of the sculpture and an engaging explanation of how it was made.	Makes a thorough presentation that includes an adequate description of the sculpture and an adequate explanation of how it was made.	Makes a presentation that includes a partial description of the sculpture and a disorganized explanation of how it was made.	Makes a presentation that includes an incomplete or misleading description of the sculpture and an incomplete explanation of how it was made.
Participating in the Group	Takes a lead in planning, constructing, and presenting the sculpture	Participates in all aspects of planning, building, and presenting the sculpture.	Participates in most aspects of planning, constructing, and presenting the sculpture.	Plays a minor role in the planning, constructing, and presenting the sculpture.

Show Some Motion

The following steps will walk you through the Chapter Project. Use the hints as you guide your students through measuring distance and time, recording this data, calculating speed, and displaying the results.

Chapter Project Overview

The basic goal of this project is for students to practice measuring a variety of speeds. They are required to choose at least one speed to measure from each of three lists and they are encouraged to measure additional speeds of their own choosing.

Through this project, your students will develop the following skills: measuring, making multiple measurements to improve accuracy, calculating, converting units, and communicating.

The menu items on the student project handout are designed so the Appetizers list contains speeds that are easy to calculate, the Entrees list contains more challenging speeds, and the Desserts list has the most difficult items.

Distribute the Project Overview and the Scoring Rubric. Review the Overview and the Rubric with the entire class so students will know what is expected of them. Encourage students to ask questions.

Set due dates for intermediate tasks and a deadline for completion of all three display cards. Have students enter the due dates in the Project Timeline.

Materials and Preparation

Review the student project handout. Try a couple of speed measurements yourself so you can anticipate some of the difficulties students will experience.

Students will need devices for measuring at home. Metric rulers will work well for centimeters and millimeters. Because most students probably don't have meter sticks at home, you can make them from posterboard in class. For measuring distances longer than 40 or 50 meters, they could make a "measuring tape" with a 10-meter piece of rope knotted with colored yarn at 1-meter intervals. Students will also need stopwatches or watches with a second

hand. Provide a few stopwatches that can be checked out on a one-night-at-a-time basis.

Students will need construction paper or large index cards to make their display cards.

Although this project is written to be completed by students individually at home, they could complete parts or all of the project in groups in class. You could even adjust the requirements of each level of success to better match the cooperative capabilities of small groups of students.

Have students complete Project Worksheet 2: Converting Units for Speed Measurements. Use of calculators might be appropriate.

Keep Students on Track—Tasks 1–5

Have students meet in small groups to discuss how they would make the measurements for speeds in the Appetizers list.

Try making one of the measurements from the Appetizers list as a class, or assign this measurement for homework. Lead students through the procedures of recording measurements and making calculations on a step-by-step basis. Make sure students label the units on their data, their partial answers, and their final answers.

Have students complete Project Worksheet 1, The Art of Measuring Speed. Students will learn the value of taking several measurements and then calculating an average. They will also learn how to measure the circumference of a circle. Discuss the answers to this worksheet in class.

Have students meet in small groups to discuss how they might make measurements of the speeds in the Entrees list and the Desserts list. Share ideas in class for some of the more difficult measurements. For instance, the speed of sound can be estimated by placing two students on opposite ends of a very large field. One person makes a loud noise, such as by clapping. The second person starts the stopwatch when the first person is seen making the sound and stops the stopwatch when the sound is heard.

Consider allowing students who are having difficulty with this project to choose their three speeds to measure from the Appetizers list.

Keep Students on Track—Task 6

Students should bring in at least one completed display card so you can make sure they are on the right track. Have students meet in small groups to share what they have done so far. Things to look for include: Are students' steps clearly organized? Are values labeled? Do the cards have titles? Are there diagrams to aid in the explanations?

Have students share techniques for making attractive and informative display cards.

Chapter Project Wrap Up

Have students review each other's display cards in small groups. Have students compare the speeds they measured.

Lead a discussion about the speeds calculated by different students for the same menu item. Have students check for possible errors in measurement or calculation. Have students brainstorm reasons for the differences between answers.

Have students convert all their speed measurements in this project to m/s for comparison purposes. They can add these values to their display cards, and then the cards can be put in order from slowest to fastest. Group cards describing the same measurement together. Put the display cards in order on the wall or make them into a booklet showing a "spectrum of speeds."

Extension

Allow students to measure speeds not included on the lists, as long as they get your approval before beginning their measurements.

Add to the "spectrum of speeds" display or booklet by finding speeds of things faster or slower than what you have already measured, such as the speed of light, the speed of Earth in orbit around the sun, the speed of a jet, and the speed of hair growth.

PROJECT OVERVIEW

Show Some Motion

Superman is faster than a speeding train, but is he as quick as lightning? Just how fast are these things? Have you ever been accused of moving like molasses or at a snail's pace? How slow is a snail?

    Your goal is to measure the speeds of various things around your home. To measure an object's speed, you need to know how far it moves in a certain amount of time. The snail in the diagram below crawled for 2 minutes to leave the 10-cm slime trail. To calculate the snail's speed, divide the distance (10 cm) by the time (2 minutes) to get 5 cm/min (5 centimeters per minute).

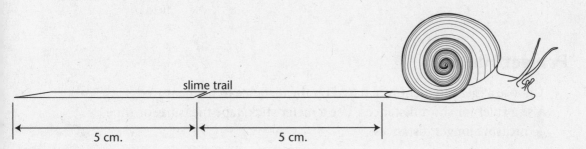

Project Rules

- You must measure the speed of three items in the Speed Choice Menu on the next page. Pick one from each list. If you would like to measure the speed of something not on the lists, ask your teacher for approval.

- For each speed measured, prepare a display card that includes: a title, a diagram of your measurement method, a table of data collected, your step-by-step procedure for calculating speed, and the speeds you calculated.

Suggested Materials

- Things to measure

- A stopwatch or other device to measure seconds and a clock to measure hours, if necessary

- A variety of tools for measuring distances, such as a tape measure, long string or rope with meters marked off, meter stick, or ruler

- Materials to make your display

- Optional: calculator

Speed Choice Menu

Appetizers	Entrees	Desserts
• you walking, running, crawling, or hopping	• a toy vehicle moving on a track or across the floor	• a point on the rim of your bicycle wheel
• a pebble falling in a glass of water	• the scent of vanilla moving across a room	• the tip of a minute or hour hand
• a walking, running, or slithering pet	• the rising water level in a bathtub	• the growth of grass or other plant
• a falling feather, tuft of down, or snowflake	• water moving through a hose	• the tip of your dog's wagging tail
• an art moving across the sidewalk or driveway	• a bird flying by	• sound moving across a playground or football field

Project Hints

- Choose a measurement tool based on the distance to be measured. Use a ruler for short distances. Use a meter stick, tape measure, or rope to measure longer distances.
- For distances longer than about 50 meters, you might want to estimate the distance by pacing. Ask your teacher if you need help to estimate a distance.
- Check your math with a calculator.

Project Timeline

Task	Due Date
1. Three speeds chosen.	_____
2. Measurements approved by teacher.	_____
3. Data collected for first measurement.	_____
4. Data collected for second measurement.	_____
5. Data collected for third measurement.	_____
6. Display cards completed for the three measurements.	_____

PROJECT WORKSHEET 1

The Art of Measuring Speed

Measuring More Than Once

1. Keisha wanted to measure the running speed of her dog, Marvin. She marked off 20 meters in her backyard, told Marvin to stay at the starting point, and then positioned herself at the finish point with a stopwatch. She started the stopwatch and called Marvin. Keisha repeated the measurement three more times. Her four measurements were: 5.6 s, 4.3 s, 4.1 s, and 4.4 s.

   a. Explain why the first measurement might be so different. Why is it a good idea to repeat a measurement several times?

   _____

   _____

   b. The first measurement was over a second longer than the other three. Give reasons for including and for excluding the first measurement from the average.

   _____

   _____

Measuring the Distance Around a Circle

2. Cara's gerbil Clancy was running in a treadmill. Cara remembered that the circumference of a circle is $\pi \times$ the diameter of the circle. ($\pi = 3.14$)

   a. Calculate how far Clancy runs for each revolution of the treadmill.

   _____

   b. The radius of a bicycle wheel is 34.5 cm. How far does your bicycle travel for each revolution of the wheel? (*Hint:* The diameter of a circle is equal to twice its radius.)

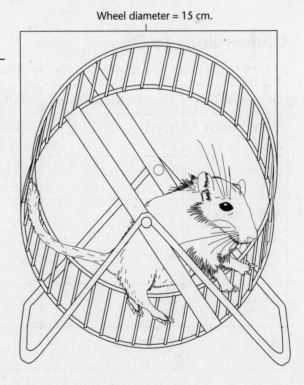

Wheel diameter = 15 cm.

PROJECT WORKSHEET 2

Converting Units for Speed Measurements

As you make speed calculations, you'll choose measurement units that are convenient for that particular measurement. If you want to compare two different speeds, it's more convenient to convert one or both measurements so that both units are the same. Work through the examples and complete the table to practice converting measurement units.

Example 1

Peyton calculated the speed of a windup toy to be 7 m/min and the speed of a grain of sand dropping through water to be 11 cm/s. He wanted to convert these measurements to the same units to compare them. In this example, Peyton converts the speed of the grain of sand from cm/s to m/min.

$$\frac{11 \text{ cm}}{1 \text{ s}} \times \frac{1 \text{ m}}{100 \text{ cm}} \times \frac{60 \text{ s}}{1 \text{ min}} = 6.6 \text{ m/min}$$

The grain of sand moves at 6.6 m/min, somewhat slower than the windup toy.

Example 2

Kaely estimated that her bean plant grew about 2 centimeters per day. She wants to know how fast that is in meters per year. She does the following calculation:

$$\frac{2 \text{ cm}}{1 \text{ day}} \times \frac{1 \text{ m}}{100 \text{ cm}} \times \frac{365 \text{ days}}{1 \text{ year}} = 7.3 \text{ m/yr}$$

Here's how she would find the growth rate of the bean plant in centimeters per hour:

$$\frac{2 \text{ cm}}{1 \text{ day}} \times \frac{1 \text{ day}}{24 \text{ h}} = \text{approximately } 0.083 \text{ cm/h}$$

Conversions to Do

Complete the table. The first two rows are done for you.

Start with this	Convert the units to	Multiply original measurement by	Answer
0.0065 m/day	mm/d	$\frac{1000 \text{ mm}}{1 \text{ m}}$	6.5 mm/d
25 m/s	km/h	$\frac{60 \text{ s}}{1 \text{ min}} \times \frac{60 \text{ min}}{1 \text{ h}} \times \frac{1 \text{ km}}{1000 \text{ m}}$	90 km/h
8,900 mm/s	m/s		
30 cm/d	m/yr		
0.9 km/yr	m/d		
6 m/d	km/yr		

SCORING RUBRIC

Show Some Motion

In evaluating how well you complete the Chapter Project, your teacher will judge your work in four categories. In each, a 4 is the best rating.

	4	3	2	1
Planning	Designs an efficient and accurate method for measuring distance and time for all three setups.	Designs a reasonable method for measuring distance and time for all three setups.	Designs a method for measuring distance and time for all three setups.	Chooses three speeds to measure. Chooses inappropriate methods to make measurements.
Measuring	All distances are measured accurately. All time measurements are accurate.	Makes one error in measuring. Otherwise, measurements are accurate.	Makes two major errors in measuring.	Makes more than two major errors in measuring.
Calculating	Makes all calculations accurately. Correct units are used throughout the project.	Makes one calculation error and includes correct units most of the time.	Makes two calculation errors. May also omit units or use incorrect units several times.	Makes more than two calculation errors. May omit most units in answers.
Presenting the information	Completes all display cards with title, diagram showing measurement method, data table with proper units, procedure for calculating speed, and speed calculated. Display cards are well organized and easy to read.	Completes all display cards with at least four of the following: title, diagram showing measurement method, data table with proper units, procedure for calculating speed, and speed calculated. May have minor errors.	Completes display cards with at least three of the following: title, diagram showing measurement method, data table with proper units, procedure for calculating speed, and speed calculated. May have errors.	Attempts display cards, but they are incomplete. Display cards may have major errors.

In Hot Water

The following steps will walk you through the Chapter Project. Use the hints and detailed instructions as you guide your students through experimental design, materials testing, device design and construction, and presentation.

Chapter Project Overview

In this project, students will conduct experiments to learn about heat loss and will construct an insulating device for a 355-ml aluminum can.

To introduce the project and stimulate student interest, perform the following demonstration. Bring an insulated container of hot water to class the day before you begin the project. Measure the temperature of the water. Leave the container in the classroom until the next day. Measure the temperature of the water again. Ask students why the temperature of the water decreased. Explain to students that even the best insulators cannot keep hot water warm indefinitely. Eventually the heat of the water will be transferred to its surroundings (the air in the room) until the water and its surroundings are the same temperature.

Have students read the Project Overview. Review the Project Rules and hand out the Scoring Rubric. Discuss with students what will be expected of them.

Set a deadline for the project presentation and interim dates for the different project tasks. Encourage students to copy the dates on the Project Timeline.

If you have grouped students during the initial testing phase of the project, have each group come up with an experimental plan and then have each student in a group test one or two materials or design features using the plan. To ensure that every student will have ample opportunity to participate in experimental planning and testing, each group should consist of no more than four students.

Distribute copies of Project Worksheet 1. This worksheet will help students collect data during the testing part of the project. Project Worksheet 2 will help students design their own insulating device. Remind students to refer to the hints in the Project Overview as they plan and carry out the project.

Materials and Preparation

Each student will need an empty aluminum soda can. Alcohol thermometers, funnels to pour hot water into cans, tongs or hot pads, and a source of hot water, such as a coffee urn should be available.

Gather an assortment of materials for students to test, such as aluminum foil, newspaper, packing peanuts, cardboard, nylon cloth, canvas cloth, cotton balls, plastic wrap, foam board, and wood chips. Encourage students to suggest and use other materials as well.

Caution students to use extreme care when transporting hot water around the classroom and when pouring hot water into containers. Students should wear goggles and oven mitts.

Students could start building their device in the early stages of the project. This tests intuitive knowledge without giving them a chance to learn through experiment.

Keep Students on Track—Tasks 1–3

Because the testing requires the use of thermometers, this part of the project may be better done in class. Many of the experiments could involve setting up the can at the beginning of class and then checking temperatures at the end of class.

This step may be difficult for some students because they are expected to design experiments. During a discussion, help students see that their experiments will fall into two areas: the type of material used for the insulation and the location and thickness of the insulation. Students should measure the insulation ability of many different materials and designs to help them in designing their own container and in predicting the insulating properties of other students' containers.

Worksheet 1 will help students decide which materials and design features work best.

Check students' experimental plans. Have they identified controls? Do they know what will be manipulated? Look over the designs to determine what other materials might be needed if currently unavailable in the classroom. Decide how much time you are going to allow students to test materials. Some students may have to rethink their experimental designs if given a time limit.

Keep Students on Track—Tasks 4–6

Have students discuss the results of their experiments in small groups. Tell students to use Worksheet 2 during these discussions. Not everyone will have tested all possible variables. Consider having a class discussion to allow students to have access to all of the data. Point out certain trends that the data are likely to support. For example, lids are important and insulation over a particular thickness is not very helpful.

Decide how much time, if any, you are going to allow students to work on their containers in class. Remind students of the date on which their containers must be finished. Remind them that they need to test their containers with water at different starting temperatures.

Chapter Project Wrap Up

Make arrangements to have a large quantity of hot water at constant temperature available on the day the devices are presented. A large coffee urn works well. At the beginning of class, quickly fill the cans in each of the students' containers. All cans should be filled with water that is the same temperature; 80–90°C should work well. Take care when pouring the water to not burn yourself or students. Students should use the temperature of the water reservoir as the starting temperature. Tell them to stir the water in the cans before taking the final temperature.

Students should present their containers to the class and explain why they chose the materials and features that they did. When making predictions, students should look for similarities to designs and materials they tested. Each student should predict the final temperature of his or her own project as well as the final temperature for 3 to 5 other projects. While the class is waiting for final temperatures, predictions can be posted.

Extension

When the devices are tested, pour water into an uninsulated can to act as a control. Subtract the final temperature of the water in the control can from the starting temperature to calculate the maximum temperature drop. You could look at each student's device from the standpoint of percent of maximum drop. For example, suppose the maximum drop was 45°C and a student's device lost 15°C. As a percent of the maximum, the drop was 33% (15°C/45°C). The lower the percentage, the better the device was at insulating the can.

PROJECT OVERVIEW

In Hot Water

In this chapter you will learn about temperature, thermal energy, and heat and how these concepts are related. Keep in mind what you learn because you will be using this information to design a container to slow the loss of heat from a 355-mL aluminum can of hot water.

This project has two parts. In the first part, you will design and conduct experiments to learn more about materials that can help prevent heat loss. In addition, your experiments will investigate whether certain container designs slow heat loss more than other designs.

The second part of the project involves building a container that insulates an aluminum can of hot water. Once you have built your device, you should test it with various water temperatures.

For your presentation, your teacher will fill your can with hot water of a known temperature. At the end of the class period, the temperature of the water in your can will be measured. If the difference between the starting and ending temperatures is small, your container is a good insulator! You will be asked to predict the final temperature of the water in your device and in the devices of other students. To make your predictions, you will need to review your notes and recall what you learned in your experiments.

Project Rules

- Have your teacher approve your plans before you begin your experiments.

- Your container must be something you assembled. You cannot use ready-made or manufactured devices. This excludes foam drink holders and commercial bottles or cups. In addition, you may not use electric current or heating chemicals.

- Your container should keep the water sample as hot as possible while using the thinnest amount of insulation. The insulation must be no thicker than 3 cm.

- The opening of the can must be easily reached so that hot water can be poured in. However, you may cover the opening of the can during the cooling period.

- The aluminum can may not have any other holes besides the opening in the top.

- When you design your project, keep in mind that a thermometer will be inserted through the opening in the top to measure the final temperature.

Safety

You will be working with hot containers and water that can burn skin. Be careful, especially when moving the hot water. Wear goggles to protect your eyes and oven mitts to protect your hands.

Suggested Materials

In your group, you will need to test many different materials for their ability to insulate. Examples include: aluminum foil, newspaper, packing peanuts, cardboard, nylon cloth, canvas cloth, cotton balls, plastic wrap, foam board, and wood chips. You can try other materials as well.

Project Hints

- Record the data from your experiments as outlined in Project Worksheet 1.
- Share the results of your experiments with other students and rank the materials and container designs with respect to their ability to minimize heat loss (see Worksheet 1). Each person can do a different experiment and learn from each other's work.
- Use Project Worksheet 2 to help you with the design and construction of your device.
- Plan on building your insulating device several days before it is due. You will need time to test your device with different temperatures of water. Record the temperature of the water in the can every 10 minutes for 40 minutes. You can then make a graph by plotting temperature against time. This graph will help you make predictions.
- Throughout the project, keep track of what you have learned about insulation devices. This will help you to predict the final temperature of the water in your classmates' devices.

Project Timeline

Task	Due Date
1. Plans for heat loss experiments completed.	_____
2. Experiments completed.	_____
3. Project Worksheet 1 completed.	_____
4. Project Worksheet 2 completed.	_____
5. Insulating device constructed.	_____
6. Tests of insulating device completed.	_____
7. Device presented and tested in class.	_____
8. Predictions made.	_____

PROJECT WORKSHEET 1

In Hot Water

Some of your experiments should help you to determine which types of materials make the best insulators. Make a table similar to the one below on a separate sheet of paper. Add a separate row for each material you test. Use it to record your data.

Material Tested	Time	Temp. (°C)	Insulating Ability Rank
	Start _____	Start _____	
	End _____ Elapsed (mins) _____	End _____ Change _____	

1. Write the name of the material to be tested in the first column.

2. Record starting and ending times of your experiment in the second column. Use these times to calculate the elapsed time in minutes. You should try to keep the elapsed time the same for all materials.

3. In column three, record the starting, ending, and change in temperature of the water in the can. The starting temperature should be the same or nearly the same for all materials tested.

4. Once you have all of your data, determine a way to rank the materials in terms of their insulating ability.

You will also need to conduct experiments to determine the best location and thickness for the insulation. Make a table similar to the one below on a separate sheet of paper. Add a separate row for each design you test. Use it to record your group's data.

Design	Time	Temp. (°C)	Insulating Ability Rank
	Start _____	Start _____	
	End _____ Elapsed (mins) _____	End _____ Change _____	

1. In the first column give a description of the design being tested (with or without lid, thickness of insulation, with or without bottom, and so on).

2. The elapsed time and starting temperature of the water should be the same or nearly the same for each design.

3. Once you have all of your data, determine a way to rank the designs in terms of their insulating ability.

PROJECT WORKSHEET 2

In Hot Water

Answer the following questions to help you design your insulating device.

1. Why was it important to keep the elapsed time and the starting temperature of each of your experiments the same or nearly the same?

_____

_____

2. What method did you use to rank the materials and designs that you tested?

_____

_____

3. Which three materials that you tested were the best at insulating the hot water? Do these materials have anything in common? What are some similar materials?

_____

_____

_____

4. Which three design features that you tested were the best at insulating the hot water? Can you think of a way to include all three design features in your device?

_____

_____

_____

5. Using the results of your experiments, choose one or more materials that are good insulators and choose the design features that you want to use. Make a sketch of your plan for your container. Label its important features.

6. On a separate sheet of paper, make a list of the materials you will need to construct your device. Be sure to identify other materials that may be needed during construction such as tape, string, or glue.

SCORING RUBRIC

In Hot Water

In evaluating how well you complete the Chapter Project, your teacher will judge your work in the following categories. In each, a score of 4 is the best rating.

	4	3	2	1
Developing Experimental Design and Testing Materials	Experimental design clearly shows understanding of the value of keeping some variables constant. Experiments test both materials and design features.	Design shows good understanding of the value of keeping some variables constant. Experiments test both materials and design features.	Design shows partial understanding of the value of keeping some variables constant. Experiments test either materials or design features, but not both.	Design shows limited understanding of the value of keeping some variables constant. Experiments test either materials or design features, but not both.
Designing, Building, and Testing the Insulation Device	Device adheres to project rules. Device is an excellent insulator. Complete testing of device performed on time.	Device adheres to project rules. Device is a good insulator. Testing of device performed on time.	Device adheres to project rules. Device is a poor insulator. Testing of device is incomplete.	Device clearly violates one or more project rules. Testing of device is incomplete.
Predicting Results	Uses knowledge learned in project. Accurately predicts final temperature of several different device designs, including own.	Uses knowledge learned in project. Accurately predicts final temperature of two or more device designs, including own.	Uses knowledge learned in project. Accurately predicts final temperature of own device only.	Guesses rather than uses knowledge learned in project. Predictions of all devices, including own, are inaccurate.
Working Cooperatively (optional)	Takes a lead in group planning. Effectively communicates container features to class.	Participates in all aspects of group planning. Communicates most container features to class.	Participates in most aspects of group planning. Communicates some container features to class.	Participates minimally in group planning. Communicates few container features to class.

The Nifty Lifting Machine

The following steps will walk you through the Chapter Project. Use the hints as you guide your students through designing and building their device.

To introduce the project and to stimulate student interest, load a soup can with sand until its mass is 600 g. Show students how you can reduce the input force required to lift this load by using a meter stick as a lever and a chalkboard eraser as a fulcrum. Invite students to lift the can with and without the lever. Use an inclined plane and/or a set of pulleys to lift the load as well.

Have students read the Project Overview. Review the Project Rules and hand out the Scoring Rubric that you will use for scoring students' work. Discuss with students what will be expected of them.

Set a deadline for the project presentation and interim dates for the different project tasks. Encourage students to copy the dates in the Project Timeline.

As a class, discuss compound machines, how one might build a machine, materials that could be used, and any initial questions students may have. Have students brainstorm ideas for a device on their own. Each student should design their own device, which must be a compound machine. Students should be grouped for the construction phase of the project. Each group should consist of no more than four students. Groups can build one or all of the designs in their group, or come up with another design to build.

Distribute copies of Project Worksheet 1. Have them read over the questions they will need to answer to help them design their device. Project Worksheet 2 will help students during the construction phase of the project. Distribute this worksheet once students have designed a device that you have approved.

Remind students to refer to the hints in the Project Overview as they plan and carry out the project.

Materials and Preparation

Provide a wide variety of materials from which students can choose to build their machine. Some possibilities include: wood scraps of all sizes, cardboard and plastic tubes, nails and screws, coat hangers, straws, spools, cups, cans, wire, toy wheels, toy cars, string, paper clips and cardboard. Keep sanding paper and a light lubricating oil on hand for when the devices are built. Encourage students to suggest and use other materials as well.

You may choose to have students work up the design stage of the project without requiring any actual construction or demonstration. The design stage still requires students to apply knowledge from the text to original solutions to a problem.

Keep Students on Track—Tasks 1–2

Assuming that the machine is under ideal conditions, then its efficiency is 100%. A 600 g mass represents a load with a force of 6 N. The distance the load must travel is 5 cm which is equal to 0.05 m. Total work (force × distance) required of the machine is $6 \times 0.05 = 0.3$ J.

The force diagram may vary considerably depending on the design of the device. Students must at least show the force of the weight of the load and the input force.

Do not let students try to build a device that is too complicated, unlikely to work, or represents a safety hazard due to its size.

Keep Students on Track—Task 3

The efficiency of the machine can be improved by sanding to smooth rough surfaces and lubricating moving surfaces that are in contact with the load. Measurements to make for calculating mechanical advantage are the weight of the load can (600 g) and the amount of the input force required to lift the load.

Encourage students to perform a simple efficiency analysis on their own machine (comparing work put into the machine versus work done by the machine). Tell them to try to improve the efficiency by sanding ramps and using lubricants to reduce friction.

Have students discuss as a group how they could change the mechanical advantage of their machine (input force versus output force). Lengthening a lever, adding a pulley, or reducing the angle of an inclined plane will all increase the mechanical advantage.

Help students with calculating the total mechanical advantage of a compound machine. It's the product of the ideal mechanical advantages of each simple machine.

Chapter Project Wrap Up

Review the rules with students the day before presentations to prevent students from missing their goals because they overlooked one of the restrictions. For instance, students may have forgotten that the load must be raised at least 5 cm, because they were focused on mechanical advantage.

Make sure that students turn in a brief description of their machine (as a group is fine) that describes how it works.

As students demonstrate their machines, ask their classmates to try to identify which of the six types of simple machine are being used in the compound machine being demonstrated.

After the presentations, ask students to reflect on their own projects by using diagrams and short paragraphs describing what they would do differently if they were just beginning the project. You can ask them to share their designs in small groups, or you can collect and comment on their diagrams and paragraphs.

Extensions

- Consider having a school-wide competition to see who can design and build the best machine to perform a particular task. Quality can be scored in terms of efficiency of the machine, the mechanical advantage, or perhaps the speed with which the task is accomplished.

- Have students design devices for performing tasks other than the one performed in this project. For fun, you could have students design (on paper) devices with very poor mechanical advantage, or have students design devices that must use all six simple machines when performing their function.

PROJECT OVERVIEW
The Nifty Lifting Machine

For this project, you will design and build a device to lift 600 grams at least 5 centimeters with as little input force as possible. You are thus trying to design and build a machine that operates at a high mechanical advantage. You must submit a brief explanation of how your device works when it is finished and demonstrate it to the rest of the class.

Project Rules

- The load can is a soup can filled with sand until it has a mass of 600 g. You can lift the load from below, or you can lift it from above using string on top of the can, or you can pull it from the side.

- The input can is identical to the load can except that it will be empty. When you demonstrate your project, you will attach the input can to your device and fill it with sand until the load can has been raised 5 cm.

- To determine the mechanical advantage of your machine, you need to determine its input force and output force. Since you know the masses of the input can and the load can, you can use Newton's second law in the form of *Weight = Mass × Acceleration due to gravity* to calculate the input force and output force. To calculate the actual mechanical advantage of your machine, you divide the output force by the input force. You can calculate the mechanical advantage of a compound machine by multiplying the mechanical advantage of each of its simple machines.

- Have your teacher approve your design before you begin building your device.

- Your device must contain a combination of at least two simple machines.

- The distance the load must be raised is 5 cm, measuring from the lowest point of the load before and after the device is used.

- Imaginary walls extend upward from a 1-m square area in which your device must be able to sit. You need to design your device with this size limitation in mind.

- Exercise caution when building your device to prevent injuries.

Suggested Materials

- You will need materials to build your device. Some possibilities include wood scraps of all sizes, cardboard and plastic tubes, nails and screws, coat hangers, straws, spools, cups, cans, wire, toy wheels, toy cars, string, paper clips and cardboard. You can use other materials but must ask your teacher's permission first.

- Ask your teacher for sanding paper and a light lubricating oil to improve the efficiency of your device.

Project Hints

- Before designing your device, you will need to get some ideas. Look at the machines around you to see how simple machines are used to perform simple tasks.

- Before you start building, draw diagrams of several different designs.

- Do not begin building until your teacher approves your design.

- Consult your textbook to learn how you might improve the device by changing the length of a lever, by adding a pulley, or by changing the angle of a plane.

- To calculate the total ideal mechanical advantage of your compound machine, multiply the individual ideal mechanical advantage of each of your simple machines.

Project Timeline

Task	Due Date
1. Individual student design finalized.	_____
2. Group design finalized (if applicable).	_____
3. Prototype built.	_____
4. Device finished; written description complete.	_____

PROJECT WORKSHEET 1
The Nifty Lifting Machine

Answer the following questions on a separate sheet of paper. Use your textbook to help you answer the questions. When you have finished, you are ready to begin designing your own machine.

1. List the six different types of simple machines (refer to your text).

When moving the load can, you can apply the force from the top, bottom, or side.

2. If you were to move the load by applying force to the top, what kind of machine might be the most appropriate to lift the load 5 cm?

3. If you were to move the load by applying force to the bottom, what kind of machine might be the most appropriate to lift the load 5 cm?

4. If you were to move the load by applying force to the side, what kind of machine might be the most appropriate to lift the load 5 cm?

5. Use your answers to Questions 1–4 to decide whether your device will apply a force to the top, bottom, or side. Write the direction on a separate sheet of paper.

6. Decide what type of simple machine you will use to apply the force to the load can in the direction you decided. Call this machine "X" and write its type on the sheet.

7. Since you must design a compound machine, you cannot use the input load to apply force directly to machine X. Instead you must apply the input force to another machine which will then apply a force to machine X. Decide what type of simple machine you will use to apply force to machine X and write it on the sheet.

8. You are now ready to draw a design of your device. Draw the design on the sheet.

9. Examine the design you have drawn. Are there modifications you would like to make that might improve your lifting machine? Repeat Steps 5 through 8 with your revisions. Draw the new design on the sheet and take it to your teacher for approval.

10. Use your drawing to predict the mechanical advantage of your machine. Take measurements of each of the two simple machines that make up your compound machine and compute their mechanical advantage. Multiply the mechanical advantage of the two simple machines to get the mechanical advantage of the compound machine.

PROJECT WORKSHEET 2
The Nifty Lifting Machine

Follow the guidelines below to help in building your machine.

Before beginning construction:

Take a look at your design and at the building materials. For each part of the device locate materials which you can use to build that part. Make sure that the materials will be able to withstand the forces that will be acting on them without breaking. Keep in mind that if parts will move, you want to try to minimize friction.

Once you have determined all the materials that you will need, collect them in one area and also obtain any glue or fasteners (screws, nails) that you require.

Show the materials to your teacher and get permission before you begin construction. You are now ready to begin building.

During construction:

You need to be careful during the construction especially if you need to use a hammer or screwdriver to attach parts together. Wear safety goggles at all times. If you need to use glue, place newspaper under the area.

As you build the machine, check each part to make sure that it is working as you expected. If you run into trouble, stop and go back to the original design and modify it as necessary. Get your teacher's permission before making any changes.

After construction:

- Make sure that your device fits within the space limitation (one meter square).

- Your device must lift the load can at least 5 cm.

- Measure the input force that is required to lift the load can 5 cm. Use this force to calculate the mechanical advantage of the machine (= output force/input force). The larger the mechanical advantage, the better your machine is.

- If you are not satisfied with the mechanical advantage of your machine or if it is unable to lift the load can 5 cm, you will have to make some changes. Small changes such as sanding or lubricating surfaces might help increase the efficiency of your machine. Also, you might want to change the machine's ideal mechanical advantage.

The presentation:

Practice with your device so that it will perform properly on the day of your presentation. During the presentation, pour sand slowly into the load bucket until just enough is present to lift the load 5 cm.

Name _____ Date_____ Class_____

SCORING RUBRIC

The Nifty Lifting Machine

In evaluating how well you complete the Chapter Project, your teacher will judge your work in four categories. In each, a score of 4 is the best rating.

	4	3	2	1
Creating the Design	Design is clear and simple. Design lists the materials that will be required to build the device.	Design is fairly clear and most of the materials that will be required to build the device are listed.	Design is somewhat unclear. Some of the materials that will be required to build the device are listed.	Design is confused. Few of the materials required for construction are listed.
Understanding Concepts	Student's written explanation shows a clear understanding of the simple machines used in the device and mechanical advantage.	Student's written explanation shows an adequate understanding of the simple machines used in the device but not mechanical advantage.	Student's written explanation shows an adequate understanding of one of the simple machines used in the device but not mechanical advantage.	Student's written explanation shows minimal understanding of a few of the simple machines used in the device but not mechanical advantage.
Working Cooperatively	Participates in all aspects of group planning, decision-making, and construction.	Participates in most aspects of group planning, decision-making, and construction.	Participates in some aspects of group planning, decision-making, and construction.	Participates in group work in a minor way. Usually lets others do the planning, decision-making, and construction.
Demonstrating the Device	Device moves load 5 cm and requires an input load of less than 200 g.	Device moves load 5 cm and requires an input load of more than 200 g but less than 400 g.	Device moves load 5 cm and requires an input load of more than 400 g but less than 600 g.	Device does not move load 5 cm or requires an input load of more than 600 g.

You're on the Air

The following steps will walk you through the Chapter Project. Use the hints and detailed directions as you guide your students through planning, data gathering and analysis, and presentation.

Chapter Project Overview

Before introducing the project, discuss communication devices with the class. List various devices on the board. Then lead the class in the identification of devices that are mobile and easy to carry around, such as cellular phones and personal music devices.

Have students read the Project Overview. Review the Project Rules and hand out the Scoring Rubric which you will use for scoring students' work. Discuss with students what will be expected of them.

Set a deadline for the project presentation and interim dates for the different project tasks. Encourage students to copy the dates in the Project Timeline.

Group students. Have them brainstorm a list of communication devices that are most commonly used. Review their ideas and discuss the advantages and drawbacks. Review each student's choice of communication devices to survey.

Distribute copies of Project Worksheet 1. Have them read over the questions they will answer to help them design their survey sheets. Project Worksheet 2 will help students through collecting data and preparing for the presentation. Distribute this worksheet once you have given students approval for the devices they plan to investigate. Remind students to refer to the hints in the Project Overview as they plan and carry out the project.

Some students might have an interest or ability to use computer programs for compiling and analyzing data. Spreadsheet programs often can both tabulate and graph data.

It will be helpful if students compose their survey questions so that a numerical answer can be provided. For example: 0 = never, 1 = rarely, 2 = once a week, 3 = often, 4 = every day. Using such a numerical system may make it easier for students to analyze and graph their data.

Have students distribute surveys to as many people as possible. Surveys should be confidential. Students need to remind classmates and other people to return surveys as soon as they are completed. Make sure students include a due date on their survey.

You might consider assigning groups of students to investigate the use of one type of communication device. The group can devise one survey form. If each student in the group distributes the forms, a much greater amount of information can be gathered.

Materials and Preparation

This project will require paper for photocopies, posterboard, graph paper, and acetate sheets for transparencies (optional). Students will need multiple copies of the survey sheet to distribute. Computer programs that create graphs or spreadsheet programs can be used to compile data.

Keep Students on Track—Task 3

The design of the survey sheet is very important. Students need to decide what information they want to collect. Brainstorming ideas with students may help them to formulate the questions that will give them the information they need. Develop criteria for selecting good questions. Some suggestions for criteria might be: (1) Clarity: Are the questions easy to understand? Will they give the student the information needed? Are they short and to the point?; (2) Time: Does the survey take a reasonable time to complete?; (3) Method of responding: Can the questions be answered with a check mark, one or few words, by numbers, or by circling a response? Have students develop other criteria.

If possible, distribute an example of a professional survey to give students ideas on how to write their questions.

Keep Students on Track—Tasks 5–6

By this time the students should have the survey sheets returned. They should begin compiling the data, recording the results, and preparing their graphs. Students may need to review methods of compiling data.

If computer programs such as spreadsheets are available, share these with the students. It may also be necessary to review graphing skills. Discuss the various types of graphs such as bar graphs, pictographs, line graphs, and so on. Have students select graphs that would be best to use for this project. Students may need to complete a bar graph for each question asked on the survey.

Chapter Project Wrap Up

Students may present their findings by using overhead transparencies, creating slide show presentations on the computer, or placing their graphs on posterboard to present to their classmates.

Students should have a written analysis for each graph. The analysis should summarize the graph and may also offer hypotheses to explain results. For example, a written analysis for a graph showing brand use would include which brands are most popular and which are least popular. If respondents did not directly say why they preferred a particular brand, students might infer that one brand was most economical, or a brand was too new to be in widespread use.

Extension

Class data can be pooled so that comparisons between the uses of different communication devices can be made. If this option is chosen, you may want to make sure that each survey has one or more questions that have the same wording, otherwise, comparisons between answers to different surveys may not be valid.

PROJECT OVERVIEW

You're on the Air

For this project, you will collect data that will give you information about when, where, and why people use radios, televisions, cellular telephones, computers, and other wireless communication devices.

You will choose one or more communication devices and conduct a survey on how and when people use them. You will also evaluate the most popular brand of device that you choose to study. These devices have features that may affect their ease of use, efficiency, and cost-effectiveness. These are topics you can include in your surveys.

You will design a survey and distribute it to friends, neighbors, and relatives. When the surveys are completed you will analyze the data, construct graphs, and interpret the results. You will prepare a poster to display your data and interpretations. Finally, you will present your findings to the class.

Project Rules

- Have your teacher approve your choice of communication devices before developing your survey.

- Have your teacher approve your surveys before you distribute them.

- Be sure to gather your survey results in time to meet the project timelines.

- Graphs of your data will be an important part of your analysis.

Suggested Materials

- You will need paper for photocopies, posterboard, graph paper, and acetate sheets for transparencies (optional).

- If you plan to use colored graphs you will need some type of coloring materials, such as colored markers or colored pencils.

Project Hints

- Brainstorm a list of devices that interest you. If you choose a communication device that is too expensive or specialized, you might not find very many people who use it and your survey results may be limited.

- Libraries, the Internet, computer stores, cellular phone stores, and many other retail outlet stores may have information for you to consider when designing your survey.

- The survey can examine many things. It can look at favorite brand choices. It can compare the efficiency of e-mail programs to phone calls. It can examine high versus low usage times. Do not feel limited in the choice of your survey questions.

- When designing your survey, remember to have at least some questions with numerical answers, or answers that can be converted to numbers, so that you can analyze the data numerically. For example, as answers for "How often do you use this device?" you might have never = 0, rarely = 1, once per week = 2, two or three times per week = 3, every day = 4, more than once per day = 5.

- There are many ways to present your results. For example, you can write a report, give a speech, or draw illustrations with captions. If possible, bring in a device of the kind you are discussing and demonstrate how it works. If you plan to demonstrate a device, take it to your teacher before the school day starts and leave it there for safekeeping. The device may be delicate and might break if it is carried all day in a backpack.

Project Timeline

Task	Due Date
1. Select device and have choice approved	_____
2. Complete research	_____
3. Write survey and have it approved	_____
4. Distribute surveys	_____
5. Collect completed surveys	_____
6. Analyze data	_____
7. Present project to class	_____

PROJECT WORKSHEET 1

Designing a Survey

Below is a sample list of survey questions. This sample asks about use of a cellular telephone. Make your own survey on a separate sheet of paper.

Survey on Cellular Telephone Use

Teacher's Name: _____ Student's Name: _____

Our class is collecting information concerning the usage of communication devices. Please complete this survey and return it to _____ at _____. It is not necessary for you to write your name on this form. Thank you for your help.

1. Do you use a cellular telephone?

2. Which brand of cellular phone do you use?

3. About how much did the device cost?

4. About how many hours a month do you use the device?

5. About what is your monthly bill for the device?

6. Do you use the device for business? Personal? Both?

7. Do you use the device while driving?

8. Where do you use the device most often?

PLEASE RETURN BY _____

PROJECT WORKSHEET 2
Analyzing Your Data

Answer the questions below on a separate sheet of paper to help you to analyze and present the data from your survey.

1. For each question in your survey that had a numerical answer, find the answer with the highest value and the answer with the lowest value. Then calculate the average response using all the data. Suppose one of your questions was "How many hours per week do you use a cellular telephone?" and you received the following answers: 5 hours, 1 hour, 2 hours, and 4 hours. To calculate the average response, you would add the answers together (5 + 1 + 2 + 4 = 12) and then divide by the total number of answers (12 ÷ 4 = 3 hours).

2. For each question you want to graph, make groups for the data if the results are not already grouped in a small number of categories. When making your categories, consider the highest and lowest values for your data as well as how the data are clustered. For example, if you asked how many hours per week a device was used, the results could be grouped into the following categories:

Average Length of Time the Device Is Used Each Week	Number of People
None	1
Up to 2 hours	6
2 to 4 hours	7
4 to 6 hours	3
Over 6 hours	1

3. Choose what kind of graphs you want to make. For the sample data above, a bar graph or a circle graph might be made.

4. If your survey has a question for which the answers can't be grouped, or a question for which the results are better explained in words, write a description of the answers.

5. Make a poster of your results. You'll probably want to include a copy of the survey on the poster. Include the graphs that you made. Be sure to add any explanations needed. Write a short summary of your results.

6. Now you are ready to decide how to present the results of your survey to the class. What kind of presentation do you want to make? You could give an oral report using your poster as a visual aid, you could make transparencies of your graphs and display them with an overhead projector, or you could use a computer to create a slide show of your graphs.

SCORING RUBRIC

You're on the Air

In evaluating how well you complete the Chapter Project, your teacher will judge your work in three categories. In each, a score of 4 is the best rating.

	4	3	2	1
Writing and Conducting the Survey	Comprehensive set of survey questions developed. Questions are clearly written and elicit useful and interesting answers. Large number of surveys are completed.	Fairly comprehensive set of survey questions developed. Most questions are clearly written and elicit useful and interesting answers. Fairly large number of surveys are completed.	Somewhat comprehensive set of survey questions developed. Some questions are unclear and elicit confusing data. An adequate number of surveys are completed.	Set of survey questions is not comprehensive. Questions are unclear and elicit confusing data. Some questions are irrelevant. Few surveys are completed.
Analyzing and Graphing the Results	Data analysis is complete and appropriate. Form of graphs is appropriate for the data. Graphs are neat, well labeled, and greatly enhance understanding of the survey results.	Data analysis is mostly complete and appropriate. Form of graphs is appropriate for the data. Graphs are fairly neat and well labeled and enhance understanding of the survey results.	Data analysis is partly incomplete but mostly appropriate. Form of one or two graphs is inappropriate for the data. Graphs are partially labeled and somewhat enhance understanding of the survey results.	Data analysis is incomplete or inappropriate. Form of some graphs may be inappropriate for the data. Graphs are hard to understand, missing many labels, and do little to enhance understanding of the survey results.
Making Class Presentation	Presentation is interesting, clear, and well organized.	Presentation is mostly complete and easy to understand.	Presentation is somewhat incomplete and difficult to understand.	Presentation is difficult to understand, incomplete, and very brief.

Design and Build an Optical Instrument

The following steps will walk you through the Chapter Project. Use the hints and detailed directions as you guide your students through planning, constructing, modifying, and presenting their optical instruments.

Chapter Project Overview

Before introducing the project, make a telescope from two lenses, a cardboard tube, and tape. Show students that the distance between the two lenses must equal the sum of the focal length of each lens for the instrument to work properly. Talk about how different instruments, such as telescopes, microscopes, and periscopes, operate by using mirrors and lenses to redirect light rays.

Have students read the Project Overview. Review the Project Rules and hand out the Scoring Rubric you will use for scoring students' work. Discuss with students what will be expected of them.

Set a deadline for the project presentation and interim dates for the different project tasks. Encourage students to copy the dates in the Project Timeline.

Group students. Have them think about different optical instruments and the materials they can use to build them.

Distribute copies of Project Worksheet 1. Have students experiment with the beam of light from a flashlight or a laser pointer. They should understand how mirrors and lenses bend this beam of light. Make sure they understand both reflection and refraction.

Project Worksheet 2 will help students prepare for their class presentations. Distribute this worksheet once they have finished making modifications to their instruments.

Remind students to refer to the hints in the Project Overview as they plan and carry out the project.

Materials and Preparation

Some miscellaneous items students will need include tape, clay, filters (colored cellophane works well), cardboard tubes, flashlights, shoeboxes, protractors, rulers, and meter sticks.

The following optical components will be required and can be purchased from a scientific supply house:

  convex and concave lenses

  plane mirrors

  concave mirrors

  convex mirrors

  optical bench or meter stick

  optical bench kit

If time is an issue, concentrate on constructing a class model of a design created by the class. Each student should take an active role in discussing the final design to be built. Furthermore, each student could be responsible for drawing diagrams of the instrument with lines representing how light rays travel through the instrument. The class can work together to assemble the parts. Continually discuss the effects of arranging the components differently.

Keep Students on Track—Task 2

Before students design their optical instruments, make sure they understand refraction and reflection. Encourage them to experiment with lenses and mirrors to see how these devices bend light rays.

Review students' design plans before allowing them to begin construction. Make sure that all materials they will require are available to them.

Keep Students on Track—Task 3

Give students time in class to construct their optical instruments. Help them use clay and/or tape to anchor all lenses and mirrors.

Encourage students to talk with one another to discuss any difficulties they may be having during this construction phase of the project.

Help students think of ways they can incorporate moving parts into their designs to allow for focusing of lenses. One suggestion would be to use two different cardboard tubes so that one can be inserted into the other. They could put lenses on the ends of the tubes so that when they slide the tubes back and forth, the lenses move closer to and further from each other.

Keep Students on Track—Tasks 4–5

Make sure students are keeping good records of all modifications they make to their instruments.

Advise students as they write their manuals. Explain that a good manual explains product use and gives a detailed description of all instrument parts.

Chapter Project Wrap Up

As students give their reports, ask their classmates to take brief notes, writing down the major characteristics of each optical instrument.

After all the presentations have been made, have students discuss their projects. Have them describe similarities and differences among the instruments.

Have students turn in any written work you require, such as their project designs, records of modifications, and manuals.

Extension

- Have students research and model existing optical instrument designs as their final design projects. They should be expected to explain the effects of reflection and refraction, as well as the effects of altering various components in their designs.

- If there is an observatory near your school, consider taking your class there to see the large telescopes that are used to view stars and planets. Ask the exhibitor to explain how the lenses in the telescope are focused to look at different astronomical features.

PROJECT OVERVIEW

Design and Build an Optical Instrument

In this chapter, you will be learning about reflection and refraction. In this project, you will demonstrate your knowledge of these principles by building an optical instrument, such as a telescope, microscope, or periscope. Once you have completed your instrument, you will write a manual that describes how to use it. Your manual will also contain a detailed diagram and a description of all of the parts of your instrument. To complete the project, you will present your instrument to the class and demonstrate how it is used.

Project Rules

- Have your teacher approve your design plans before you begin building your optical instrument.

- You may not use any pre-assembled parts—only those items listed in the materials section are allowed. If you wish to use a material that is not listed, you must obtain your teacher's permission.

- You must keep records of any modifications that you make to your original design plans.

- During a class presentation, you will demonstrate how your instrument functions and describe all of its parts.

Suggested Materials

- Some miscellaneous items you will need include tape, clay, filters (such as colored cellophane), cardboard tubes and boxes, flashlights, protractors, rulers, and meter sticks.

- Some optical components you will require include concave lenses, convex lenses, flat mirrors, concave mirrors, and/or convex mirrors.

Name _____ Date_____ Class_____

Project Hints

- Brainstorm a list of optical instruments that you could model. Think about how these instruments work. Do they contain mirrors? Do they contain lenses? If so, what type? Think about the path that light takes as it travels through these instruments.

- When making your design plans for your optical instruments, include measurements such as distances between lenses.

- On your design plans, draw the path that light will take as it travels through your instrument. Think about the angles of the light rays as they reflect off mirrors or are bent by lenses.

- Try to incorporate moving parts into your design so that you will be able to focus your lenses or adjust mirrors. One suggestion would be to use two cardboard tubes, one of which fits inside the other. Attach your mirrors or lenses to opposite ends of the tubes. You can adjust the distance between the lenses or mirrors by sliding the tubes back and forth.

- Make sure that you test your instrument before your class demonstration. Record any modifications that you make to the original design.

Project Timeline

Task	Due Date
1. Type of optical instrument selected	_____
2. Design plans completed and approved	_____
3. Optical instrument constructed	_____
4. Tests and modifications of instrument completed	_____
5. Manual written	_____
6. Class presentation	_____

Light

PROJECT WORKSHEET 1
Experimenting With Reflection and Refraction

Complete the following tasks using a separate sheet of paper. When the tasks have been completed, you are ready to obtain your teacher's permission to begin building your optical instrument.

1. Direct a beam of light from a flashlight or laser pointer into a flat mirror at a 45° angle. Measure the angle between the mirror and the reflected light ray. Draw a diagram of the path of light and label these angles. Repeat this activity using 30° and 60° angles.

2. Using two flat mirrors, reflect a light beam from a flashlight or laser pointer such that the light ray leaving the second mirror runs parallel to the ray leaving the flashlight or laser pointer, but is six inches to the right. Measure the angles of the light rays as they are reflected in the mirrors. Also measure the distances between the mirrors. Draw a labeled diagram that illustrates this activity.

3. Make at least three tests using concave and convex mirrors. Shine a flashlight or laser pointer into these mirrors at different angles and record the results. Draw labeled diagrams of the arrangements.

4. Find the focal length of a convex lens by focusing light from a window through the lens and onto a piece of paper. The focal length is the distance between the lens and the paper when the image of a distant object is clear.

5. Make tests with at least four combinations of convex or concave lenses and light from a flashlight or laser pointer. Make labeled drawings of the arrangements of lenses and light and how the light rays bend.

6. Decide what kind of optical instrument you want to build. Then, using the information that you have learned about reflection and refraction of light beams, draw a diagram of the instrument. Label all the parts and make a materials list. On the plan, trace the path that light will take as it passes through your instrument. Note all distances between instrument parts. Also note the angles at which light hits and reflects from the mirrors.

Name _____ Date _____ Class _____

Preparing for the Class Presentation

Complete the following tasks on a separate sheet of paper. When they have been completed, you are ready to put together your presentation.

1. In designing your instrument, how did you select the materials, types and dimensions of mirrors and/or lenses, and the locations of important components?

2. Describe what your instrument accomplishes. Does it function as you hoped it would?

3. Use words and diagrams to explain how light is reflected and/or refracted as it moves through your instrument. Make sure you discuss how your instrument's design accomplishes its intended function.

4. Describe the effect of altering different components of the optical instrument. For example, what would happen if you placed the mirrors and/or lenses farther apart? What would happen if you placed them closer together? What would happen if you rotated the lenses or mirrors?

5. What possible modifications could be made to your instruments? Are there any materials that you would have liked to have used that were unavailable to you? If so, how would these have changed your design?

6. Compare your instrument with a commercially available one. What similarities and differences are there? Make sure you compare the major features of each instrument.

SCORING RUBRIC

Design and Build an Optical Instrument

In evaluating how well you complete the Chapter Project, your teacher will judge your work in four categories. In each, a score of 4 is the best rating.

	4	3	2	1
Planning and Building the Instrument	Makes a thorough design plan and materials list. Plan accurately indicates the path light will take, is clearly labeled, and includes distances between parts and angles of reflection.	Makes a fairly thorough design plan and materials list. Plan indicates the path light will take, is labeled, and includes most distances between parts and angles of reflection.	Makes a somewhat incomplete design plan and materials list. Plan indicates the path light will take, is missing some labels, and includes some distances between parts and angles of reflection.	Design plan and materials list are incomplete. Path of light is inaccurate, many parts are not labeled, and many distances between parts and angles of reflection are missing.
Testing and Modifying the Instrument	Many tests are performed. Extensive modifications are made. Tests and modifications are recorded in detail.	Quite a few tests and modifications are made. Records of tests and modifications made are fairly complete.	Some tests are performed. Some modifications are made. Some records of tests and modifications are made.	Few tests are performed. Few modifications are made. Records of tests and modifications are incomplete.
Writing the Manual	Manual is organized and accurately describes and diagrams all parts of the instrument in detail.	Manual fairly accurately describes and diagrams nearly all parts of the instrument.	Manual describes and diagrams the instrument in general, but important details are missing.	Manual is disorganized and cursorily describes and diagrams parts of the instrument.
Making the Class Presentation	Presentation is thorough and well organized. Student explains in accurate detail how the instrument functions.	Presentation is fairly thorough and well organized. Student explains in some detail how the instrument functions.	Presentation is adequate. Student explains in some detail how the instrument functions.	Presentation is brief and disorganized. Student explains very generally how the instrument functions.

Music to Your Ears

The following steps will walk you through the Chapter Project. Use the hints and detailed directions as you guide your students through planning, construction, testing, improvement, and presentation.

Chapter Project Overview

Before you introduce the project, bring in some musical instruments for a class discussion. Encourage students to understand that all instruments depend on vibrations moving through air. Using both well-known and unusual instruments as examples, explain that the principles of sound that they will learn in this chapter apply to musical instruments.

Distribute the Project Overview and the Scoring Rubric. Discuss the purpose of the project and your expectations of what students should be able to do with the final product. Explain that students will be demonstrating their instruments to the class and that they must test and modify their instruments before the class demonstrations. Review the Project Rules and Scoring Rubric with the entire class so that students will be clear about your expectations.

Set a deadline for the project presentation and interim dates for the different project tasks. Encourage students to copy the dates in the Project Timeline.

Distribute copies of Project Worksheet 1. Have students complete the worksheet, then discuss the answers as a class.

After students have designed their instruments, distribute the Project Worksheet 2. Have students complete the worksheet and keep it for use in the testing and modification phase of this project.

Materials and Preparation

Students will need a variety of materials to build their instruments. Some ideas are different sizes of rubber bands, cardboard boxes, different lengths of cardboard tubes or plastic pipes, string, wooden craft sticks or tongue depressors, boards, nails, drinking straws, plastic bottles, wooden sppons, and dowels.

If time, space, and resources are limited, have students work in small groups on this project. You will have to ensure, however, that all of the students participate equally in instrument design, construction, and performance.

Keep Students on Track—Task 1

Check to make sure students have identified appropriate concepts that will apply to their design. If they are having difficulty identifying concepts, make suggestions of appropriate headings under which to look.

Keep Students on Track—Task 2

Review students' instrument design sketches and prototypes. Make sure that there is a way to vary the pitch of the sounds produced by their instruments. Make suggestions for materials they can use if the materials they have selected are not effective.

Set aside time in class for students to discuss their instruments with other students. Peer input may help them improve their instruments.

Keep Students on Track—Tasks 3–4

By now students should have finished and started testing their instruments. Remind them to keep accurate records of the testing process, either in a notebook or on separate sheets of paper. They should also note how they will modify their instruments to improve them and then make the changes described to see if their instruments are improved. Check that they can successfully control pitch and loudness.

Keep Students on Track—Task 5

Students should be in the final stages of modifying their instruments. If you can, bring in a pitch pipe or keyboard so students can tune their instruments. Students may also want to find out what range of notes their instruments can play.

If some of the students' instruments are horns that use a mouthpiece, have students that already play a brass instrument explain or demonstrate how a variety of notes can be played simply by varying the position of the lips when blowing.

You may want to have available simple tunes already written out. Some students may want to compose their own simple tune to play.

Chapter Project Wrap Up

Allow each student to present his or her instrument, and encourage class members to ask questions about features on the instrument. Each presentation should also include a brief explanation of the student's design, construction, and modification process.

Each student must play a short, simple tune on his or her instrument, as well as demonstrate how the instrument can play different notes and notes at different volumes. Performing can be anxiety-producing, so don't make this seem like a recital.

Be sensitive to students whose instruments fail to operate properly. Encourage these students to think about what might have gone wrong with the construction of their instruments, and how they might have proceeded differently.

After all the presentations have been made, discuss with the class different ways in which students could have improved their instruments. Allow them to think freely and to include ideas that would not have been possible because of limited materials.

Extension

- If you or some of your students have musical training, pick one or several students' designs on which different notes or even a scale can be played. Students could make enough copies of the instrument to form a band, and the band could play a tune.

- At the end of the project, have students research instruments of other cultures. Students could pick a country or part of the world to study, and write a report on the instruments used there.

Name _____ Date_____ Class_____

PROJECT OVERVIEW

Music to Your Ears

Humans have been making and playing musical instruments for thousands of years. New instruments are invented, and existing instruments are modified to produce different sounds. Probably many cultures have used a hollow log as a simple drum.

Many instruments are based on vibrating strings. One category of instrument, horns, depends on the vibrating lips of the player to create sound. Other instruments use vibrating reeds. The many flutelike instruments create sound by causing a column of air to vibrate.

In this project, you will design, build, test, and modify your own musical instrument. At the end of the project, you will demonstrate your instrument in a class presentation.

Project Rules

- Have your teacher approve the design of your instrument before you begin construction.

- You must be able to demonstrate how to change the loudness and pitch of the sound produced by your instrument.

- Your instrument must be made of safe materials. Cover any sharp edges with tape.

- Loud sounds can damage hearing. Do not play your instrument too near other students' ears.

- You may not use electric current in your instrument in any way.

- You must keep a logbook of the design, construction, testing, and modification of your instrument.

- You must demonstrate and play a simple tune on your instrument in a class presentation.

Suggested Materials

Your teacher will have on hand a supply of materials to build your musical instrument, such as different sizes of rubber bands, cardboard boxes, different lengths of cardboard tubes or plastic pipes, string, wooden craft sticks or tongue depressors, drinking straws, and bottles. You may use other materials of your own choosing that you bring from home, as long as you discuss this with your teacher first. Practically anything can be incorporated into a musical instrument.

Project Hints

- Think about whether you will want to play your instrument by blowing into it, strumming it, striking it, or by some other method.

- Be creative! Don't limit yourself to the materials supplied by your teacher. And don't just copy an existing instrument. Part of your teacher's assessment of your project will be based on originality.

- As you decide on the design of your instrument, remember that you will need to play something on it. Your instrument must not only make sounds, but it must make different sounds.

Project Timeline

Tasks	Due Date
1. Complete instrument design and submit it for approval	_____
2. Construct instrument	_____
3. Complete testing of instrument	_____
4. Modify instrument	_____
5. Test redesigned instrument	_____
6. Present instrument and design process to the class	_____

PROJECT WORKSHEET 1

Planning Your Musical Instrument

The following tasks will help you start the design phase of this Chapter Project.
Use another sheet of paper if you need more room.

1. Brainstorm all the ways you can think of that musical instruments make and modify sound. You might want to begin with instruments that are familiar to you, either because you or someone you know plays them, or because music you like is played on them. Then think of instruments you may not know as much about. As you brainstorm, you may find it helpful to classify instruments into categories, such as instruments with a mouthpiece and instruments in which strings make the sound. Finally, try to think of ways to make and modify sound that may not be used in a conventional instrument.

2. Draw a diagram of your proposed instrument. Be sure to label its parts, and the materials you will use.

3. How will you play your instrument? Exactly how will your instrument make sounds? What will vibrate to create sound waves? How will your instrument make sounds of different pitch and volume?

4. Make detailed notes on the construction of your instrument. Will you need to use other materials for certain parts of your instrument? How will the parts fit together? Will you need glue or special tools to make your instrument?

PROJECT WORKSHEET 2

Improving Your Musical Instrument

After making an instrument from your original design, you must test, modify, and test your instrument again. The following tasks will help you as you improve your instrument in preparation for the class presentation.

Answer the following questions on a separate sheet of paper.

1. Describe what kinds of sounds your instrument can make. How can you vary the volume? How can you vary the pitch of notes played?

2. Now write out a plan for testing your instrument. Keep in mind the principles of sound you have learned from the chapter. Be specific about the changes you will make. Can you use other materials for your instrument? What happens when you vary the size of different parts? Is there more than one way to play your instrument? Write down what tests you perform on your instrument and what the results of those tests are.

3. After you test your instrument, write out a plan to modify and improve it. You may even want to redesign and rebuild the entire instrument, based on your experience so far.

4. Based on the plan you devised above, modify your instrument. Test the modified instrument, and write down the results of those tests.

5. Write out a plan for your class presentation.

SCORING RUBRIC
Music to Your Ears

In evaluating how well you complete the Chapter Project, your teacher will judge your work in three categories. In each, a 4 is the best rating.

	4	3	2	1
Creating Design, Planning and Building the Instrument	Design is very creative. Planning is thorough, with detailed and useful notes, sketches, and materials list. Student follows all Project Rules. Instrument is well made.	Design is fairly creative. Planning is good, with useful notes, sketches, and materials list. Student follows most Project Rules. Instrument is fairly well made.	Design is somewhat creative. Planning is adequate, with somewhat useful notes, sketches, and materials list. Student follows some Project Rules. Instrument construction is adequate.	Design is not creative. Planning is minimal, with brief notes, sketches, and materials list. Student does not follow many of the Project Rules. Instrument construction is poor.
Testing and Modifying Instrument	Extensive testing performed on instrument led to significant modifications of the instrument.	A fair amount of testing performed on instrument led to some modifications of the instrument.	Some testing performed on instrument. Modifications to the instrument are minor. Some are related to testing.	Very little testing performed on instrument. Modifications to the instrument are minimal and unrelated to testing.
Making Class Presentation	Presentation is thorough and well organized. Student explains the process of design, construction, testing, and modification in detail. Student plays a simple tune and demonstrates all characteristics of the instrument.	Presentation is good. Student explains most of the process of design, construction, testing, and modification. Student plays a simple tune and demonstrates most characteristics of the instrument.	Presentation is adequate. Student explains some of the process of design, construction, testing, and modification. Student plays a simple tune and demonstrates some characteristics of the instrument.	Presentation is brief and hard to follow. Student omits major parts of project. Student demonstrates a few characteristics of the instrument, but does not play a tune.

Over and Over and Over Again

The following steps will walk you through the Chapter Project. Use the hints and detailed directions as you guide your students through discussion, observation, analysis, and presentation.

Chapter Project Overview

In this project, students will observe periodic events that occur in their lives. They will be asked to apply terms such as *amplitude, wavelength,* and *frequency* to these events.

To start students thinking about this project, describe several examples of periodic motions and events. For example, describe how the school bell rings at the end of every period or how the moon goes through the same phases month after month. Introduce the project by telling students they will observe and measure periodic motions or events such as these.

After introducing the project, have students brainstorm periodic events they can observe for this project. Have them discuss the types of measurements they will need to make for each of these periodic events.

Have students read the Project Overview. Review the Project Rules, and hand out the Scoring Rubric, you will use for scoring students' work. Discuss with students what is expected of them.

Set a deadline for the class presentations and some interim dates for the different project tasks. Encourage students to copy the dates in the Project Timeline.

Urge students to be creative when thinking about periodic events to observe. If they need more help thinking about events, you might suggest some of the following: pendulums, carousels, hamster wheels, ocean tides, bicycle or car wheels, the flashing light on a lighthouse, the sound of a nearby ambulance siren, the shadow length of a stationary stick observed at different times during the day, or Earth's rotation every 24 hours.

Distribute copies of Project Worksheet 1. This worksheet will help students begin thinking about things that they can observe. It will also help them organize their data charts to record their observations.

Once students have observed at least two different periodic events, distribute Project Worksheet 2. This worksheet will help them graph their periodic events so they can apply terms such as amplitude, wavelength, and frequency to one of them.

Materials and Preparation

Students will need graph paper for graphing observations, clocks or stopwatches to measure the frequency of periodic events, and rulers and measuring tape for making other measurements.

Keep Students on Track—Tasks 1–2

Make sure students have observed at least two different periodic events.

Check students' description and sketches to be sure that they include information about the duration of one complete cycle of each event and other measurable qualities about the events (e.g., how long an object's shadow is at a given time and place, or how wide a pendulum swings).

Keep Students on Track—Tasks 3–4

Check that students understand how to apply terms such as amplitude, wavelength, and frequency to their periodic events. Also check that students have correctly measured the properties.

Check that students understand how to graph or diagram their data and how to properly label their graphs or diagrams.

Chapter Project Wrap Up

Make sure students have made a poster, display, or demonstration for their class presentations. Their poster, display, or demonstration should include data tables, charts, and diagrams that summarize their findings.

Students should make brief presentations to the class in which they present their posters, displays, or demonstrations and describe the events they observed. They should be able to apply terms such as *amplitude, wavelength,* and *frequency* to their observations.

Have students turn in any written work you require.

Encourage the class to discuss the presentations.

PROJECT OVERVIEW

Over and Over and Over Again

In this chapter you will learn about waves, how they are produced, and how to measure and describe their properties. In this Chapter Project, you will be introduced to periodic motion and events and will observe and measure periodic events in your own life. This will help you to better understand waves and allow you to apply the terms that you will be learning in this chapter.

A periodic event is one that repeats itself at regular intervals. Examples of periodic events include the movement of the hands on a clock, the rotation of a tire on a vehicle traveling at a constant speed, and the swinging of a pendulum.

In this project you will be asked to observe at least two periodic events. Start out by describing the events you observe. You will also need to make a data table in which you can record measurements that describe these events, such as how frequently each event repeats and other measurable qualities about the event (for example, how wide a pendulum swings). Once you have your data organized in a data table, you will graph one event that you have observed. You will then be asked to apply such terms as *amplitude, wavelength,* and *frequency* to that event. Finally, you will summarize all of your findings in a poster, display, or demonstration, and present your findings to the class.

Project Rules

- Observe at least four periodic events.

- Make detailed records of the periodic events that you observe by describing and measuring the events. These observations and measurements should be organized into a data table.

- Graph one of the periodic events you observed. You must be able to apply terms such as *amplitude, wavelength,* and *frequency* to the periodic event you graph.

- Present a summary of your findings to the class. For this presentation, make a poster, display, or demonstration that summarizes your findings in a clear and concise way. Your poster, display, or demonstration must contain a graph of at least one of the periodic events you observed. On the graph, label the amplitude and wavelength. Also, determine the frequency of the event. When you present your poster, display, or demonstration, you should demonstrate your knowledge of the properties of waves.

Suggested Materials

You will use graph paper for graphing observations, clocks or stopwatches to measure the duration of the periodic events, and rulers and measuring tape for making measurements.

Project Hints

- Be creative when looking for periodic events to observe.

- Consider observing light and sound as well as objects in motion.

- Brainstorming is a good way to come up with ideas. Talk to friends and family members to see if they can suggest some periodic events for you to observe.

- If you are still having difficulty identifying periodic events, ask your teacher for some suggestions.

- Some periodic events may be difficult for one person to record. Consider working with a partner to make measurements—one person could time the events while the other measures distances or heights.

Project Timeline

Task	Due Date
1. Complete Project Worksheet 1	_____
2. At least four observations made	_____
3. Complete Project Worksheet 2	_____
4. One observation completely graphed and labeled	_____
5. Poster, display, or demonstration made	_____
6. Make presentation to class	_____

PROJECT WORKSHEET 1
Observing Periodic Motion

The following tasks will help you get started on the chapter project.

1. Brainstorm periodic events or motions that you could observe. Try to think of different types of periodic events, such as some that involve changes in light, some that involve changes in sound, and some that involve changes in movement. Also, think of events that vary in the length of time they take to complete. In the space provided below, make a list of at least ten events.

_____

_____

_____

_____

_____

_____

2. Choose at least four of the events on your list to observe. Use a chart similar to the one below to record your observations of each periodic event. Note that you may have to make more than one measurement for each periodic event. On a separate sheet of paper, describe and make a sketch of each of the events that you observe.

Periodic Event	Time Begin	Time End	Duration	Other Meas.	Comments
Swinging of a pendulum backward	11:10:30	11:10:31	1 s	15 cm	I observed that it took one second for the pendulum to swing backward 15 cm.
Swinging of a pendulum forward	11:10:31	11:10:32	1 s	15 cm	I observed that it took one second for the pendulum to swing forward 15 cm.
Swinging of a pendulum backward	11:10:32	11:10:33	1 s	15 cm	I observed that it took one second for the pendulum to swing backward 15 cm.

PROJECT WORKSHEET 2
Describing Period Events
Interpreting Your Data

The following exercises will help you think about how to interpret your periodic events.

Periodic Event	Time Begin	Time End	Duration	Other Meas.	Comments
Girl on swing moving forward	2:34:40	2:34:42	2 s	5 m	In two seconds the girl's swing moved forward 5 m.
Girl on swing moving backward	2:34:42	2:34:44	2 s	5 m	In two seconds the girl's swing moved backward 5 m.
Girl on swing moving forward	2:34:44	2:34:46	2 s	5 m	In two seconds the girl's swing moved forward 5 m.
Girl on swing moving backward	2:34:46	2:34:48	2 s	5 m	In two seconds the girl's swing moved backward 5 m.

1. A girl was observed while swinging on a playground swing. The data collected from the observations are listed in the table above. Use the data from the table to graph the motion of the swing as a series of waves. Label the rest position, a crest, and a trough. Label the amplitude of the wave produced by the motion. What is the amplitude of the wave produced? How long does it take for one complete motion of the swing? What is the frequency of the motion of the swing?

2. Graph the data you have recorded for one of the events you observed. Try to represent the data as a wave. Label the rest position, a crest, a trough, and the amplitude of the wave. Determine the amplitude, wavelength, and frequency of the wave. Try to use other terms you have learned in the chapter to describe the motion or event.

SCORING RUBRIC

Over and Over and Over Again

In evaluating how well you complete the Chapter Project, your teacher will judge your work in four categories. In each, a score of 4 is the best rating.

	4	3	2	1
Listing Periodic Events	Lists at least four periodic events. Includes a variety of periodic events.	Lists four periodic events. Includes some variety of periodic events.	Lists at least three periodic events. Events listed are similar.	Lists fewer than three periodic events, or events that are not periodic.
Making Observations	Makes complete entries into data tables. The data tables and other observations are well organized.	Makes fairly complete entries into data tables. The data tables and other observations are fairly well organized.	Makes incomplete entries into data tables. The data tables and other observations are not very well organized.	Makes incomplete entries into data tables. The data tables and other observations show little or no organization.
Applying Concepts	Completes graphs and accurately labels. Correctly applies chapter terms to the observations.	Completes graphs, but has some difficulty labeling them. Applies chapter terms to most of the observations.	Makes incomplete graphs, and has some difficulty labeling them. Has problems applying chapter terms to the observations.	Attempts but is unable to graph the data. Is unable to apply chapter terms to the observations.
Presenting Data	Makes a thorough, well-organized presentation with well-designed visual aids and a complete written analysis.	Makes a good presentation with some well-designed visual aids and a fairly complete written analysis.	Makes a presentation, but it is somewhat hard to follow, there are few visual aids, and the written analysis is incomplete.	Gives only a brief presentation without visual aids. The written analysis is inaccurate, incomplete, or missing.

Answer Key

Science, Society, and You: Science in the Community
Worksheet 1
1. False
2. True
3. b
4. c
5. Evidence
6. Opinion
7. Answers will vary.
8. Answers will vary.

Worksheet 2
1–7. Answer will vary. Samples are given.

1. An understanding of science is important because people in a democracy must decide many issues that depend in part on understanding the science involved.
2. I listen closely to scientists on network news.
3. I ask friends or relatives who have more scientific literacy than I what they think.
4. Question 3: Most people knew that a cell is the basic unit of living things; Question 2: Most people did not know that spiders don't have backbones.
5. The average was 73% correct; The average was 11.2 correct out of 15.
6. The most frequent number of correct answers was 9.
7. Most people I surveyed did, because most of them answered the Evidence/Opinion questions correctly.
8. One person said she had a career in science. 60% said they sometimes use science at work or at home; 5% said they do not use science at all.

Scientific Inquiry: Is It Really True?
Worksheet 1
1–3. Answer will vary. Samples are given.

1. Common belief: A piece of buttered bread usually falls buttered side down. This could be investigated by dropping or pushing a piece of buttered bread off a table many times and observing each time how the bread hits the floor.
2. Common belief: When a person's arms are fully extended to the sides, the measurement of a person from left fingertip to right fingertip is the same as that person's height. This could be investigated by measuring the fingertip-to-fingertip length of many people and comparing those measurements to measurements of height.
3. Common belief: It is darkest just before dawn. This could be investigated by observing how far away a person has to stand to read an unlighted clock at various times before dawn. The phrase "just before dawn" would have to be defined as a certain time before dawn.

Worksheet 2
1–7. Answer will vary. Samples are given.

1. A piece of buttered bread usually falls buttered side down.
2. When a piece of buttered bread is dropped, it lands on the floor buttered side down.
3. A slice of bread buttered on only one side
4. A piece of bread buttered on only one side is dropped.
5. On which side the piece of bread lands on the floor
6. Size of the piece bread, amount of butter on the piece of bread, height from which the bread is dropped, person dropping the bread, the way the bread is dropped each time
7. Take 20 pieces of bread from the same loaf, and butter each with the same amount of butter on one side. Hold a piece perpendicular to the floor at a height of 1 meter, and drop it to the floor. Observe on which side the piece falls. Repeat until all 20 pieces have been dropped, observing how each piece lands on the floor.
8. Record in a data table how each piece lands.

Technology and Engineering: Design and Build a Chair
Worksheet 1
1–3. Answer will vary. Samples are given.

1. Examined chairs included one of the straight-backed chairs in the classroom, a kitchen chair at home, and a desk chair at home.

2. The design features that might be used are the way some wooden chairs are put together without nails or screws and the dimensions of the back and seat of a straight-backed chair.

3. Useful ideas included the dimensions of the back and seat of the chair and the way in which cardboard pieces could be put together in an interlocking way.

Worksheet 2
Students should note the ideas and tasks that take place at each of the stages of the technology design process.

Tools of Science: Design and Build a Scale Model
Worksheet 1
1. Students might choose a room in the school, their home, or some other familiar place. They also might choose a local landmark building or a famous building from another city.

2. See Worksheet 2.

3. Students' scales will vary depending on the size of the room or building they are modeling. Sample scale: 1 meter = 1 cm.

4. Materials will vary. Sample materials: cardboard, construction paper, flexible wire, craft sticks, pipe cleaners, toothpicks

Worksheet 2
Students should complete the data table with measurements they have made or researched.

Ecosystems and Biomes: Breaking It Down
Worksheet
Students should construct two simple compost chambers and carry out an experiment using them.

Energy Resources: Energy Audit
Worksheet
1. 526
2. 532
3. 6,560; 656,000
4. 11,700
5. 2,907,876
6. 8,500,000

Land, Air, and Water Resources: A Precious Resource
Worksheet 1
1. The basic setup should look like the figure shown on the worksheet. The sequence of layers will vary. A typical sequence of layers might have larger pieces of gravel on the top and fine sand on the bottom.

2. The water might be described as brown and cloudy, with suspended particles throughout.

3. The water should be cleaner after filtration. Comparisons to the "cleanness scale" will vary.

Worksheet 2
1. Students' first step will vary. A typical first step might be a coagulation process.

2. Students' second step will vary. A typical second step might be a filtration process.

3. Students' flowcharts should show input of dirty water, a first step, a second step, and an outflow of clean water.

4. Students' sketches should reflect the two steps described on the worksheet.

Populations and Communities: What's a Crowd?
Worksheet 1
1. Accept all reasonable hypotheses. Sample: Plants that are crowded closely together will not grow as tall and bushy as plants that are not crowded.

2. The type of seeds that are used, the containers in which the seeds are planted, the oil used, the spacing of the seeds, the amount of light the plants receive, the amount of water they receive

Answer Key

3. Students' data tables should include, at a minimum, the container numbers (or other codes) in the left column and the day numbers in a row across the top (or vice versa), with plant heights to be recorded in each box. Groups may also provide for recording other information such as the number and color of leaves and the number of flower buds.

Worksheet 2

The Scoring Rubric stipulates criteria for evaluating students' written reports and class presentations.

Resources and Living Things: Variety Show
Worksheet 1

1. 15 cm
2. 1 cm = 10 cm (Calculation: 15 cm = 1.5 m; 1 cm = 0.1 m)

Worksheet 2

Students' work will vary.

Cell Processes and Energy: Shine On!
Worksheet 1

Students' data tables should be similar to the sample data table below.

| Date and Time | Plant ID Number/ Letter | Lighting Conditions | Measures of Plant Growth | | | |
			Plant Height (mm)	Plant Diameter (mm)	Number of Leaves	Comments
October 1, 2:00 PM	1	High	130	100	15	Looks healthy
October 1, 2:00 PM	2	Low	134	124	18	Looks healthy
October 3, 2:00 PM	1	High	132	120	17	Very green
October 3, 2:00 PM	2	Low	134	124	18	A little pale

Worksheet 2

1. Sunlight, water, and carbon dioxide
2. Sugars (food) and oxygen
3. It makes the plant get bigger, or grow.
4. The plant would remain the same size, because it would not have the food it needed for growth.
5. Answers depend on the variables that are tested.

Cells: Egg-speriment With a Cell
Worksheet 1

Students' data tables and graphs will vary somewhat. In general, eggs will increase in size when they soak in vinegar and plain water, and they will decrease in size when they soak in liquids that have a lower concentration of water, such as salt water.

Worksheet 2

Column 4 in the table should read: 70 percent (liquid A); 92 percent (liquid B); 87 percent (liquid C); 79 percent (liquid D).

1. Liquids A and D would cause the cell to lose water; liquids B and C would cause the cell to take in water.
2. Possible answers might include shampoo, syrup, ketchup, or honey.

Change Over Time: Life's Long Calendar
Worksheet 1

Students' timelines will vary.

Worksheet 2

Students' timelines will vary.

DNA: Proteins From a Double Helix
Worksheet 1

1. Chromosomes are mostly composed of DNA. A gene is a section of a DNA molecule.
2. The shape of a DNA molecule is a double helix, or a twisted ladder.
3. The order of nitrogen bases along a gene forms a genetic code that specifies what type of protein will be produced.
4. Adenine always pairs with thymine, and guanine always pairs with cytosine.
5. A sugar molecule that alternates with phosphate molecules along the sides of a DNA double helix
6. Phosphate
7. One of the nitrogen bases that make up the rungs of DNA; represented by the letter *A*

Chapter Activities and Projects

Copyright © Pearson Education, Inc., or its affiliates. All rights reserved.

Answer Key

8. Thymine

9. One of the nitrogen bases that make up the rungs of DNA; represented by the letter *G*

10. Cytosine

Worksheet 2

1. A protein molecule is made up of molecules called amino acids.

2. Protein synthesis is when the cell uses information from a gene on a chromosome to produce a specific protein.

3. RNA is ribonucleic acid. It is a genetic messenger that carries the genetic code from the DNA inside the nucleus to the cytoplasm.

4. The two types are mRNA, which copies the message from DNA in the nucleus and carries the message to the ribosome in the cytoplasm; and tRNA, which carries amino acids to the ribosome and adds them to the growing protein.

5. nucleus	6. mRNA
7. uracil	8. cytoplasm
9. ribosome	10. tRNA
11. bases	12. amino acids
13. mRNA	14. tRNA

Genetic Technology: Teach Others About a Trait

Worksheet 1

1. Students could research traits such as night blindness, hitchhiker's thumb, ability to roll the tongue, a widow's peak, or presence of free-hanging ear lobes.

2. Student responses will vary but may include a description of the trait; the factors that control the inheritance of traits; a way to predict what traits from parents will probably show up in their offspring; the purpose/importance of studying how traits are inherited.

3. Student responses will vary but may include introducing and explaining key terms such as *trait, heredity, genetics, gene, dominate,* and *recessive.* The plan must also include a process for predicting probability and at least one sample problem for younger students to solve.

4. Student should add components that will be engaging for younger students, such as visual or audio effects, moving parts, or other props.

5. Materials will vary.

6. Check students' sketches to ensure that their ideas are reasonable.

Worksheet 2

Topic: How traits are inherited; which alleles are dominant and recessive; how to predict the probability that a trait will be visible in an offspring.

Goal: Responses may include: Students should be able to give examples of traits that are inherited, tell how an offspring inherits one gene from each parent for a given trait, and solve a simple probability problem.

Purpose: Responses may include: Inherited traits determine what an organism is like and can predict to a degree what its offspring will be like.

Materials: Besides the materials in the display board, student responses may include worksheets, recording equipment, or other props.

Lesson Content: Student responses will vary, but may include a set of vocabulary terms and an explanation of inherited traits, how they are passed on from parent to offspring; how inherited traits affect an organism; and how to predict what traits might show up in offspring.

Teaching Steps: a. Student responses will vary, but may include giving examples of inherited traits: night blindness, freckles, curly hair, ability to roll the tongue, a widow's peak, or presence of free-hanging earlobes. **b.** Responses will vary but may include: an explanation of the factors that control the inheritance of traits; a discussion of dominant and recessive alleles; a process for predicting probability of the occurrence of a trait; the purpose/importance of studying how traits are inherited. **c.** Responses may include asking questions during the lesson presentation to check students' understanding. **d.** Responses may include asking questions to activate prior knowledge about the topic or preparing an introduction that is entertaining, informative, and makes students feel comfortable. **e.** Responses should include a process for summarizing and reviewing what was taught in the lesson.

Answer Key

Genetics: All in the Family
Worksheet 1
Paper pets will vary depending on the traits chosen.

Worksheet 2
Paper pet offspring will vary depending on the genotypes of the parent pets.

Animal Behavior: Bird Watch
Worksheet 1
1. Answers may vary. Examples of birds with widespread distribution in the U.S. include house sparrow, cardinal, blue jay, starling, house wren, and mourning dove.
2–5. Answers will vary.

Worksheet 2
1–3. Answers will vary.

Animal Movement: Animal Adaptations
Worksheet 1
catfish: detects food by taste
lamprey: feeds on other fish
spring peeper: inflatable throat for loud voice
adult salamander: gets oxygen from the air
king cobra: builds nests and guards eggs
Jackson's chameleon: climb trees

Worksheet 2
Answers may vary. Sample: My adaptation is the tail fin of a barracuda, the hind leg of a bullfrog, and the tail of an alligator. Each one is an adaptation for moving the animal through the water, so each has a flat surface with which the animal pushes against water to move forward. Also, the bullfrog's leg has powerful muscles for jumping long distances on land. The alligator's tail is heavy and powerful and can be used as a weapon.

Animals and Energy: Animals in the Neighborhood
Worksheet 1
Animals students list will vary. For each animal listed, students should provide information about location observed, classification, feeding adaptation, and feeding group.

Worksheet 2
Animals students include will vary. For each animal, students should include information about the digestive, respiratory, circulatory, and excretory systems. Students should also list the sources they used in their research.

Animals: Design and Build an Animal Habitat
Worksheet 1
1. Answers will vary; suitable animals might include anole lizards, crickets, earthworms, fruit flies, guppies, millipedes, pill bugs, slugs, snails, and spiders.
2. Characteristics of the natural habitat will vary depending on the animal selected.
3. Feeding habits will vary depending on the animal selected.
4. Water requirements may vary depending on the animal selected.
5. Answers will vary. Special needs might include structures to climb or bask on, a place to hide, or a substrate.
6. Sketches will vary.

Worksheet 2
1. Specific needs will vary depending on the animal selected. General needs include: access to food, water, light, warmth, and space; a safe environment free of any materials that might harm the animal(s).
2. Answers will vary depending on the animal selected. Habitats should include features that address any specific needs of the animal.
3. Responses will vary.
4. Sketches will vary. Parts of the habitat including any special features should be clearly labeled.

Answer Key

Living Things: Mystery Object
Worksheet 1

1. Students should write a few sentences that describe characteristics of living organisms.

2. Students should come up with two different tests to examine characteristics described in Question 1. The descriptions should include how he or she would analyze possible outcomes.

3. Students should list materials that he or she needs to conduct the tests outlined in Question 2. Be sure that the student knows whether such materials are available.

4. Students should make an initial hypothesis about whether or not the object is living. He or she should write a few sentences justifying the hypothesis.

5. If necessary, students should modify any tests described in Question 2.

6. Students should write out a clear plan for what tests he or she will conduct and how often he or she will conduct these tests.

Worksheet 2

The student's data table should be well organized and show a regular schedule of observations.

1. The student should write several sentences describing the research, including a description of why some tests worked better than others did.

2. The student should write several sentences summarizing observations and drawing a conclusion as to whether the object is living. If the mystery object is living, the student should try to classify the object into a domain and kingdom.

3. This paragraph should include the student's plan for how to present his or her project to the class.

Plants: Design and Build an Interactive Exhibit
Worksheet 1

1–9. Answers will vary.

Worksheet 2

1–9. Answers will vary.

Viruses, Bacteria, Protists, and Fungi: A Mushroom Farm
Worksheet 1

1–6. Answer will vary. Samples are given.

1. Availability of nutrients

2. I predict that mushrooms will grow better in a substrate with nutrients than in a substrate without nutrients.

3. In the treatment with a manipulated variable, the spores will be spread on vermiculite, which does not contain nutrients. In the treatment with the controlled variables, the spores will be spread on peat moss, which contains nutrients.

4. Both containers will be kept in the dark. Both will be kept under the same constant heat source. Both will be watered the same amount by spraying each container the same number of times.

5. My hypothesis would be supported if mushrooms first appeared in the container with peat moss or if more mushrooms grew in this container. It would also be supported if the mushrooms in the peat moss container were taller or had larger caps.

6. My hypothesis would be shown to be incorrect if mushrooms first appeared in the container with vermiculite or if more mushrooms grew in this container. It would also be shown to be incorrect if the mushrooms in the vermiculite container were taller or had larger caps.

Worksheet 2

Check that daily measurements are made. Students' data and graphs will vary. Graphs should be line graphs. Plotted along the x-axis should be time or day. Plotted along the y-axis should be the number of mushrooms, average height of mushrooms, and/or average diameter of mushroom caps.

Answer Key

Bones, Muscles, and Skin: Design and Build a Hand Prosthesis
Worksheet 1

1. It must be able to grasp, lift, and release; it must be activated by a pulled cord or string; it must spring back when the cord is released.
2. The model must have movable parts that can perform the specified activities. The actions must be under the control of the person using the model prosthesis.
3. Groups should decide on their own method of selecting the design, but one way would be to use a point system to rate each design criterion on a scale of 1 to 4; the design with the most points wins.
4. Descriptions will vary but must include all the elements needed for the model to perform the required activities.
5. Materials will vary based on students' designs.
6. Designs will vary.

Worksheet 2

1. The models must meet the following criteria: the prosthesis must be able to grasp, lift, and release; it must be activated by a pulled cord or string; it must spring back when the cord is released.
2. Responses will vary based on the performance of students' models.
3. Responses will vary depending upon students' critiques of their models.
4. Solutions will vary.
5. Designs will vary.

Circulation: Travels of a Red Blood Cell
Worksheet 1

Students should make a drawing of the heart with all parts labeled and the direction of blood flow indicated. They should also make a drawing that shows the two loops of blood circulation from the heart to the rest of the body.

Digestion: What's for Lunch?
Worksheet 1
Food logs will vary.

Worksheet 2

1. Answers will vary. Look for completeness. Check also that foods are classified in more than one food group when necessary.
2. Answers will vary. Check that graphs are properly labeled. The easiest way to compare the food log results with recommended diet is to have the two graphs for each food group on the same grid.
3. Answers will vary. If what students actually ate was far from the ideal diet, students should pick one aspect of diet to change, rather than try to change to an ideal diet for three days. This increases the likelihood of success.
4. Answers will vary. Students should keep another three-day food log, also spanning two weekdays and one weekend day.
5. Answers will vary. Answers should reflect students' actual experiences in this project.

Endocrine System and Reproduction: A Precious Bundle
Worksheet 1

Check students' versions of the Task Table. The Task Table should be complete, with other tasks listed, such as Visit to Doctor. Be sure steps for each task are detailed enough, that the How Often column is realistic, and that there is a checkbox for each performance of a task. Sample: Feeding; Steps: Get formula from refrigerator, heat it up, prepare milk bottle, sit in a comfortable chair and feed baby, clean up afterward; How Often: every 3–4 hours for 20 minutes; 6 checkboxes per day.

Worksheet 2

Check that data tables are complete and that students' responses are realistic.

1. Answers will vary. Students may find that letting the baby nap takes little time, because they can do something else while

the baby is napping. They may find that bathing a baby takes a long time.

2. Answers will vary. Some students may find that changing a diaper is easier than they had expected, especially after doing it several times a day for several days. Some students may find that bathing a baby is harder than they had thought, because you have to do a lot of preparation, and because you have to be careful not to injure the baby while bathing it.

3. Answers will vary. Some students may find that the evening feeding is quite satisfying. Some students may find that the 2:00 A.M. feeding is not very satisfying to do.

4. Answers will vary. All students will likely report that having help in raising a baby is better for performing all tasks.

5. Answers will vary. Students will likely write that having a real baby would be a life-changing event, and that nearly every activity in one's life changes in some way when you have a baby to care for.

Human Body: Working Together
Worksheet 1

Activities will vary. Sample:

Activity: Doing homework

Main Body System Involved: Nervous system

Interacting Body Systems: Respiratory and circulatory systems

Worksheet 2

1–10. Answers will vary. Samples are given.

1. System of roads, highways, and bridges
3. All the vehicles in the city
4. The water delivery system throughout the city
5. The post office and companies that deliver packages
6. The supermarkets and restaurants
8. The mayor and city council
9. The police department
10. The chamber of commerce, which brings in new businesses to the city

Immune System and Disease: Stop the Invasion!
Worksheet 1

1–6. Answers will vary. Samples are given.

1. In newspaper articles, the opening sentence summarizes the rest of the story. Sometimes the opening sentence tells how the events described in the story could affect the reader's life. This makes the reader want to finish the story to get more information. Sample: "Area clinics are reporting high numbers of students coming in complaining of flu symptoms, and they predict the situation will get worse before it gets better."

2. An article about the flu discusses a predicted outbreak. Then it describes flu outbreaks in the past, and then discusses this disease in general. This article moves from the specific to the general.

3. A story about Nobel Prize winners helped readers understand the behavior of some electrons by comparing them to balls on a billiard table.

4. A story about conflict in Eastern Europe summarizes a previous day's story in a short paragraph.

5. A story about a flu outbreak ends with a quote from a doctor that states that too few people are getting the flu vaccine.

6. A story about conflicts in Eastern Europe includes a map that shows the site of a battle. This helps the reader to visualize the part of the world where the conflict is taking place.

Worksheet 2

Students' tables will vary depending on the disease they select.

1. Answers will vary. Students should choose newspaper articles, television broadcasts, or radio broadcasts.

2. Answers will vary. Sample: My first report will describe how the pathogens entered the person's body and the first symptoms of the disease. My second report will describe how the disease spreads through the body, the new symptoms that appear, and how the body fights back. My third report will describe how the disease is fought off by the body and how the person recovers.

3. Answers will vary. Sample: I want to include sound effects of an interview with a disease organism and an interview with the person who has the disease.

Nervous System: Tricks and Illusions

Worksheet 1

1. Vision and touch

2. Yes, it seemed larger when I looked at it through the hand lens than when I just felt it.

3. Answers may vary. Sample: Looking through a hand lens fooled my brain into thinking that the coin was larger than it really was.

4. In the bowl of cool water

5. No, I took off the glove and saw that my hand wasn't really wet.

6. The sense of touch was involved in tricking me. The sense of sight was involved in figuring out the illusion.

7. Answers may vary. Sample: My brain assumed my hand was wet when it felt cool water through the glove.

8. Answers may vary. Sample: The room seemed to spin, and I almost fell over.

9. The senses of balance and sight were involved in tricking me.

Worksheet 2

1-2. Answers will vary depending on the illusion selected. Students should have two sets of answers to these questions—their own and those of another student to whom they have presented the illusion. Students' data sheets will vary depending on the illusion selected. However, they should include typical answers that can easily be checked off as well as blank spaces for recording more variable responses.

Respiration and Excretion: Get the Message Out

Worksheet 1

Answers will vary. Samples:

- An ad on TV for a fast food restaurant is aimed at children. The restaurant sells hamburgers but the ad shows free toys that people get when they buy a certain meal. Kids will want their parents to take them to the restaurant so they can get the toys.

- An ad for expensive running shoes appears in a magazine for teenagers. The ad shows a professional basketball player wearing the brand of shoes being sold. The basketball player is a great athlete who makes a lot of money and is admired by teenage boys and girls.

- A newspaper has an ad for a clothing sale at a department store. The ad is aimed at adults. It has lots of bright colors and starburst shapes to attract attention to the low prices. Adults would probably be attracted to the ad because the products are all being sold for less than their regular prices.

Worksheet 2

1-3. Answer will vary. Samples are given.

1. The main reason children start to smoke is that they see adults and teenagers smoking and want to be like them. Teenagers, too, often start smoking because they want to be more grown up, but many simply do it to fit in with friends who already smoke.

2. Most adults actually want to quit smoking but find it hard to do so because they are addicted to it.

3. Tar inhaled in smoke makes cilia in the respiratory system less effective at moving contaminants out of the air passages, so smokers get sick more often. Smoke is irritating, too, so smokers have an uncomfortable cough. Carbon monoxide in smoke takes the place of oxygen and binds to hemoglobin so smokers have higher heart rates and breathing rates. They can't exercise as hard as people who don't smoke. Various chemicals in smoke have been shown to cause cancer, which can be fatal. Smokers are more likely to have heart attacks or develop bronchitis and emphysema.

4-6. Answers will vary. Students' ads should be appropriately geared to appeal to the particular age group at whom they are aiming.

Answer Key

Earth: Make a Model of Earth
Worksheet 1
1. 6,371 km
2. Model sizes will vary; a typical diameter may be 50 cm.
3. Answers will vary; a typical scale might be 1 cm = 130 km.
4. Crust, 5–40 km, 1 cm; Mantle, 2,900 km, 22 cm; Outer Core, 5,150 km, 39 cm; Inner Core, 6,371 km, 50 cm
5. Students' designs will vary. A typical design might be a wedge or a sphere with a section cut away.
6. Materials will vary, though most students will probably suggest papier-mâché or modeling compound for at least part of the model.
7. Students' sketches will vary but should include all layers of Earth's interior drawn to scale.

Worksheet 2
1. Mid-ocean ridge, ocean floor
2. Ocean floor, continent, deep-ocean trench
3. Materials will vary. A typical suggestion might include modeling compound.
4. A divergent boundary, in which two plates pull apart from each other; a convergent boundary, in which two plates collide; a transform boundary, in which two plates slide past each other
5. Answers will vary. A typical answer might suggest using paint.
6. Other features include continents and a rift valley.
7. A typical answer will suggest using modeling compound.
8. Students' sketches will vary but should include a mid-ocean ridge, ocean floor, deep-ocean trench, continents, plates and plate boundaries, and a rift valley.

Earthquakes: Design and Build an Earthquake-Safe House
Worksheet 1
1. 1 cm =2 cm.
2. *Length:* 15 cm; *Width:* 7. 5 cm; *Height:* 12.5 cm

3. The floor plan should be a rectangle 15 cm by 7. 5 cm. The wall elevation should be a rectangle 15 cm by 12. 5 cm. Make sure students label their drawings with the scale.

Worksheet 2
4. The frame bends sideways; the paper wrinkles or may start to tear.
5. The paper will tear.
7. Students could try placing straws horizontally, vertically, and/or diagonally within the frame; diagonal straws will offer the best support. Toothpicks or straws could be used to make diagonal braces at the corners. Students might suggest that craft sticks or triangular pieces cut from index cards would be even stronger as corner braces.

Minerals and Rocks: Growing a Crystal Garden
Worksheet 1
Students may choose their own containers and materials. Sketches will vary.

Plate Tectonics: Plates Move!
Worksheet 1
1. Earth's plates are in slow, constant motion, driven by convection currents in the mantle.
2. Divergent boundaries, convergent boundaries, transform boundaries
3. The movement of Earth's plates
4. The plates are on top of the large convection currents in Earth's mantle.

Students' tables will vary.

Worksheet 2
1. Plates pull apart at divergent boundaries.
2. Plates collide at convergent boundaries.
3. Plates slip past each other at transform boundaries.

Volcanoes: Volcanoes and People
Worksheet 1
1. Ethiopia, Tanzania, Zaire
2. Guadeloupe, Iceland, Indonesia, Japan, Martinique, Montserrat, New Zealand,

465
Chapter Activities and Projects

Papua New Guinea, Philippines, St. Vincent, USA (Hawaii)

3. USA (Alaska, California, Oregon, Washington), Chile, Colombia, Costa Rica, Ecuador, El Salvador, Guatemala, Indonesia, Japan, Kamchatka (Russia), Mexico, New Zealand, Nicaragua, Papua New Guinea, Peru, Philippines

Worksheet 2

1. Paragraphs 4 and S

2. Students' notes will vary. Sample: Solfatara (Naples, Italy); steam and sulfur gas believed to have special healing powers; since the Romans, people take steam baths for arthritis, breathing problems, benefits of "sweat baths," soak in mud pools to soften skin.

3. Myths and legends; geothermal energy; uses of volcanic materials in manufacturing

Erosion and Deposition: Design and Build a Dam
Worksheet 1

1. Student answers should reflect a choice in materials showing three different grain-sized soils.

2. Students should respond as follows: Collect selected soils. Set up three test tubes. Collect water to pour over each soil and a stopwatch to time each experiment.

3. Students should respond as follows: Place selected soils in one of the three test tubes. Carefully pour water over each soil and, using the stopwatch, time each experiment to determine which soil is most permeable and which isn't.

4. Students should respond as follows: Collect selected soils. Set up three test tubes. Collect water to pour over each soil.

5. Students should respond as follows: Place selected soils in one of the three test tubes. Carefully pour water over each soil and watch to see which soil sample erodes easiest.

6. Students should find that they may need to change the placement of the soils when building their dam, based on the results of their experiments.

Geologic Time: A Journey Back in Time
Worksheet 1

1–9. Students' answers will vary and depend on the geologic time period chosen. Make sure students' answers are accurate for the chosen time period.

Worksheet 2

1–6. Students' answers will vary and depend on the geologic time period chosen.

Mapping Earth's Surface: Getting on the Map
Worksheet 1

Students' answers will vary depending on the site chosen.

Worksheet 2

5–7. Answers will vary.

Weathering and Soil: Soils for Seeds
Worksheet 1

1. Soil, or growing material

2. Answers may vary. Amount of sunlight and amount of water are the two other major variables. Students should suggest that all pots be given the same amount of sunlight and water throughout the project.

3. Answers may vary. A typical answer might suggest that plants will grow well in potting soil and poorly in gravel.

4. Answers may vary. A typical answer might suggest measuring plant height, leaf size, or the number of leaves.

5. Answers may vary. A typical answer might suggest observing changes in color or general appearance.

Atmoshpere: Watching the Weather
Worksheet 1

Students should combine the information given in the two tables to create their own scale to measure wind speed.

Worksheet 2

Students' weather logs may vary. Check to make sure they have recorded their observations for a two-week period.

Climate and Climate Change: Investigating Microclimates
Worksheet 1

1. Students should describe what the area looks like, such as whether the area is near a building, a pond, or woods, or whether it is on a hillside or in a meadow. They should also describe whether it was warm, cool, moist, dry, shady, or sunny. They should include any plants or animals that they observed.

2. Students might list temperature, precipitation, relative humidity, wind speed, wind direction, and the amount of light.

3. Students might list thermometer, rain gauge, anemometer, wind vane, wet- and dry-bulb thermometers, light meter, hand lens, and field guides.

4. Students should describe exactly when and where in each study area they plan to collect data.

5. Students' logbook pages may vary. A typical page will include spaces to record such factors as temperature, precipitation, wind speed and direction, relative humidity, amount of light, living things observed, and general comments.

Worksheet 2

1. In general, Site 1 has slightly higher temperatures than Site 2. Site 2 is shaded and receives less sunlight through the day than Site 1.

2. The building probably blocks some precipitation from falling at Site 2.

3. Site 2 has slightly higher relative humidity readings than Site 1.

4. Site 1 seems to be sheltered from the north winds because it is located on the leeward side of a hill.

Fresh Water: Every Drop Counts
Worksheet 1

The total reading for the dials in Figure 1: 68,923 cubic feet, in Figure 2: 37,049 cubic feet

Worksheet 2

Figure 1: 68,923 cubic feet ÷ 28.5 = 2,420 liters; Figure 2: 37,049 cubic feet ÷ 28.5 = 1,300 liters

Oceans: Design and Build an Erosion-Proof Beach
Worksheet 2

Answers will vary. Possible estimated sizes are 20 m (lighthouse), 2 m (adult human), 1.3 m (child), 1.5 m (bush), 0.4 (sea gull), 0.2 m (beach pail), 2.3 m (beach umbrella), 3 m (lifeguard stand), 1.6 m x 0.6 (beach towel), 1.5 m (fence). Corresponding model sizes would be 20 cm (lighthouse), 2 cm (adult human), 1.3 cm (child), 1.5 cm (bush), 0.4 cm (sea gull), 0.2 cm, (beach pail), 2.3 cm (beach umbrella), 3 cm (lifeguard stand), 1.6 cm × 0.6 cm (beach towel), 1.5 cm (fence). Waves could be 2 to 5 cm high.

Weather: The Weather Tomorrow
Worksheet 1

Students' weather maps should include weather symbols that illustrate their prediction for tomorrow's weather at their assigned locations. They should also indicate the predicted positions of fronts and large weather systems, such as high- and low-pressure systems.

Worksheet 2

1. occluded; west
2. warm; southwest
3. cold; northeast
4. stationary; not moving
5. warm; east
6. cold; south

Earth, Moon, and Sun: Track the Moon
Worksheet 1

Check that students' direction maps have accurate compass directions on them.

Worksheet 2

Check that students have made and recorded moon observations over several weeks.

Answer Key

Exploring Space: Space Exploration Vehicle
Worksheet 1

Planets and Major Moons	Description of Planet or Moon	Landscapes — Check all that exist on the planet or moon.							
		Dirt or Gravel	Rocks	Ice	Craters	Volcanoes/ Geysers	Cliffs/ Cracks	Bodies of Water or Other Liquid	Others (Please explain.)
Mercury	Small, rocky surface, virtually no atmosphere, heavily cratered; resembles Earth's moon	X	X	?	X		X		
Venus	Rocky surface, thick atmosphere, very high surface temperature	X	X	X	X	X	X		
Earth	Thick atmosphere, liquid oceans, rocky surface	X	X	X	X	X	X	X	
Moon	Orbits Earth, rocky surface, heavily cratered, maria, highlands	X	X	?	X		X		
Mars	Rocky surface, polar ice caps, thin atmosphere	X	X	X	X	X	X		
Phobos	Larger of the two moons of Mars; covered with craters	X	X		X		X		
Deimos	Smaller of the two moons of Mars; covered with craters	X	X		X				
Jupiter	Largest planet in the solar system; gas giant								No solid surface
Io	One of Jupiter's Galilean moons; one of the most volcanically active bodies in the solar system; surface covered by sulfur compounds	X				X			
Europa	One of Jupiter's Galilean moons, covered by a thin layer of water ice	X		X			X	?	
Ganymede	Largest moon in the solar system;		X	X	X		X		

Answer Key

Planets and Major Moons	Description of Planet or Moon	Landscapes — Check all that exist on the planet or moon.							
		Dirt or Gravel	Rocks	Ice	Craters	Volcanoes/ Geysers	Cliffs/ Cracks	Bodies of Water or Other Liquid	Others (Please explain.)
Callisto	Second-largest of Jupiter's Galilean moons; heavily cratered icy crust covered by blanket of dark, dusty material	?	X	X	X		X		
Saturn	Gas giant								No solid surface
Titan	The largest of Saturn's moons; very little known about the surface because of thick atmosphere		?	?	?	?	?	?	
Uranus	Gas giant								No solid surface
Miranda	Best-known of Uranus's moons as a result of close fly-by by Voyager		X	X	X		X		
Neptune	Gas giant								No solid surface
Triton	Largest of Neptune's moons; surface covered by nitrogen and methane ice		X	X		X	X		
Pluto	Smaller than Earth's moon		?	?	?				Very little known about its surface
Charon	Pluto's moon; very little known about its surface		?	X	?				Very little known about its surface

Worksheet 2

Students' answers and sketches may vary.

Answer Key

Solar System: Build a Model of the Solar System

Worksheet 1

Distance From Sun: 1:10,000,000,000 Scale: Sun Center; Mercury 5.8 m; Venus 10.8 m; Earth 15.0 m; Mars 22.8 m; Jupiter 77.9 m; Saturn 143.4 m; Uranus 287.3 m; Neptune 449.5 m; Pluto 587.0 m

1:50,000,000,000 Scale: Sun Center; Mercury 1.2 m; Venus 2.2 m; Earth 3.0 m; Mars 4.6 m; Jupiter 15.6 m; Saturn 28.7 m; Uranus 57.5 m; Neptune 89.9 m; Pluto 117.4 m

Planet Size: 1:1,000,000,000 Scale: Sun 1.39 m; Mercury 5 mm; Venus 12 mm; Earth 13 mm; Mars 7 mm; Jupiter 14.3 cm; Saturn 12.1 cm; Uranus 5.1 cm; Neptune 5.0 cm; Pluto 2 mm

1:500,000,000 Scale: Sun 2.78 m; Mercury 10 mm; Venus 24 mm; Earth 26 mm; Mars 14 mm; Jupiter 28.6 cm; Saturn 24.1 cm; Uranus 10.2 cm; Neptune 9.9 cm; Pluto 5 mm

Model Objects: These will vary but should be about the diameters computed for the scales chosen by students.

Worksheet 2

Combination Model: Diameter of Objects: Sun 13.9 cm; Mercury 0.5 mm; Venus 1.2 mm; Earth 1.3 mm; Mars 0.7 mm; Jupiter 14.3 mm; Saturn 12.1 mm; Uranus 5.1 mm; Neptune 5.0 mm; Pluto 0.2 mm

Distance From Sun: Sun Center; Mercury 5.8 m; Venus 10.8 m; Earth 15.0 m; Mars 22.8 m; Jupiter 77.9 m; Saturn 143.4 m; Uranus 287.3 m; Neptune 449.5 m; Pluto 587.0 m

Model Objects: These will vary, but they should be about the size indicated in Diameter of Objects, above.

Analyzing and Presenting:

1. Students should describe their experiences, including information on the scales that they used, why they chose those scales, and what problems they encountered.

2. Students should include distances between the planets and the sun, discussing how the solar system is largely empty space. The spacing between the planets is not equal; some planets are much closer together than are others.

3. Students should discuss scaling. One of the advantages of using scale models is that it allows one to work with measurements that are too large to visualize easily. A disadvantage is that it is difficult to choose a scale that is convenient for showing both large distances and relatively small diameters in one model.

Stars, Galaxies, and the Universe: Star Stories

Worksheet 2

Encourage students to use the sequence described as they write their constellation story.

Acids, Bases, and Solutions: Make Your Own Indicator

Worksheet 1

1. Answers will vary. Sample: cherries, blueberries, and grass

2. Answers will vary. Sample: Cut 5 g of cherries into small pieces and place in blender. Blend for two minutes, adding water 2 mL at a time if the cherry mixture is too dry. Pour mixture through cheesecloth, squeezing out as much liquid as possible. Store the liquid in a labeled container in the refrigerator.

3. Answers will vary. Sample: Brand X cleaning solution, Brand Y bleach, apple juice, Brand Z baby shampoo.

Worksheet 2

1. A good indicator should show distinct colors for different pH values (e.g., bright red for a pH of 1, pink for a pH of 2, etc.). Students may notice that some of their indicators worked better for acids than bases and vice versa. Good acid and base indicators could be used together when making a test kit.

2. A bad indicator is one that either does not change for various pH values or shows only slight variations in color, for example making it difficult to distinguish a pH of 1 from a pH of 4.

3. Check that answers reflect actual experiences doing the research, including both successes and problems.

4. Answers will vary, depending on the indicators chosen. Check that answers reflect actual observations from the data table. Some substances may work well as indicators, others may work poorly. Some indicators will test only acids, others only bases. It is probable that some will work well only for strong acids or for strong bases, or a limited range of pH.

5. Answers will vary. Samples: Class presentation, poster display, demonstration of testing and results of the best indicator. The list of materials will include the substances to test, the indicators to do the testing, and test tubes and bottles to hold the substances.

Atoms and Bonding: Models of Compounds
Worksheet 1

1. Answers will vary. Sample: different fruits, gumdrops, various balls. Examples for covalent bonds are toothpicks, pipe cleaners, and small springs.

2. Answers will vary. Choices for nuclei should be something that will distinguish between different kinds of nuclei, such as different fruits or different colored gumdrops. The choice for covalent bonds must adequately connect nuclei, and the material must differentiate between single, double, and triple bonds.

3. Answers will vary. Samples: writing on the surface of the nucleus, small blobs of clay stuck to the nucleus

4. The first column of this table should read as follows: carbon 4, chlorine 7, fluorine 7, hydrogen 1, iodine 7, magnesium 2, nitrogen 5, oxygen 6, sodium 1, and sulfur 6. Students' answers in the second column will depend on the materials that they choose. Make sure that they have thought of a way to distinguish between the different types of elements.

Worksheet 2
Compounds Containing Ionic Bonds: The charges of the given ions are as follows: sodium (1+), chloride (1–), potassium (1+), and oxide (2–). Other compounds and their ions will vary. Be sure students have selected compounds with

ionic bonds, not covalent bonds. They should give the charge of the compound's ions and briefly describe their model plans for these compounds.

Molecules Containing Covalent Bonds: Water contains single bonds. Carbon dioxide contains double bonds. Hydrogen (H_2) contains a single bond. Some compounds that students choose will contain more than one kind of bond. Be sure students have selected compounds with covalent bonds, not ionic bonds. Students should briefly describe their model plans.

Chemical Reactions: Design and Build a Closed Reaction Chamber
Worksheet 1

1–6. Check that students follow the procedures outlined in Steps 1–6.

7. Students should obtain your approval before beginning Step 7.

Worksheet 2
Data in both tables should generally support the principle of conservation of mass. The initial and final mass of each chamber will be about the same, with a nearly zero change in mass, unless students make errors in measurement and/or the reaction chambers are not sealed.

Elements and the Periodic Table: Survey Properties of Metals
Worksheet 1

1. Sample answers: shininess, malleability, ductility, conductivity (thermal and electrical), solid at room temperature.

2. Magnetic, reactive

3. Data tables should correctly reflect information from the periodic table.

Worksheet 2
Initial Observations: Students should complete the data table with their observations.

Test Design:

1. Properties student may choose to test include conductivity (thermal and electrical), magnetism, and ease of corrosion.

Answer Key

2. Check student's design of testing procedures for completeness, feasibility, and practicality. Also, make sure the tests are safe to perform.

3. Students should describe expected outcomes and give reasons. Sample: Copper will be a good conductor because I know it is used in electrical wire. I expect it to be less likely to corrode than iron because it is to the right of iron in the periodic table.

4. Data table should leave adequate room for recording test results and comments.

Matter: Design and Build a Density-Calculating System
Worksheet 1

1. The object to be measured is placed on one side of the balance. Objects with known masses are placed on the other side of the arm until the balance arm is level.

2. Sample answer: Balance arm, center pivot point, containers to hold objects at each end of the balance arm, indicator scale to show when the balance arm is level

3. Sample answer: Volume; I can measure the mass of the substance in the same container I will use to measure volume.

4. Sample answer: Each substance will have its own container. I will use identical containers for each substance.

5. Sample answer: I will measure an exact volume of water, such as 20 mL in a graduated cylinder, pour it into my container, and draw a line at the water level. I will test the accuracy by filling the container with water to the line and measuring the volume of the water in the graduated cylinder. If it doesn't measure 20 mL, then I will readjust the line.

Worksheet 2

1. Most students will have the same volume for each material, but the mass for each will differ depending on the density of the material.

2. Density = [Mass (g) × Volume (cm^3)]

3. In most cases, students will measure mass in grams and volume in milliliters. 1 mL = 1 cm^3

4. Check student calculations for accuracy.

Solids, Liquids, and Gases: A Story of Changes in Matter
Worksheet 1
Answers will vary. Check that students understand how to make a storyboard. Be sure that the storyboards include descriptions of both visual and narrative parts of the cartoon or skit, as shown in the example. Make sure students understand the particle nature of matter and how movement and arrangement of particles differ for the states of matter.

Worksheet 2
For both columns of table: Particle speed increases, attraction between particles decreases, distance between particles increases, and temperature of sample increases.

1. Solids have a definite shape and volume. Liquids have a definite volume, but their shape depends on the container that holds them. Gases have no definite shape or volume. Their volume depends on pressure and temperature. As pressure increases, volume decreases. As temperature increases, volume increases.

2–3. Answers will vary. Check that answers indicate that students have considered the details of the presentation and are adequately prepared.

Electricity: Cause for Alarm
Worksheet 1

1. Answers will vary. Sample: The rising water level in a jar could cause a floating ping pong ball covered with aluminum foil to contact another piece of foil stretched across the top of the jar.

2. Answers will vary. Sample: Place the bare ends of two wires in a tiny pile of salt. When a drop of water is placed on the salt pile, the resulting salt water will conduct current.

3. Answers will vary. Sample: Build a sensitive balance with a 100 cm^2 platform on one end. The added weight of mist sprayed onto the end will tip the balance and cause two pieces of metal to make contact.

Answer Key

4. Answers will vary. Sample: Tape one paper clip near the hinge on the inside of a box lid. Bend one end of the clip so that when the lid swings open, the bent end will make contact with a second paper clip taped to the inside wall of the box.

5. Answers will vary. Sample: Tape a paper clip to the inside of a box so that the end just barely protrudes above one of the corners. Line the inside of the lid with aluminum foil. When the box is closed, the aluminum foil will make contact with the paper clip end.

6. Answers will vary. Sample: Attach a 1-m^2 piece of cardboard onto one end of a 1-m dowel. Attach a small piece of metal to the other end of the dowel. Pivot the dowel on a nail so that the end with the cardboard "sail" is at least twice as long as the other end. Attach a nail to the base at a position where the metal on the end of the dowel will come in contact with the nail when a slight breeze pushes the sail, moving the short end of the dowel.

7. Answers will vary. Sample: Attach a thread to the object, insert the thread through a hole in a board, through a metal washer, and then tie the free end to the middle of a toothpick. Tape a piece of aluminum foil on either side of the hole in the board. The aluminum foil must be close enough to the hole so that the washer will contact both pieces when it is lifted up by the thread.

Worksheet 2

1–7. Answers will vary. Samples are given.

1. The event chosen to detect can be nearly any kind of movement.

2. Sketches should be detailed and clearly labeled.

3. The materials list should be complete.

4. Paragraph should give an overview of the operation of the circuit.

5. Problems and their solutions will likely include difficulties in the mechanics of assembly of the circuit, such as keeping the wires connected, but may also relate how students were able to make a subtle event close an electric circuit.

6. Students' circuits may have hidden parts. If they do, students should provide a labeled sketch.

7. (NOTE: Some student products may not have a practical application.)

Energy: Design and Build a Roller Coaster
Worksheet 1

1. The vehicle will not have enough energy to get up the second hill. The potential energy of a vehicle on the first hill would be less than the potential energy of a vehicle on the second hill. The vehicle would require energy input to get up the second hill.

2. In a frictionless system this would work; however, the vehicle will lose energy because of friction against both the track and the air. The vehicle would not make it up the second hill.

3. It might be possible for the vehicle to complete this type of track. However, success will depend on the height of the first hill and the distance between the hills. If the vehicle has enough potential energy on the first hill and does not expend the energy on long distances between the hills, this setup would work.

4. The materials that the students select may vary. Make sure they are readily available to the students at a reasonable price. Also, make sure the students have selected materials that are easy to modify.

5. The students' vehicle choices will vary. Again, make sure that they are readily available to the students at a reasonable price. Also, be sure that the students' vehicles are compatible with their choice of track.

6. This measurement will vary, depending on the student's vehicle. Students might need help measuring the mass of their vehicles.

7. Make sure that students draw their sketches to scale. The scale that they use should be clearly indicated.

8. Heights of hills and distances between hills should conform to the scale that the student selected. The point of maximum potential energy is at the top of the first hill. The point of maximum kinetic energy is at the bottom of the first hill.

473
Chapter Activities and Projects

Answer Key

Worksheet 2
Part I
Make sure students keep thorough records of their modifications.

1. If the second hill is shorter, the vehicle will travel further up the third hill.
2. The answer to this question will vary depending on the type of track that the student has designed.
3. The students' answers will vary depending on the track, vehicle choices, and distances between hills.

Part II
4. The answer to this question will vary depending on the type of track that the student has designed.
5. It is likely that the student will need to change the heights of the hills to include additional features.
6. The answer to this question will vary depending on the type of track that the student has designed.

Forces: Newton Scooters
Worksheet 1
Everyday Examples
1. The stretched rubber of the inflated balloon rapidly pushes air molecules out of the nozzle. The force from the rapid expulsion of air in one direction results in an equal force in the opposite direction.
2. A squid fills an internal pouch with water and then rapidly expels it. This water quickly being pushed in one direction results in an equal push in the opposite direction, and the squid moves forward.
3. The flipping of the salmon's tail pushes water downstream. The water being pushed pushes back with an equal force, propelling the salmon upstream.
4. The hummingbird flaps its wings rapidly, pushing air downward. The air being pushed down pushes up with equal force, keeping the hummingbird suspended in the air, against the force of gravity.

Energy Sources
Answers may vary. Samples: springs pushing off the back of a ramp, mousetrap pushing off the ground, windup clock turning wheels that push against the ground, rubber band turning a propeller that pushes against the air

Worksheet 2
The Spring-Loaded Design
Answers may vary. Samples: shape of vehicle, length of ramp, length of spring, type of wheels
Your Own Vehicle
Answers may vary. Students should include at least one experiment for every variable listed in their table.

Magnetism and Electromagnetism: Magnet Art
Worksheet 1
Students should record basic information about magnetic poles and magnetic domains, including the information they learn in their text, encyclopedias, and other books or Web sites they might consult. In making notes on how to make temporary magnets, they might describe a demonstration by you or experiments that they carry out on their own.

Worksheet 2
Students should record the results of their tests of materials that are and are not attracted to magnets. They will discover through these tests a basic property of a magnet: that it attracts iron and materials that contain iron. They will also discover that magnets do not attract all metals, including the metals that compose some coins.

Motion: Show Some Motion
Worksheet 1
1. a. Answers may vary. Marvin might not have started running as soon as Keisha called. Repeating experiments lets you get an average speed, and average speed may be more representative of an animal's speed than just one measurement.
    b. Answers may vary. Sample: You may want to include the first measurement because it increases the number of measurements, and the more measurements used, the more accurate the speed calculation. You may want to exclude the first measurement because it is atypical.

2. a. about 47.1 cm
    b. about 2.17 m

474
Chapter Activities and Projects

Worksheet 2

$$\frac{1\text{ m}}{1{,}000\text{ mm}}; 8.9\text{ m/s}$$

$$\frac{1\text{ m}}{1{,}00\text{ cm}} \times \frac{365\text{ d}}{1\text{ yr}}; 109.5\text{ m/yr}$$

$$\frac{1{,}000\text{ m}}{1\text{ km}} \times \frac{1\text{ yr}}{365\text{ d}}; 2.5\text{ m/d}$$

$$\frac{365\text{ d}}{1\text{ yr}} \times \frac{1\text{ km}}{1{,}000\text{ m}}; 2.19\text{ km/yr}$$

Thermal Energy and Heat: In Hot Water
Worksheet 1
Part I

Data will vary depending on the materials tested. Materials should be ranked according to difference between starting and ending temperatures.

Part II

Data will vary depending on the design features tested. Features should be ranked according to difference between starting and ending temperatures.

Worksheet 2

1. Keeping these two variables the same acts as a control. It allows you to use the ending temperatures of the experiments to determine the best insulators.

2. Answers may vary. Sample: The materials and designs with the highest ending temperatures will make the best insulating devices.

3. Answers may vary depending on materials tested. Students may notice that materials such as packing peanuts and foam board that contain enclosed air pockets make good insulators, and materials that hold air less tightly, such as cotton balls, are less effective as insulators.

4. Answers may vary depending on design features tested.

5. Sketches may vary. Check that students have labeled the important features of their containers.

6. Lists may vary. Check that lists are complete and feasible.

Work and Machines: The Nifty Lifting Machine
Worksheet 1

1. inclined plane, wedge, screw, lever, wheel and axle, pulley

2. pulley

3. lever

4. inclined plane

5. Answers will vary: top, side, or bottom

6. Answers will vary; only one of the six simple machines must be mentioned.

7. Answers will vary; only one of the six simple machines must be mentioned.

8–10. Students' designs will vary.

Electromagnetic Waves: You're on the Air
Worksheet 1

Check that students' survey questions are clear and specific enough so that respondents can give precise answers.

Worksheet 2

1–6. Answers will vary. Check that all data are tabulated and graphed where possible.

Light: Design and Build an Optical Instrument
Worksheet 1

1–6. Answers will vary. Check that students' sketches and notes of tests with mirrors and lenses are accurate and detailed. Answers should demonstrate an understanding of how light is reflected and refracted by the various mirrors and lenses.

Worksheet 2

1–6. Answers will vary. Check that students' answers accurately describe their instruments.

Sound: Music to Your Ears
Worksheet 1

1. Answers will vary. Check that students have been thorough in describing the ways instruments make sounds.

2. Answers will vary. Check that drawings are clear and that parts and materials are labeled.

Answer Key

3. Answers will vary. Sample: The vibrations will be created when I rub my wet finger slowly around the rim of the jar. Based on what I've read in the text, I think that the part of the jar vibrating and actually making the sound will be the part of the jar from the water level to the rim. Pressing harder and softer might have an effect on the volume. I will use 13 identical jars, each filled with a different amount of water, to make the 13 notes within an octave.

4. Answers will vary. Sample: All 13 jars need to be identical. The amount of water in each jar will determine the pitch. I will have a bowl of water nearby that I will use to wet my fingers as I play. After I figure out how much water needs to be in each jar for the correct pitch, I will place a small piece of tape at the water line to help in setting the instrument up each time. When the jars are not being played, I will keep lids on them to maintain the proper amount of water in each one. For carrying the instrument, I will get two medium-sized cardboard boxes. Each jar will be carefully wrapped in newspaper and old towels before moving. When played, the instrument will be placed on a 15 cm by 50 cm board to protect other surfaces from drops of water and to give the instrument a solid surface on which to be played.

Worksheet 2

1. Answers will vary. Sample: My jar instrument makes a fairly pure, constant tone when I wet my finger and slowly rub it around the rim of the jar. I found that I cannot vary the volume of sound produced. Increasing the amount of water in a jar makes the pitch higher. There is a point above which when I add water no sound is produced. There is also a minimum amount of water needed to make a sound.

2. Answers will vary. Sample: I am now using small jars and rubbing my wet finger around the rim. I will try jars and glasses of different sizes and kinds of glass. I will also run tests where I tap the glasses with a pencil and other objects to make sounds. Students' responses to this question should include their record of test results.

3. Answers will vary. Sample: I discovered that thin glass makes the best tone, so I will buy some inexpensive wine glasses from a thrift store to use along with some glass jars. I will use the largest jar that will make a tone for low notes. Tapping the jars and glasses with a pencil makes a different sound at the same pitch. The completed instrument will use a variety of jars and glasses.

4. Students should make modifications based on their answers to the previous questions. Check that students test the modified instruments and keep a record of the results of those tests.

5. Answers will vary, but should indicate that students will describe the process of design, construction, testing, and modification of their instrument. Their plan should also include the simple tune they plan to play.

Waver Characteristics: Over and Over and Over Again
Worksheet 1

1. Make sure that students have thought of at least ten different types of events to observe. Discuss any events listed that will be difficult to observe. Identify any that are not periodic.

2. Check students' observation tables. Make sure they are making thorough observations and are recording all necessary details of the observations in the tables. Also, make sure that students make sketches of their observations.

Worksheet 2

1. The wave produced should have two crests and one trough. The rest position should be midway between the crest and the trough, producing an amplitude of 2.5 m. The period is 4 s, and the frequency is 1 complete swing per 4 s. Make sure that students understand that their wave should begin at the top of the backswing.

2. Students' graphs will vary depending on the data that they collected. Check students' graphs to make sure that they are correctly drawn and labeled.